OPERATIONS ECONOMY:

Industrial Applications
of Operations Research

PRENTICE-HALL INTERNATIONAL SERIES IN MANAGEMENT

PRENTICE-HALL, INC.
PRENTICE-HALL INTERNATIONAL, INC., UNITED KINGDOM AND EIRE
PRENTICE-HALL OF CANADA, LTD., CANADA
J. H. DE BUSSY, LTD., HOLLAND AND FLEMISH-SPEAKING BELGIUM
DUNOD PRESS, FRANCE
MARUZEN COMPANY, LTD., FAR EAST
HERRERO HERMANOS, SUCS., SPAIN AND LATIN AMERICA

OPERATIONS ECONOMY:

Industrial Applications of Operations Research

W.J. Fabrycky
Virginia Polytechnic Institute

Paul E. Torgersen
Oklahoma State University

Prentice-Hall, Inc., *Englewood Cliffs, N.J.*

PRENTICE-HALL INTERNATIONAL, INC., *London*
PRENTICE-HALL OF AUSTRALIA, PTY. LTD., *Sydney*
PRENTICE-HALL OF CANADA, LTD., *Toronto*
PRENTICE-HALL OF INDIA (PRIVATE) LTD., *New Delhi*
PRENTICE-HALL OF JAPAN, INC., *Tokyo*

© 1966 by
Prentice-Hall, Inc.
Englewood Cliffs, New Jersey

Current Printing (last digit):

10 9 8 7 6 5 4 3 2 1

Library of Congress Catalog Card Number 66-19247

Printed in the United States of America
63796C

to **H. G. Thuesen,** Head Emeritus
School of Industrial Engineering and Management
Oklahoma State University

"education is society's most profitable activity"

PREFACE

Progress in the areas of operations research and management science has produced a large body of systematic knowledge about operational systems. Continued progress in the application of science to managerial problems may be expected to extend and refine the quantitative approach to decision making. Anyone who aspires to a managerial position, or who is a part of the management process as a decision maker or as the member of a staff group, will find an understanding of these exciting developments to be helpful if not essential. The purpose of this text is to help the reader grasp the significance of the analytical approach to decision making, and to help him become proficient in the application of quantitative models in operational systems.

The title *Operations Economy* is based on the observation that economic criteria are of primary importance in most decision situations. Therefore, the decision models presented in this text are directed toward optimizing the economic outcome of managerial decisions. In this regard, operations economy is similar to the well established body of analysis techniques known as engineering economy. It extends these familiar procedures of economic evaluation to include methods for evaluating operational alternatives. Thus, operations economy is the applied counterpart of operations research. It deals with established quantitative methods for providing management with a basis for decision making.

No attempt is made in this text to describe management information and control systems in their various and complex forms. Emphasis is placed on the task of explaining fundamental quantitative relationships common to most operational systems. Since paperwork and other procedural instruments differ from firm to firm, this text gives precedence to decision model formulation, manipulation, and implementation. The principles presented find universal application and, as such, are useful in the study of quantitative decision processes. It is assumed that the reader already has some appreciation for the complex of organized activity to which these models are directed.

Prerequisite concepts are presented early in the text. The initial chapter presents the viewpoint that operations economy should not be an end in itself, but should be a means for improving the want satisfying capability of organized activity. The second chapter presents the decision model as a simulation device for achieving optimum effectiveness. It provides a conceptual background for the models developed in subsequent chapters. Some fundamentals of statistics and probability are presented in the third chapter for the convenience of those who do not have a working knowledge of this important prerequisite material.

Production operations are given analytical treatment by the presentation of break-even models, production functions, manufacturing progress models, models for economic equivalence, depreciation models, and models for equipment replacement. Economy in the control of operations is presented within the framework of statistical control through control charts and methods of acceptance sampling. Economy of procurement and inventory operations considers both deterministic and probabilistic models useful in deriving operational policy for the procurement and inventorying of goods. Deterministic and probabilistic models for waiting line situations are presented as a means for achieving economic operation of queuing systems. Finally, programming for economy of operations includes the distribution models of linear programming, the general linear programming model, and some applications of dynamic programming. To facilitate the learning and application of the concepts and quantitative methods presented, a complete set of questions and problems is included at the end of each chapter. Statistical tables, progress function tables, interest tables, and finite queuing tables are given in the appendix in support of the models presented in the text.

We have attempted to treat each topic in a concise manner so that each page would have high information content. Each topic is organized within chapters so that the more advanced may be omitted without destroying continuity. Thus, the text contains sufficient material and is so organized to allow flexibility in the design of a course. Although a knowledge of elementary calculus is helpful in understanding the derivations of some models, it is not essential for a successful study of the applications. Omission of the derivations makes the material useable in those situations where the student has not been introduced to the calculus.

Indebtedness is gratefully acknowledged to the many students who have assisted in the refinement of this material by permitting its use in class. Their helpful suggestions have been of immense value in producing what we hope is a teachable volume. Specific credit is due Dr. P. M. Ghare for his direct contributions and to Dr. R. W. Gibson and Mr. W. M. Zimmerman for reviewing and commenting on portions of the manuscript. Finally, Mrs. Frank Roberts and Miss Velda Davis deserve the credit for typing the draft and final editions of the manuscript.

W. J. Fabrycky
Paul E. Torgersen

CONTENTS

OPERATIONS ECONOMY:

Industrial Applications of Operations Research

Part I

PREREQUISITE CONCEPTS
IN OPERATIONS ECONOMY

one

OPERATIONS ECONOMY
AND THE MANAGEMENT PROCESS

*In dealing with the physical aspect of his environment, man has
accumulated an expanding body of physical laws upon which to base his
reasoning. With every advance in the physical sciences, new relationships are
discovered which provide further understanding of physical phenomena.
Although much less is known about the science of the management of
organized activity, this important area is now receiving continued attention.
The increasing difficulty of rational decision making has been followed by
numerous efforts to put this process on a more quantitative, objective,
and routine basis.*

*As introductory material, this chapter will begin with
an explanation of the process of want satisfaction.
Knowledge about physical phenomena, together with the appropriate
selection and effective pursuit of objectives through organized
activity has enabled man to satisfy his wants more fully and
continually to improve his standard of living. Operations economy will
be discussed as a means for evaluating operational alternatives
in terms of their effectiveness in achieving organizational objectives.
Finally, a systematic plan for applying operations economy
within the management process will be presented. Thus, this
chapter emphasizes that operations economy should not be an end in
itself, but should be a means for improving the want satisfying capability
of organized activity.*

1.1. THE PROCESS OF WANT SATISFACTION

Man's wants exceed his means to satisfy them. The scarcity of goods and services is a relative economic dilemma that all must face. Some wants cannot be satisfied at all; others can be only partially satisfied; only a few wants can be fully satisfied. The huge investment in producer goods, together with the existence of complex industrial organizations, indicates that changing the physical environment through organized activity has been found to be an effective means for satisfying human wants. In many parts of the world where this means is not fully operational, human wants are generally unsatisfactorily met.

The creation of utilities. An accepted economic definition of the term *utility* is the power to satisfy human wants. The utility that an object represents is determined by an individual's subjective evaluation. Thus, the utility of an object is not inherent in the object, but depends on the esteem that a person has for it. It follows that the utility of an object is not ordinarily constant, but may be expected to change over time as the wants of the individual change.

Most things that have utility for an individual are physically manifested. This is readily apparent in regard to physical objects, such as a house, an automobile, or a pair of shoes. This situation is also true in regard to more intangible things. One can enjoy a television program because light waves impinge upon the retina and sound waves strike the ear. Even friendship is realized through the senses and therefore has its physical aspects. From this reasoning it follows that utility may be created by changing the physical environment.

Two kinds of utility may be considered: The first involves the utility of goods and services that are consumed by the individual. The second is the utility that an object may have as a means to an end, as is the case with producer goods and services. This class of goods includes such items as machine tools, construction equipment, factories, rolling stock, and digital computers. Each has utility as an intermediate step in man's effort to satisfy his wants. They are desired not for themselves, but because they may be coupled with organized activity as an effective means for altering the physical environment to produce consumer goods and services.

Certain human wants are more predictable than others. The demand for food, clothing, and shelter needed for bare physical existence is more stable and predictable than the demand for those things that satisfy man's emotional needs. The number of calories of energy needed to sustain life may be fairly accurately determined. Clothing and shelter requirements may be predicted within narrow limits from climatic conditions. Once man is assured of physical existence, he demands satisfactions of a less predictable nature resulting from his being a member and product of a society rather than only a simple biological organism.

The economy of organization. Organizations are a means for creating and exchanging utility. Through cooperative action, man has been able to overcome his individual limitations. It is apparent that many desired ends may be obtained from the environment more easily by joint action than by individual action. For example, the utility of the harmonic sounds in music is usually increased by the precise coordination of the efforts of a group of musicians. The utility of steel is increased by a complex manufacturing process which ultimately results in an automobile. Even friendship is enhanced by participation in certain forms of organized activity. To a large degree, the high standard of living enjoyed by modern man may be attributed to the ability of organizations to change the physical environment more effectively than is possible through individual action alone. In this respect, organization may be called mankind's most important innovation.

The function of an organization is to change the physical environment through the appropriate utilization of the activities of contributors. In order for the organization to be successful, not only must the total of the tangible and intangible satisfactions of all contributors exceed the total of all their contributions, but also each individual contributor's satisfactions must exceed his contributions as he subjectively evaluates them. Essentially, organizations are devices to which individuals contribute what they desire less to gain what they desire more.

Organizations come into being as a means for creating and exchanging utility. Their success is dependent upon the appropriateness of the series of acts contributed to the system. The majority of these acts are purposeful; that is, they are directed to the accomplishment of some objective. These acts are physical in nature and find purposeful employment in the alteration of the physical environment. As a result, utility is created which, through the process of distribution, makes it possible for the cooperative system to endure.

The function of the management process is the delineation of organizational objectives and the coordination of activity toward the accomplishment of these objectives. The system of coordinated activities must be maintained so that each contributor, including the manager, gains more than he contributes. To maintain this system in equilibrium, the decision maker must constantly choose from among a changing set of alternatives. Each member of a set of alternatives may contribute differently to the effectiveness with which organizational objectives are achieved and the contributors satisfied. It is evident from this that managerial talent is a valuable resource.

1.2. THE OBJECTIVES OF ORGANIZED ACTIVITY

Objectives pursued by organizations should be directed to the satisfaction of demands resulting from the wants of mankind. Therefore, the determination of appropriate objectives for organized activity must be preceded by an effort to determine precisely what their wants are. Industrial organizations conduct market studies to learn what consumer goods should be produced. City commissions make surveys to ascertain what civic projects will be of most benefit. Highway commissions conduct traffic counts to learn what construction programs should be undertaken.

Major and subordinate objectives. Any organized effort will involve major and subordinate objectives. For example, an objective to produce and market automobiles is an aim realized only through the accomplishment of subordinate objectives. Design, procurement, and manufacturing objectives must be defined and undertaken. These subordinate objectives will then have objectives subordinate to them that also must be appropriately executed. Specialization in an organization is a direct result of the necessity for executing subordinate objectives.

After the kinds and amounts of required consumer goods have been predicted, the kinds and amounts of producer goods and organized activities needed may be objectively ascertained. If it has been determined that the demand for transportation may be met by producing and marketing 400,000 automobiles of a certain model during a certain period, then the organization of personnel, materials, equipment, and capital becomes a matter of objective determination. The number of assembly workers needed may be determined from production standards. The quantity of steel needed may be calculated from design requirements and a predicted scrap loss. The number of supervisory personnel required may be estimated from past experience. From such data, the objectives that must be achieved by each member of the organization may be specified.

Before the Industrial Revolution, most productive activity was accomplished in small owner-manager enterprises, usually with a single decision maker and simple organizational objectives. Increased technology and the growth of industrial organizations made necessary the establishment of a hierarchy of objectives. This, in turn, required a division of the management function until today a hierarchy of decision makers exists in most organizations. Each decision maker is charged with the responsibility of meeting the objectives of his organizational division. He may therefore be expected to pursue these objectives in a manner consistent with his view of what is good for the organization as a whole. For example, the manager of production strives to meet production requirements and minimize production cost. The marketing manager seeks to maximize sales and minimize selling expense. The personnel manager strives to level out the fluctuations in the work force and to retain competent people. These objectives, and those that are subordinate, are not always consistent with each other.

The conflict of objectives. Although high productivity is due in part to the functional division of objectives in organizations, these objectives are often pursued in ways that conflict with each other. Consider the clashing viewpoints of various departments with respect to the inventory policy of a corporation. The production department strives for long uninterrupted production runs which will minimize set-up and tear-down costs and hence, total production cost. The end result will be a large inventory of a relatively few product lines. Marketing desires a large inventory, but also requires the availability of diverse product lines so as to maximize sales. Finance strives to minimize inventory levels to reduce capital investment. A stabilized labor force desired by the personnel director can be achieved only by building inventory during periods of slack demand. Conflicting objectives such as these may occur at any level in the organization.

Whenever a hierarchy of objectives is required for the accomplishment of an objective, conflicts are likely to occur. Limited perception at subordinate levels, together with the desire to pursue assigned objectives effectively, may result in action that is appropriate for the subordinate objective, but less than best for the organization as a whole. Choice of operating policies for maximum over-all economy requires consideration of how all segments of the whole are related. An attempt is then made to select that course of action which results in the best outcome evaluated with regard to the entire system.

1.3. ALTERNATIVE COURSES OF ACTION

Courses of action, among which one expects to choose, are conveniently called alternatives. The term *alternative* implies both a means and an end. For example, purchasing from vendor A is a course of action which results in the accumulation of an inventory. But accumulating an inventory may be considered a course of action which will result in the support of manufacturing operations. All proposed alternatives are not equally desirable since each will involve the consumption of different amounts of scarce resources. The accumulation of an inventory required for the support of manufacturing operations may be accomplished by means other than purchasing from vendor A. Quantitative methods of analysis for evaluating alternatives relative to objectives are finding increased use as an aid in decision making. That course of action most appropriate in the light of the over-all objective sought, and the resources consumed, will be considered to be best.

Seeking courses of action. Alternatives not considered cannot be adopted no matter how desirable they might prove to be. Rarely indeed are all possible courses of action known and defined, for the conception of alternatives is a creative process requiring the consumption of time. A fully defined course of action rarely emerges in its final form; it usually begins as an interesting but poorly defined idea requiring further effort for full development. Ordinarily, too few alternatives are considered, but there is a limit beyond which consideration of new possibilities cannot be economically justified.

An important facet of the management process involves identifying factors standing in the way of attaining objectives. Once limiting factors have been identified, they may be examined to determine those which may be altered or removed to permit the attainment of the objective. Those limiting factors that may be successfully and expediently altered are called *strategic factors*. Effort directed to accomplishing an objective may then be applied to these strategic factors by choosing means appropriate to the situation at hand.

The effect of counteractions. A *counteraction* is a course of action chosen by an opponent which may change the expected outcome of a course of action recently initiated. Evaluating the effects of possible counteractions is important, since an anticipated gain can be converted into a loss by the action of a competitor.

Anticipating and allowing for the results of counteractions is a creative process. It requires considerable experience in situations involving interaction between competing forces. Sometimes a study of the history of competitive counteraction will be helpful. In other cases a rational evaluation of the given situation will help the decision maker. In either case extrapolation to future situations cannot be made with certainty. Since, however, counteractions will modify expected outcomes, one should try to evaluate their probable effect.

1.4. EFFECTIVENESS AND EFFICIENCY

The objectives of organized activity are not ends in themselves; they are chosen and pursued as a means for satisfying human wants. The success of the organization ultimately depends upon its ability to achieve such objectives. But achievement is meaningless in itself unless the economic resources consumed are included in the criterion of success. Therefore, the term *effectiveness* will be defined and used as a measure of the economic outcome of a course of action relative to an objective. *Efficiency*, on the other hand, will be applied as a measure of the want-satisfying power of cooperative action for the contributors as subjectively evaluated by them.

Effectiveness. In general, effectiveness, as used here, means the degree to which an action leads to the result it was planned to achieve expressed in economic terms. The following examples illustrate this concept: In production operations, one objective is manipulating the process so that the resulting product will conform to specifications. An indication of when the process needs attention may be obtained by sampling from the stream of product and plotting the sample data on a control chart. If the control limits are set close, the chart will frequently indicate an out-of-control condition, often when the process is actually in control. If the control limits are set far apart, the chart will not be as sensitive to an out-of-control condition. In the first case, a cost will be incurred due to production lost while an attempt is made to find the out-of-control condition that may not exist. In the second case, defective product will be produced while the process is out of control, resulting in an associated cost. In order to optimize the effectiveness with which the objective is achieved, the decision maker must set the control limits so as to minimize the sum of the costs arising from lost production on the one hand and from defective product on the other. Thus, the objective of having the product conform to specifications is achieved to the degree that results in optimum effectiveness.

In procurement and inventory operations, the objective is to meet demand. This may be achieved by maintaining a large stock on hand so that a shortage rarely occurs. As a result, the inventory holding cost will be high and the shortage cost, low. On the other hand, the procurement level and the procurement quantity may be chosen so that the stock on hand is low and shortages occur frequently. In this case the holding cost will be low and the shortage cost, high. In order to optimize the effectiveness with which the demand is met, the decision maker should choose the procurement level and the procurement quantity so that the sum of the inventory holding cost and the shortage cost is minimized.

In waiting-line operations, the objective is to service units that arrive. This may be achieved by providing a large service capability so that the units requiring service will rarely need to wait. On the other hand, the service capability may be chosen at some low level that requires considerable waiting. In the first case, the cost of the service facility will be high and the cost of waiting, low. In the second, the cost of the facility will be low but the cost of waiting will be high. In this operation the decision maker should choose that service capability which minimizes the cost of the facility and the cost of waiting. By doing so the objective will be met to the degree that results in optimum effectiveness.

Examples such as these emphasize that the decision maker should meet his assigned objectives to the degree that results in optimum effectiveness. In order to do so, he must understand the relationships embraced by the operations under his control and trade off the relevant economic values.

By so doing he will be contributing to the over-all efficiency of the organization of which he is a part.

Efficiency. Efficiency is defined as a measure of the result of cooperative action for the contributors as subjectively evaluated by them. The effective pursuit of appropriate organizational objectives contributes directly to organizational efficiency. As used here, efficiency is a measure of the want-satisfying power of the cooperative system as a whole. Thus, efficiency is the summation of utilities received from the organization divided by the utilities given to the organization, as subjectively evaluated by each contributor.

Consider the following illustration: Assume that the organizational objective to produce 400,000 automobiles is being pursued with optimum effectiveness. That is, assume that each objective subordinate to the over-all objective is being met in a manner similar to the examples discussed previously. If this is true, the organization will be able to distribute a greater amount of tangible benefits to its contributors. The assembly line worker will evaluate the time and effort given to the organization against the wages and intangible benefits he receives. The person is more likely to make a favorable evaluation if he contributes to a cooperative system with a relatively large amount of tangible benefits to distribute. Similarly, an effective organization can produce more automobiles per unit of labor input and thereby contribute to the maximum satisfaction of its customers. In addition, the owners will enjoy a larger return on their investment, and the material suppliers will find a market for large quantities of their product at an acceptable price.

Man is continually seeking to satisfy his wants. In so doing, he joins with others in cooperative action and gives up certain utilities to the joint effort in order to gain others which he values more. The efficiency of the organization as a whole is the summation of the utilities gained by the individual contributors divided by the summation of the utilities contributed, subjectively evaluated. It is evident that this ratio must be greater than unity if the organization is to survive. In fact, the value of the ratio is a conceptual measure of the want-satisfying power of the cooperative system. The relationship of effectiveness and efficiency, as it pertains to the satisfaction of human wants, leads to understanding of the function of the decision maker and the management process. Included within this concept is the idea that the effective pursuit of appropriate objectives usually results in organizational efficiency and the satisfaction of human wants.

1.5. OPERATIONS RESEARCH AND OPERATIONS ECONOMY

The management process involves a multitude of decisions that determine the present and future status of the organization. These decisions deal with many types of operational activity. They may range from routine recurrent decisions required in finance, production, marketing, or distribution, through top level policy determination for the firm as a whole. Science in management has the task of developing and recommending logical bases for choosing from among available operational alternatives. Although intuition, experience, and subjective judgment are still the predominant ingredients in top level decisions and in most operating level decisions, considerable progress has been made in the adoption of quantitative decision rules. This section presents the contributions of operations research and operations economy to a science of decision making.

Operations research. The initial application of scientific methodology to military decision making was called *operations research* and was undertaken by interdisciplinary teams at the onset of World War II. Complex military operations required that scientists provide information about the effective use of military resources. The first operations research groups were formed in England and given the task of recommending courses of action associated with tactical problems. In the United States, similar research groups were organized in the respective military branches. These groups were attached to operational commands at various levels to recommend policies that would improve military effectiveness and end the war sooner. Mathematicians, engineers, psychologists, physicists, and others were recruited to assist in the complex task of military decision making.

Although the military retained its capability in operations research after the war, many military operations researchers found ample demand for their talent in industrial operations research. Many large corporations and civil governmental agencies created research activities dealing with operational problems similar to those directed to product development and marketing. In this role, operations research may be described as the application of scientific methods to problems arising from operations involving integrated systems of men, machines, and materials. It normally utilizes the knowledge and skill of an interdisciplinary research team to provide the managers of such systems with optimum operating solutions. The importance of this research activity in government and industry has led to the development of course work and degree programs in many leading universities. The concepts and principles of operations research may be found in such disciplines as industrial administration, industrial engineering, business administration, engineering administration, mathematics, and economics.

From one viewpoint, operations research may be seen as the development and extension of the scientific management movement usually credited to Taylor, Gantt, Gilbreth, Fayol, and others. The contributions of these pioneers provided the foundation for the present body of concepts, methods of analysis, and decision rules available to the decision maker. The continued development of the management sciences through the efforts of operations researchers, industrial engineers, mathematical economists, social scientists, and others will contribute further to the use of science in management.

Operations economy. Operations economy is the applied counterpart of operations research. As used in this text, an *operation* is a set of coordinated acts required for accomplishing an objective. Thus, operations are made up of purposeful physical activities coupled with machines, materials, and other factors which comprise the complex man-machine system of organized activity. The noun *economy* is defined as management with thrift. This meaning, when used with the term *operations*, should convey the ideal of achieving maximum effectiveness in organized activity against an economic measure of success.

In operations economy, we seek an effectiveness function that relates the variables under the direct control of a decision maker to those not under his direct control. One selects a specific operating policy so as to maximize an economic measure of effectiveness. Thus, the function of operations economy is the quantitative evaluation of operational alternatives in terms of their effectiveness before they are implemented. In this regard, operations economy is similar to engineering economy, whose function is evaluating the economic desirability of alternative engineering proposals before they are undertaken.

1.6. APPLYING OPERATIONS ECONOMY

Operations economy is the application of scientific methods to problems arising within the management process embracing integrated systems of men, materials, and machines. Its purpose is to provide the decision maker with a quantitative basis for evaluating the operations under his control. This aim may usually be achieved with greater success if pursued in accordance with a systematic plan. Such a plan is a conceptual construct useful in placing the area of analysis in proper perspective; such a plan seeks to provide a procedure that will result in sound conclusions. The remainder of this chapter presents a systematic plan for the application of operations economy.

Define the problem. The problem to which operations economy may be profitably directed is made up of four major components: The environment, the decision maker, the objectives, and the alternatives. These components must be studied and related to each other before the problem is fully defined.

Of these four components, the environment is the most comprehensive since it embraces and provides a setting for the other three. In general, the *environment* may be described as the framework within which a system of organized activity is purposefully directed to accomplishing an organizational objective. It involves physical, social, and economic factors which may bear on the problem at hand. For example, such diverse influences as the social acceptance of the product or the legal requirement to acknowledge and deal with a labor union may be important. Defining the problem involves a search for, and a study of, those variables that are significantly related to the effectiveness with which the desired objective is achieved.

The decision maker is the second component of the problem. Implied here is the desire of an individual or group of individuals to achieve an organizational objective, or set of organizational objectives, by the conscious choice from among several possible alternatives. Facts upon which to base the decision are sought as part of the task of defining the problem. But before this search can be successful, one must study the decision maker and his relationship to the problem in order to determine precisely what the objectives are or should be.

Objectives are the third component of the problem to which analysis must be directed. Questioning by the decision maker is rarely sufficient to formulate all pertinent organizational objectives. Sometimes these objectives may be detected by noting organizational activity. A company may move a plant from one location to another in order to escape from an area of strong union influence. Often it will be necessary to study a situation such as this to uncover objectives not specified by the decision maker. Such study is creative in nature and is an important facet of operations economy.

Alternatives are the final component of the problem requiring definition. This involves the task of identifying those variables which significantly affect the effectiveness with which the objective may be achieved. When this phase is completed, it is necessary to separate the variables subject to direct control by the decision maker from those not subject to his direct control.

Formulate the model. The first step in formulating an appropriate model is usually taken when the problem is being defined. Models are useful in choosing from among a set of alternatives since they enable us to determine how various aspects of the modeled entity may respond to a given decision. Thus the decision maker can evaluate the probable outcome of a given decision without changing the modeled entity itself. The advantage of being able to do this is obvious. Because of the importance of models in operations economy, this topic is treated in detail in the next chapter.

Operations researchers have identified and modeled many recurrent processes. An increasing number of common problem areas will be explained by the use of models as this research effort continues. These models, in their aggregate, provide a body of quantitative relationships that may be applied, with modification, to the operational problem at hand. In other cases it may be necessary to formulate a model unlike any that exist.

One should not overlook a very useful by-product of model formulation: The individual constructing the model will almost always gain a better understanding of the problem. Since the model must express the relationship of the variables involved, these relationships must be understood initially.

Manipulate the model. In manipulating a model, we seek to determine, for the variables under the control of the decision maker, values which will yield optimum effectiveness. This may be accomplished analytically or numerically. Each of these has advantages and disadvantages in regard to a given model. Where the model is complex, or where a wide range of operating policies are to be evaluated, a digital or analog computer may be needed. In some cases a large-scale system model applied to a recurrent process will require the permanent use of a computer for that model alone.

A model is never a perfect representation of reality, but if it is properly formulated and correctly manipulated, the model will be useful in predicting the effects of changes in controllable variables on the over-all system effectiveness. The usefulness of a model may be judged on how well it does predict the effect of these changes. This may be tested in two ways: First, apply the model to historical data and evaluate the difference in system effectiveness that would have resulted had the model been used; second, apply the model in a parallel fashion to the current decision-making process. One may then judge the worth of the model on the basis of the difference between the current procedure and the procedure that results with the use of the model. If the model proves itself by such a testing procedure, it is then ready to implement as an aid in decision making.

Making the decision. Models of operations are essentially means for taking the decision maker part way to the point of decision. They supply him with a quantitative basis for evaluating the operations under his control. If the model were a complete and accurate representation of reality, the results that it yielded could be accepted and applied without judgment. Since, unfortunately, this is not true, it is necessary to give the decision maker both the results derived by use of the model and a formal list of important elements not included in the model. Then, before making the decision, he may consider the quantitative result together with the irreducible elements. This dual presentation usually improves the decision-making process.

Models, together with automatic data-processing equipment, can be very useful in making routine or repetitive decisions. This process will never completely replace the decision maker because many decisions are based on factors which cannot be included in a model. The general economic situation, world politics, actions of competitors, and technological advances are examples of these. In addition, the judgment of decision makers will always be needed to identify appropriate objectives in a changing environment.

Implementing solutions derived from models requires action on the part of many people in the organization. Therefore, one should encourage close coordination between those responsible for developing the decision model and those who will use it as a basis for decision making. Where manipulation of the model is to be assigned to the decision maker, it is advisable to take extra time to be sure that the computational procedure is as understandable as possible. This may require the development of a nomograph, a set of tables, or graphs. The importance of making the results of operations economy analysis acceptable to those who will benefit from their use cannot be overemphasized.

QUESTIONS

1. Explain how advances in the physical sciences enable men to satisfy their wants more fully.

2. Define utilities and explain how they are created.

3. Contrast the utility of consumer goods and the utility of producer goods.

4. Explain why desired ends may be obtained more easily by joint action than by individual action.

5. What is the function of a manager?

6. Explain why the objectives of organized activity should be directed to the wants or needs of mankind.

7. State an over-all objective and list the necessary subordinate objectives for its attainment.

8. Describe the conditions under which conflicts of objectives are likely to occur.

9. Give an example to show that the term *alternative* implies both a means and an end.

10. State an objective and list alternative courses of action that will achieve the objective.

11. What is a counteraction?

12. Contrast the meaning of *effectiveness* and *efficiency*.

13. How is the degree of effectiveness related to efficiency?

14. Explain why it is possible for organizational efficiency to exceed 100 per cent.

15. What is the function of operations research; operations economy?

16. Define operations economy.

17. Outline the steps that should be taken in a systematic operations economy study.

18. Describe the four major components of a problem.

19. In what way have operation researchers provided the foundation for operations economy?

20. Should decision making be classified as an art or as a science?

two

MODELS AND SIMULATION

IN OPERATIONS ECONOMY

Models, and their manipulation through the process of simulation, are essential in operations economy analysis. The decision maker is concerned with understanding the operations under his control in order to select courses of action appropriate for attaining organizational objectives. The method of experimentation employing decision models may be used to gain this understanding. Experimentation implies manipulation; simulation is the process of manipulating a model of reality rather than reality itself.

A model may be used as a representation of an operational system. It is employed to explain and describe some aspect of the system under study. A model is usually an abstraction of those aspects of reality being investigated. Models provide the basis for experimental investigation which yields information in less time and at less cost than direct manipulation of the system itself. One value of a model lies in the ease with which it may be manipulated. This is particularly apparent when we realize that manipulating reality is often impossible, as with the solar system, or very costly, as with complex industrial systems. Much of this text has the primary purpose of giving the reader an understanding of models and model formulation, and describing their usefulness in operations economy analysis.

to explain operational systems incorporate two classes of variables: Those under the control of a decision maker and those not directly under his control. The objective is to select values for the variables under his control so that some measure of effectiveness is optimized. Thus, these models are directed to decision situations instead of to physical phenomena.

2.2. THE SIMULATION PROCESS

The operations with which the decision maker is concerned may be manipulated for experimental purposes over a number of alternative states. This process is costly, and in the case of a corporate organizational structure or its operational procedures, it may be destructive. For example, a plant manager might lose most of his work force by experimenting with different lengths of work week. Models and the process of simulation provide a convenient means whereby the decision maker may be provided with factual information regarding the operations under his control without disturbing the operations themselves. Thus, the simulation process is essentially one of indirect experimentation involving the testing of alternative courses of action before they are adopted.

Direct and indirect experimentation. In direct experimentation, the object, state, or event, and/or the environment is subject to manipulation and the results are observed. For example, the housewife might rearrange the furniture in her living room by this method. Essentially, she, or her husband under her direction, moves the furniture and observes the results. This process may then be repeated with a second move and perhaps a third, until all logical alternatives have been exhausted. Eventually, one such move is subjectively judged best; the furniture is returned to this position, and the experiment is completed. Direct experimentation such as this may be applied to the rearrangement of machinery in a factory. Such a procedure is time consuming, disruptive, and costly. Hence, simulation or indirect experimentation is employed, with templates representing the machinery to be moved.

Direct experimentation in aircraft design would involve constructing a full-scale prototype which would be flight-tested under real conditions. Although this is an essential step in the evolution of a new design, it would be very costly as the first step. The usual procedure is evaluating several proposed configurations by building a model of each and then testing in a wind tunnel. This is the process of indirect experimentation, or simulation. It is extensively used in situations where direct experimentation is not economically feasible.

In operations economy, indirect experimentation is effected through the formulation and manipulation of decision models. This makes it possible to determine how changes in those aspects of the system under control of the decision maker affect the modeled system. Indirect experimentation enables the decision maker to evaluate the probable outcome of a given decision without changing the operational system itself. In effect, indirect experimentation in the study of operations provides a means for making quantitative information available to the decision maker without disturbing the operations under his control.

Simulation in operations economy. In operations economy, the objective sought is the maximization of an economic measure of effectiveness. Rarely, if ever, can this be done by direct experimentation with the operations under study. For example, a sales price which maximizes profit cannot be determined by changing price over a range of values until the optimum price level is located. Such a method is expensive, time consuming, and in addition, may eventually destroy the price structure itself. Hence, operational policies are usually established by intuition, judgment, and simulation rather than by direct experimentation. Mathematical models and other quantitative procedures for doing this are currently being developed at an increasing rate.

In production operations, operational cost models are available which provide a means for determining the level of operational activity that will maximize profit. Manufacturing progress models explain the reduction in the number of direct labor hours required per unit as the number of units produced increases. Replacement models provide a quantitative basis for evaluating the effect of alternative replacement policies on the production operations of the firm.

Statistical control models are available for monitoring the stability of an operational process. They may be applied to situations in which the quality of a product is of concern or to other facets of organized activity in which a knowledge of control or lack of control is important. Methods of acceptance sampling may be used to evaluate incoming product beyond the point of process control.

Procurement and inventory operations may be managed by the choice of operational policy resulting from the manipulation of procurement and inventory models. In this case, the decision maker wishes to know when to procure, how much to procure, and from what source to procure, in order to minimize the sum of all costs associated with the procurement and inventory process. These questions could be answered, in time, by direct experimentation. But the availability of both deterministic and probabilistic models in this area makes this direct approach unnecessary.

Waiting-line operations may be studied by direct experimentation. This would be accomplished by altering the service capability over several states until the least-cost state for the system as a whole was achieved. Fortunately, many models are available for solving these problems. These are either deterministic or probabilistic, depending upon the system to which they are directed. They make it possible to evaluate alternative service policies without disturbing the operations under consideration.

Other operations may be simulated by various programming models. Involved here is the general class of optimization problems dealing with the interaction of many variables subject to certain constraints. These constraints arise because the operations under consideration compete for scarce resources. In these operations, a measure of effectiveness is to be optimized through the use of an algorithm rather than through direct trial-and-error experimentation.

The rest of this chapter, and those which follow, will be directed to developing and explaining mathematical decision models as a means for effecting indirect experimentation. In so doing it must be remembered that the result sought is the effectiveness with which organizational objectives are achieved.

2.3. FORMULATING AND MANIPULATING THE MODEL

Verbal statements usually precede the construction of a mathematical model. These statements provide a word picture of reality from which the mathematical model may evolve. The mathematical model and the verbal description are closely related, with the mathematical model being an extension and quantification of verbal statements. Ordinarily, the model will be more precise, orderly, and sharply defined, but this does not mean that the model is more accurate than the verbal description. Actually, the first formulation of a mathematical model may differ more from reality than the verbal statements which preceded it. After formulating a model it must be manipulated as a means for evaluating alternative operating policies.

Formulating the model. Formulation of the mathematical model requires that we construct an effectiveness function embracing two classes of variables. These have been identified as a dichotomous classification of those factors of importance in the system under consideration. An *effectiveness function* is a mathematical statement formally linking a measure of effectiveness with variables under the direct control of the decision maker and variables not under his direct control. It provides a means whereby various values for controllable variables, designated x_i, can be tested in the light of uncontrollable variables, y_j. The test is an experimental process performed mathematically. The experimental result is an outcome value for effectiveness, E. This functional relationship is usually expressd as[1]

$$E = f(x_i, y_j).$$

_____

[1] A more complete discussion of this relationship may be found in C. W. Churchman, R. L. Ackoff, and E. L. Arnoff, *Introduction to Operations Research* (New York: John Wiley and Sons, Inc., 1957).

As an example of the nature of the effectiveness function, consider an economic procurement quantity model. Here the economic measure of effectiveness is total system cost, and the objective is to choose a procurement quantity in the light of demand, procurement cost, and holding cost, so that total cost is minimized. The procurement quantity is the variable directly under the control of the decision maker. Demand, procurement cost, and holding cost are not directly under his control. The use of a model such as this allows the decision maker to arrive at a value for the variable under his control that will trade off conflicting cost elements. This is accomplished by indirect means instead of by direct experimentation with the actual operation. Thus, the mathematical model provides a convenient means for finding the least-cost procurement quantity without disturbing the system under study.

In formulating a mathematical model one attempts to itemize all components of the system which are relevant to the system's effectiveness. Because of the impossibility of considering all parameters in constructing the effectiveness function, it is common practice to consider only those upon which the outcome effectiveness is believed to depend significantly. This necessary viewpoint sometimes leads to the erroneous conclusion that certain segments of the environment are actually isolated from each other. It may be feasible to consider only those relationships that are significantly pertinent; still, we should remember that all elements of the total environment are interdependent.

Even though a diligent search for relevant parameters is made, it is almost certain that some will be unknowingly omitted. Others may be deliberately omitted if their impact upon the performance of the model is thought to be small and their contribution to the mathematical complexity, large. To the extent that omitted parameters are significant, the model will provide misleading results until they are detected and included.

Model formulation is often simplified by constructing the model as though it were to be used in a static decision environment. This assumption makes it unnecessary to incorporate dynamic elements into the model. But the model must be updated as the environment changes over time. Finally, some additional simplifications may be made: A variable may be replaced by a constant; a discrete distribution may be replaced by a continuous distribution; or a nonlinear relationship may be replaced by one which is linear. If the effect of these simplifications is known to be insignificant, they may be made with confidence. The model should be simplified to the point where the gain in ease of formulation and manipulation ceases to be greater than the loss resulting from an abridged model.

Manipulating the model. The decision model is not a solution in itself but is a means for deriving a solution to an operational problem. Once a model has been formulated, it must be manipulated in an experimental sense to test alternative policies. Since models may take on a variety of mathematical forms, they may require one of several mathematical procedures in the manipulation process.

If the effectiveness function can be differentiated, we can often find by direct means the value or values of the variable or variables under management control that result in optimum effectiveness. This will require taking a derivative, if one independent variable is involved, or partial differentiation, if more than one independent variable is present. Application of these calculus techniques will be used to minimize or maximize, depending on the manner in which the model was formulated. When the effectiveness function is to be maximized subject to certain constraints, it may be necessary to use linear or dynamic programming algorithms.

Often an effectiveness function can be manipulated only by numerical means. This involves the substitution of different values for controllable variables and a comparison of the outcome. That value of the variable or variables resulting in optimum effectiveness is then recommended as operating policy. When a decision model incorporates probabilistic elements, it may be necessary to employ *Monte Carlo analysis* for its manipulation. This is a method whereby statistical sampling is repeatedly used to obtain many estimates of the outcome of the process under study. These estimates are then treated as a sample and used in predicting the results to be obtained from a given decision.

2.4. CONTROL OF THE SOLUTION

Even though the model may adequately represent the system under study when it is constructed, it may become useless in decision making. This usually occurs as a result of the changing nature of most operational systems. Avoiding obsolescence of the model requires that it incorporate dynamic relationships or that it be modified over time. Since very few models are designed to cope with a dynamic environment, it will be necessary to review the environment periodically for the purpose of modifying the model under consideration.

The appropriate frequency of review depends on the nature of the changing environment. Two cost elements are pertinent: First, as the frequency of review increases, the cost of review will increase; second, the cost of incorrect output decisions from the model will decrease with a frequently updated model. The review process should be designed so as to minimize the sum of these two cost components. In effect, a secondary model may be conceived and employed to specify the optimum review period for operational models.

Control of input parameters. The input parameters to a decision model are those uncontrolled system elements which may significantly affect the model output or effectiveness. These parameters may include various cost elements as well as such factors as procurement lead time, waiting time, form of arrival distribution, and so forth. Each of these may change over time at a rate depending upon a multitude of environmental factors.

Determination of specific values for input parameters involves a process of estimation. Costs may be determined by collecting and analyzing cost accounting data and by projecting anticipated labor, material, and overhead estimates. Distribution parameters may be estimated and distribution forms may be determined. The frequency with which this procedure is followed should be based on the costs involved.

If, upon review of the relevant inputs to the model, the values obtained are significantly different from those currently being used in the model, modification is required. In this way the model is like a road map. All roads shown on the map may still exist, but if new roads have been built, proper information as to the best route to travel is not provided. By frequent revision, the value of the map in decision making is improved. Similarly, revision of input parameters gives assurance that the results obtained from the model can be used with assurance that they are based upon the environmental conditions as they currently exist.

Control of functional relationships. An effectiveness function is the basic form of the mathematical model used in decision making. It exhibits functional relationships between effectiveness and the two classes of parameters. Any or all of these functional relationships are subject to change over time. If they do change, the model will yield erroneous results.

For example, suppose that an inventory model includes the cost of holding stock based upon the average amount on hand during the year. Although this assumption may have been correct when the model was formulated, it may no longer be true. Warehousing practices may now exclude stock consolidation, thus making space vacated by a given product unavailable for other products. If this is so, the cost of holding inventory must now be based on the maximum amount on hand for the year. The decision model must be modified to express holding cost per year as a function of maximum inventory on hand if it is to represent accurately the decision situation as it currently exists.

2.5. THE APPLICATION OF MODELS

One must be cautious in applying a model, since one can come to believe that the model is reality in itself and forget that a model is only an approximation of the situation under study. When the solution derived by the use of a model is not plausible, or when it seems to disagree with what can reasonably be expected, the model should be reevaluated. This is particularly difficult to do when the model is computerized and used to make recurrent decisions.

A decision model cannot be classified as accurate or inaccurate in any absolute sense. It may be considered to be accurate if it is an idealized substitute of the actual system under study. If manipulation of the model would yield the identical result that manipulation of reality would have yielded, the model would be true. If, however, one knew what the manipulation of reality would have yielded, the process of simulation would be unnecessary. Hence it is difficult to test a model except by an intuitive check for reasonableness.

The value of models in decision making. Models are valuable primarily because they permit indirect experimentation or simulation; this advantage is particularly worthwhile where direct experimentation is not possible. Indirect experimentation with a model makes it possible to consider a greater range of operating policies at less cost and in less time.

A *decision model* is essentially a device that relates two classes of variables to over-all system effectiveness. Without such a device, the decision maker is forced to estimate values for the policy variables directly. When a model of the situation is formulated, however, the relationship of the controllable variables, uncontrollable or system variables, and effectiveness is explicitly stated. One can choose values for the controllable variables with much more certainty by making estimates for the system variables. The values for the policy variables resulting in optimum effectiveness will then depend upon a composite of many estimates. It is generally recognized that the accuracy of estimation can be considerably improved by estimating elements upon which an outcome depends, for example, one can probably estimate the volume of a room more accurately by estimating the length, width, and height of the room, than by estimating volume directly. The effectiveness function allows this principle to be applied to operational systems.

Rarely, however, is it necessary to determine all input parameters to a model by estimation. Usually there exists a certain amount of data that can be used to specify the values that should be assigned to uncontrolled variables. In fact, one advantage of the model is that it specifies which uncontrollable variables are important in the decision situation. We may then begin collecting data directed to the assignment of values to these parameters.

Often, a model is of value in the decision-making process even though it gives biased results. Here the model is valuable because it is consistent; that is, a decision model gives results that do not vary from decision to decision. It is often easier to correct for a biased decision than to compensate for a policy that changes for no apparent reason.

Automation of the management process. The delay in developing models to explain complex operational systems may be attributed to an early pre-occupation with the physical aspects of the environment. This can be justified, however, since during much of history, the limiting factors in the satisfaction of human wants were predominantly physical. But, with the accumulation of knowledge about physical phenomena, man has been able to employ complex systems of productive factors to satisfy his wants. Decision makers are becoming increasingly aware that experience, intuition, and judgment are insufficient for the effective pursuit of operational objectives.

Automation of production has resulted in reducing the number of direct labor man hours per unit produced. This reduction may be expected to continue as the move toward more complete automation continues. Decision models are finding increased use as a means to automate the management and decision-making process. Routine decisions embracing recurrent operations may be conveniently handled by properly formulated decision models. We may expect such use of models to improve the over-all effectiveness with which organizational objectives are achieved.

Although, admittedly, mathematical models can be only a partial representation of reality, they do provide a quantitative basis for decision making. This is useful because a model takes the decision maker part way to the point of decision. He may then add intuition and judgment to cover that portion of the situation not explained by the model. Thus, this augmented approach to decision making may be expected to improve the decision-making process and the economy of operations.

QUESTIONS

1. Discuss the various meanings of the word *model*.

2. Briefly describe physical models, schematic models, mathematical models.

3. How do mathematical models directed to decision situations differ from those traditionally used in the physical sciences?

4. Contrast direct and indirect experimentation.

5. Describe an operational situation that may be fruitfully explored by the use of a model.

6. Write the general form of the effectiveness function and define the symbols.

7. Identify a decision situation and indicate the variables under the control of the decision maker and those not directly under his control.

8. Why is it not possible to formulate a model that accurately represents reality?

9. What means may be employed to simplify model construction?

10. Under what conditions might variables be omitted from a model?

11. What means may be employed to manipulate a decision model?

12. Under what conditions may a properly formulated model become useless as an aid in decision making?

13. Explain the nature of the cost components that should be considered in deciding how frequently to review a dynamic environment.

14. In operations economy, models are used for prediction and control. Why is it necessary to be concerned with the control of the model itself?

15. What caution must be exercised in the use of models?

16. Discuss several specific reasons why models are of value in decision making.

17. What should be done with those facets of a decision situation that cannot be explained by the model?

18. Discuss mathematical models with regard to the automation of the decision-making process.

three

SOME FUNDAMENTALS
OF STATISTICS AND PROBABILITY

*Variation is inherent in most aspects of the decision environment.
In production operations, variation will occur in the quality
characteristics of incoming material, in the time required to complete
a work cycle, in the number of production workers absent, in the
dimensions of the finished part, in the deterioration of equipment, and so
forth. In inventory operations, variation will occur in the demand for
a given item and in the time required to procure replenishment stock.
In waiting line operations, variation will occur in the number of individuals
requiring service and in the time required to serve a given individual.
Examples such as these show that variation
is common.*

*Some decision models formulated to evaluate operations
will give satisfactory results if variation is not incorporated.
Most models must include statistical and probabilistic elements if
meaningful results are to be obtained. This chapter presents methods for
describing a mass of statistical data, concepts of probability and
probability distributions, the basics of inferential statistics,
linear regression and correlation, and Monte Carlo analysis. Understanding
these fundamental topics is necessary in order to
understand many decision models presented
in this text.*

29

3.1. DESCRIPTIVE STATISTICS

The body of analysis techniques directed to the description of collected data is called *descriptive statistics*. Such data may be either discrete or continuous and are usually the result of a series of observations taken over time. In its raw form, a mass of data communicates very little information. Therefore, it is often desirable to develop a frequency distribution which describes the data in compact form. In addition, it is common practice to calculate a measure of central tendency and a measure of dispersion for a mass of data. Each of these descriptive techniques is developed and explained in this section.

Discrete and continuous data. Discrete data are composed of separate, individually distinct elements which usually come from a counting process. For example, the data listed in Table 3.1 give the number of arrivals counted

Table 3.1. THE NUMBER OF ARRIVALS PER HOUR FOR A 30-HOUR PERIOD

Hour	Arrivals	Hour	Arrivals	Hour	Arrivals
1	2	11	1	21	1
2	0	12	4	22	1
3	1	13	2	23	2
4	1	14	2	24	0
5	1	15	1	25	0
6	3	16	1	26	1
7	0	17	4	27	0
8	0	18	3	28	2
9	2	19	1	29	3
10	1	20	0	30	1

each hour during a 30-hour period. Each arrival is an integral unit. A fraction of an arrival cannot occur. For each hour, the number of arrivals is a whole number which differs from the number of arrivals in any hour by multiples of one. Data are usually discrete if they result from a counting process.

Continuous data can take on any value within some range. The actual recorded observation may appear to be discrete, but this occurs because of the physical limitation of the measurement process. Hence two or more observations may have the same value although the characteristic under study is unique in each case. For example, consider the data of Table 3.2 pertaining to the distance between two machined surfaces on 50 similarly produced items. The smallest distance is 0.9963 in. and the largest is 1.0048 in. Other measurements may fall anywhere within these limits and possibly

Table 3.2. THE DISTANCE BETWEEN TWO MACHINED SURFACES (inches)

1.0003	0.9982	1.0007	1.0013	0.9968
1.0017	0.9970	1.0003	1.0006	0.9970
0.9987	1.0025	1.0021	0.9976	0.9993
1.0010	0.9990	1.0035	0.9997	1.0001
1.0015	0.9996	0.9998	1.0019	1.0007
1.0004	0.9989	0.9975	1.0023	1.0000
1.0001	1.0006	0.9991	0.9993	1.0028
0.9991	0.9997	1.0012	0.9979	0.9998
0.9987	0.9987	1.0015	1.0026	1.0010
1.0048	1.0041	0.9975	0.9963	0.9996

even outside this range. If the distances had been measured to the nearest one-tenth of an inch, it is likely that all would have been recorded as exactly 1 in. These data would still be continuous in nature. If measurements to the nearest one-millionth of an inch were made, it is likely that no distances would have been recorded as identical. Even then, however, the data would still appear to be discrete; it would appear to vary in increments of one-millionth of an inch. Data that result from a characteristic which varies through a continuum is continuous in nature.

Frequency distributions. The data exhibited in Table 3.1 and Table 3.2 can be expressed in a compact form by grouping into frequency distributions. Table 3.3 shows the frequency distribution of the number of arrivals per hour given in Table 3.1. Table 3.4 shows the frequency distribution of the distance between two machined surfaces given in Table 3.2. In Table 3.4 it was necessary to define class intervals into which the continuous data could be grouped.

These frequency distributions indicate that the data tend to cluster near the middle, and that the frequency of occurrence of higher and lower values decreases. Tabular presentations such as these convey more meaning than the data in raw form. The tabulated frequencies may be plotted to facilitate their description, as is shown in Figure 3.1 for the arrival data and

Table 3.3. DISTRIBUTION OF THE NUMBER OF ARRIVALS PER HOUR

Arrivals	Number of Hours	Fraction	Relative Frequency
0	7	7/30	0.2333
1	12	12/30	0.4000
2	6	6/30	0.2000
3	3	3/30	0.1000
4	2	2/30	0.0667
Total	30	30/30	1.0000

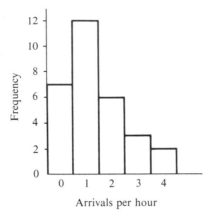

Figure 3.1. Frequency distribution of the number of arrivals per hour.

Figure 3.2 for the measurement data. If the ordinate is changed from absolute to relative frequency, the area under the distribution will be equal to unity. This transformation is shown in the last column of Table 3.3 and Table 3.4.

Relative frequency can be accumulated and plotted as a cumulative distribution. Each cell then represents the cumulative relative frequency up to and including that interval. The intervals will then have the appearance of a series of uneven ascending steps terminating at a value of unity. This is shown in Figure 3.3 for the data of Table 3.1. For the continuous distribution, the cumulative relative frequency distribution will appear as in Figure 3.4 for the data of Table 3.2. The cumulative function for continuous

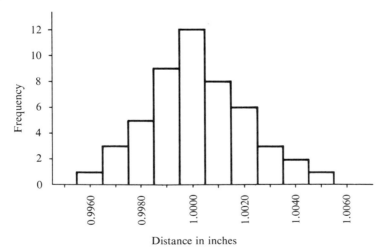

Figure 3.2. Frequency distribution of the distance between
two machined surfaces.

Table 3.4. DISTRIBUTION OF THE DISTANCE BETWEEN TWO MACHINED SURFACES (inches)

Class Interval	Number of Measurements	Fraction	Relative Frequency
0.9955–0.9964	1	1/50	0.02
0.9965–0.9974	3	3/50	0.06
0.9975–0.9984	5	5/50	0.10
0.9985–0.9994	9	9/50	0.18
0.9995–1.0004	12	12/50	0.24
1.0005–1.0014	8	8/50	0.16
1.0015–1.0024	6	6/50	0.12
1.0025–1.0034	3	3/50	0.06
1.0035–1.0044	2	2/50	0.04
1.0045–1.0054	1	1/50	0.02
Total	50	50/50	1.00

data is sometimes smoothed as in Figure 3.4 so that it approximates the form a function would assume if the class intervals were made infinitesimally small with the number of observations substantially increased.

Measures of central tendency. A number of measures may be used to describe the central tendency of a mass of data. Of these, the mean is the most commonly used and may be expressed as

$$\bar{x} = \frac{\sum_{i=1}^{n} x_i}{n} = \frac{x_1 + x_2 + x_3 + \cdots + x_n}{n}. \tag{3.1}$$

The mean of the data given in Table 3.2 may be calculated from Equation

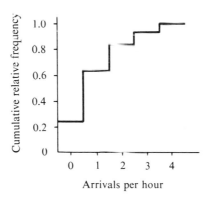

Figure 3.3. Cumulative relative frequency distribution of the number of arrivals per hour.

(3.1) as
$$\bar{x} = \frac{1.0003 + 1.0017 + \cdots + 0.9996}{50} = 1.0001.$$

Where data have already been grouped into class intervals, as in Table 3.4, the following equation may be used to yield an approximate value of the mean.

$$\bar{x} = \frac{\sum\limits_{i=1}^{k} f_i x_i}{\sum\limits_{i=1}^{k} f_i} = \frac{f_1 x_1 + f_2 x_2 + \cdots + f_{k-1} x_{k-1} + f_k x_k}{f_1 + f_2 + \cdots + f_{k-1} + f_k}. \tag{3.2}$$

Equation (3.2) requires that the mid-point of each class interval, x_i, be

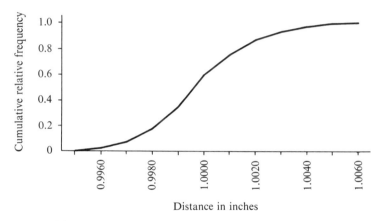

Figure 3.4. Cumulative relative frequency distribution of the distance between two machined surfaces.

multiplied by the number of units in that class interval, f_i, and summed over k, the number of cells. For the data of Table 3.4

$$\bar{x} = \frac{(1)(0.996) + (3)(0.997) + \cdots + (1)(1.005)}{50} = 1.0002.$$

The *median* is a measure of central tendency defined as that value lying in the middle of an ordered set of data. Its computation requires that data be ranked from the smallest value to the largest, or from the largest to the smallest. The median is that value lying in the middle, if the data consist of an odd number of values. Should the data consist of an even number of values, there is no middle value, and the median is the mean of the two central values. In the data from Table 3.2, the twenty-fifth value in ascending order is 1.0001. The twenty-sixth value is also 1.0001; hence, the median would be (1.0001 + 1.0001)/2 or 1.0001.

The *mode* is another measure of central tendency. It is defined as that value which occurs most frequently. In continuous data, there may be no value occurring more than once. The mode is then specified as the mid-point of the class interval of greatest frequency. Referring to Figure 3.2, the modal value would be 1.0000.

If a distribution is symmetrical with a central peak and tapering off uniformly on either side, the mean, median, and mode coincide. This is not the case only when a distribution tapers off more rapidly to one side than to the other. The continuous distribution of Figure 3.5 is said to be *skewed to the right*. In this case the mode, median, and mean would assume ascending values approximately as indicated. This distribution might typify procurement lead time for an inventory item. If this is the case, the mean gives a value of average lead time which is higher than either the median or the mode.

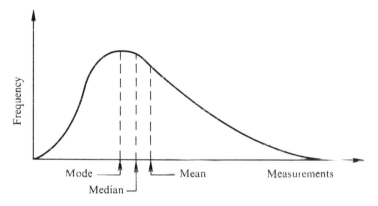

Figure 3.5. A skewed distribution illustrating three measures of central tendency.

Since the measures of central tendency do not assume the same value in all applications, it is necessary to specify which measure is being used.

Measures of dispersion. In addition to information concerning the central tendency of data, it is desirable to describe the extent to which the data cluster about their central value. For this purpose, two measures of variation or dispersion are customarily employed. Of these, the *range* is the least complex and is obtained by calculating the arithmetic difference between the largest and the smallest value. The range is not a very stable measure of variation since it depends upon only two values. Its advantage lies in the ease with which it may be calculated. The range is equal to 1.0048 − 0.9963 or 0.0085 for the data of Table 3.2.

The *variance* is a much more stable measure of dispersion. It may be computed as

$$s^2 = \frac{\sum_{i=1}^{n}(x_i - \bar{x})^2}{n-1} = \frac{(x_1 - \bar{x})^2 + (x_2 - \bar{x})^2 + \cdots + (x_n - \bar{x})^2}{n-1}. \quad (3.3)$$

Computing the variance calls for an evaluation of the difference between each value and the mean. These differences are then individually squared and added. The sum of these squared differences is divided by a number equal to one less than the number of observations. This definitional formula for the variance requires the lengthy series of calculations just described. Fortunately, the numerator can be modified by algebraic manipulation and the variance expressed as

$$s^2 = \frac{\sum_{i=1}^{n} x_i^2 - \left[\left(\sum_{i=1}^{n} x_i\right)^2 / n\right]}{n-1}. \quad (3.4)$$

Although Equation (3.4) looks more complex than Equation (3.3), it permits more rapid computation since the necessity for successive subtraction is eliminated.

The variance of the data given in Table 3.2 would be found from Equation (3.3) as

$$s^2 = \frac{(1.0003 - 1.0001)^2 + (1.0017 - 1.0001)^2 + \cdots + (0.9996 - 1.0001)^2}{49}$$

$$= 0.00000365.$$

And, use of Equation (3.4) gives

$$s^2 = \frac{[(1.0003)^2 + \cdots + (0.9996)^2] - [(1.0003 + \cdots + 0.9996)^2 / 50]}{49}$$

$$= 0.00000365.$$

Where data have been converted to a frequency distribution, Equation (3.4) becomes

$$s^2 = \frac{\sum_{i=1}^{k} f_i(x_i)^2 - \left[\left(\sum_{i=1}^{k} f_i x_i\right)^2 / n\right]}{n-1}. \quad (3.5)$$

The variance is a useful and descriptive measure of the dispersion of data. It may be converted to a closely related measure of dispersion referred to as the *standard deviation*. The relationship between these two measures is quite simple; the standard deviation is the positive square root of the variance.

3.2. CONCEPTS OF PROBABILITY

Probability may be defined either as a measure of certainty or of uncertainty. It provides a means for mathematically expressing a degree of assurance or of doubt. As a concept, probability may be used to describe the outcome of a random event. An event with a probability of unity is certain to occur. On the other hand, an event with a probability of zero is certain not to occur. These extremes rarely exist in reality, but they establish limits between which a measure of certainty or uncertainty may fall.

The concept of relative frequency is often employed to establish the probability of occurrence of an event. As an example, consider the tossing of a coin. It may be established from experience that a fair coin will come up heads as often as tails. Thus, for any toss it is said that the probability of a head will be 0.5. This notion need not be restricted to such a simple case. In the following sections, we consider probability distributions establishing the outcome of variables taking on many values.

The addition theorem. The probability of the occurrence of either one or another of a series of mutually exclusive events is the sum of the probabilities of their separate occurrences. If a fair coin is tossed, and success is defined as the occurrence of either a head or a tail, then the probability of a head or a tail would be

$$P(H + T) = P(H) + P(T)$$

$$- 0.5 + 0.5 = 1.0.$$

The key to use of the addition theorem is the proper definition of mutually exclusive events. Such events must be distinct one from another. If one event occurs, it must be impossible for the second to occur at the same time. For example, assume that the probability of having a flat tire during a given time period, on each of four tires on an automobile, is 0.3. Then, the probability of having a flat tire on any of the four tires during this time period is not given up by the addition of these four probabilities. If $P(T_1) = P(T_2) = P(T_3) = P(T_4) = 0.3$ are the respective probabilities of failure for each of the four tires, then

$$P(T_1 + T_2 + T_3 + T_4) \neq P(T_1) + P(T_2) + P(T_3) + P(T_4)$$

$$\neq 0.3 + 0.3 + 0.3 + 0.3 = 1.2.$$

This is not true because the failure of tires is not mutually exclusive. During the time period established, two or more tires may fail, whereas in the example of the coin tossing, it is not possible to obtain a head and a tail on the same toss.

The multiplication theorem. The probability of occurrence of independent events is the product of the probabilities of their separate events. Implicit in this theorem is the successful occurrence of two events simultaneously or in succession. Thus, the probability of the occurrence of two heads in two tosses of a coin would be

$$P(H \cdot H) = P(H)P(H)$$
$$= (0.5)(0.5) = 0.25.$$

The tire failure example can now be resolved by considering the probabilities of each tire not failing. The probability of tire one not failing is given by $P(\bar{T}_1) = 0.7$. The probability of no tire failing is then given by

$$P[(\bar{T}_1)(\bar{T}_2)(\bar{T}_3)(\bar{T}_4)] = P(\bar{T}_1)P(\bar{T}_2)(P(\bar{T}_3)P(\bar{T}_4)$$
$$= (0.7)(0.7)(0.7)(0.7) = 0.2401.$$

And the probability of a tire failing, or of one or more tires failing, is

$$P(T_1 + T_2 + T_3 + T_4) = 1 - 0.2401 = 0.7599.$$

This approach is valid, since the probability of one tire not failing is independent of the success or failure of the other three tires.

The conditional theorem. The probability of the occurrence of two dependent events is the probability of the first event times the probability of the second event, given that the first has occurred. This may be expressed as
$$P(W_1 \cdot W_2) = P(W_1)P(W_2 \mid W_1).$$

This theorem is similar to the multiplication theorem, except that consideration is given to the lack of independence between events.

As an example, consider the probability of selecting two successive white balls from an urn containing three white and two black balls. This problem reduces to a calculation of the product of the probability of selecting a white ball times the probability of selecting a second white ball, given that the first attempt has been successful.

$$P(W_1 \cdot W_2) = \left(\frac{3}{5}\right)\left(\frac{2}{4}\right) = \frac{3}{10}.$$

The conditional theorem makes allowances for a change in probabilities between two successive events. This theorem will be helpful in constructing finite discrete probability distributions.

3.3. DISCRETE PROBABILITY DISTRIBUTIONS

A probability distribution may be differentiated from a frequency distribution in that the latter describes what has occurred in the past, whereas the former predicts what might occur. Thus, the outcome of a coin-tossing exercise may be plotted as a frequency distribution of heads and tails. A probability distribution for coin tossing would express the expected number of heads and tails established by theoretical considerations. A frequency distribution is a historical record; a probability distribution is a forecast.

Probability distributions may be discrete or continuous, depending upon the nature of the event they are used to predict. They provide a means for assigning the likelihood of occurrence of all possible values. Variables described in terms of a probability distribution are conveniently called *random variables*. The specific value of a random variable is determined by the distribution. The occurrence of that value is then governed by the associated probability. Some discrete probability distributions are presented in this section.

The hypergeometric distribution. The hypergeometric is the most fundamental discrete probability distribution. It describes the case of sampling without replacement and is a simple extension of the conditional probability theorem. This distribution can be developed from the theory of combinations, where the number of combinations of n things taken x at a time is given by the expression

$$C_x^n = \frac{n!}{x!\,(n-x)!}.$$

For example, suppose there are four items labeled A, B, C, and D. The number of possible pairs which can be made up of these four items can be enumerated as A-B, A-C, A-D, B-C, B-D, and C-D for a total of six such pairs. Alternatively, this same solution is

$$C_2^4 = \frac{4!}{2!\,2!} = \frac{(4)(3)(2)(1)}{(2)(1)(2)(1)} = 6.$$

Likewise, the number of combinations of four units taken three at a time is

$$C_3^4 = \frac{4!}{3!\,1!} = 4.$$

And the number of combinations of four units taken four at a time is

$$C_4^4 = \frac{4!}{4!\,0!} = 1.$$

Note that $0! = 1$. At the other extreme, where very large factorials are encountered, it is convenient to work with logarithms of factorials.

Combinations are used in the construction of the hypergeometric distribution by defining the probability of each occurrence as a fraction consisting of all favorable combinations divided by the total number of combinations. As an example, consider an urn containing two black balls and one white ball. Two balls are selected at random from this urn. The probability that one is white and one is black is sought. The denominator of the fraction is the total number of combinations of three balls taken two at a time. The numerator is the number of combinations which will satisfy the requirement of selecting exactly one white and one black ball. This is the product of the number of combinations of one white ball selected from the one which is available times the number of combinations of one black ball selected from the two black balls which are available. The probability of drawing exactly one white and one black ball is

$$\frac{C_1^1 C_1^2}{C_2^3} = \frac{(1!\,2!)/0!\,1!\,1!\,1!}{3!/2!\,1!} = \frac{2/1}{6/2} = \frac{2}{3}.$$

The only remaining alternative is that of drawing exactly two black balls. The probability of so doing is given by

$$\frac{C_2^2 C_0^1}{C_2^3} = \frac{(2!\,1!)/2!\,0!\,0!\,1!}{3!/2!\,1!} = \frac{2/2}{6/2} = \frac{1}{3}.$$

These two probabilities represent the relative frequencies for a hypergeometric probability distribution.

Another example can be used to illustrate this distribution. Assume a container of 50 items includes three which are defective. A sample of five is selected from the fifty. The probability is desired that exactly zero, one, two, or all three defectives will be contained in the sample of five. These probabilities may be calculated as

$$P(0) = \frac{C_0^3 C_5^{47}}{C_5^{50}} = \frac{(3!\,47!)/0!\,3!\,5!\,42!}{50!/5!\,45!} = 0.7240$$

$$P(1) = \frac{C_1^3 C_4^{47}}{C_5^{50}} = \frac{(3!\,47!)/1!\,2!\,4!\,43!}{50!/5!\,45!} = 0.2525$$

$$P(2) = \frac{C_2^3 C_3^{47}}{C_5^{50}} = \frac{(3!\,47!)/2!\,1!\,3!\,44!}{50!/5!\,45!} = 0.0230$$

$$P(3) = \frac{C_3^3 C_2^{47}}{C_5^{50}} = \frac{(3!\,47!)/3!\,0!\,2!\,45!}{50!/5!\,45!} = 0.0005$$

$$P(0) + P(1) + P(2) + P(3) \;= 1.0000.$$

The probability distribution would assume the form shown in Figure 3.6. Note that the distribution is skewed and that the area it encompasses totals

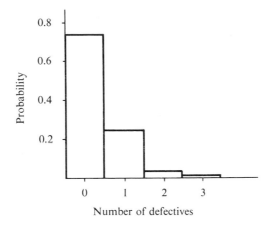

Figure 3.6. A probability distribution of the number of defectives in a sample of five from a lot of fifty containing three defectives.

unity, since the sum of the probabilities of drawing zero, one, two, or three defectives is 1.0000.

Hypergeometric distributions have no typical form. They may be symmetrical or they may be skewed either to the right or to the left. They are representative of sampling distributions where the population is finite and replacement between items is not effected.

The binomial distribution. The binomial probability distribution is also a sampling distribution. It is applicable where the probability is sought of exactly x occurrences in n trials of an event that has a constant probability of occurrence p. The requirement of a constant probability of occurrence is satisfied when the population being sampled is infinite in size, or where replacement of the sampled unit is effected. This distribution is used as an approximation to the hypergeometric distribution when the population is relatively large when compared to the sample which is drawn. Under these conditions, the constant probability of occurrence is approximated.

The probability of exactly x occurrences in n trials of an event that has a constant probability of occurrence p is given as

$$P(x) = C_x^n p^x q^{n-x} = \frac{n!}{x!\,(n-x)!}\, p^x q^{n-x}, \qquad 0 \leq x \leq n \qquad (3.6)$$

where $q = 1 - p$. The mean and variance of this distribution are given by np and npq respectively.

As an example of the application of the binomial distribution, assume that a fair coin is to be tossed five times. The probability of obtaining

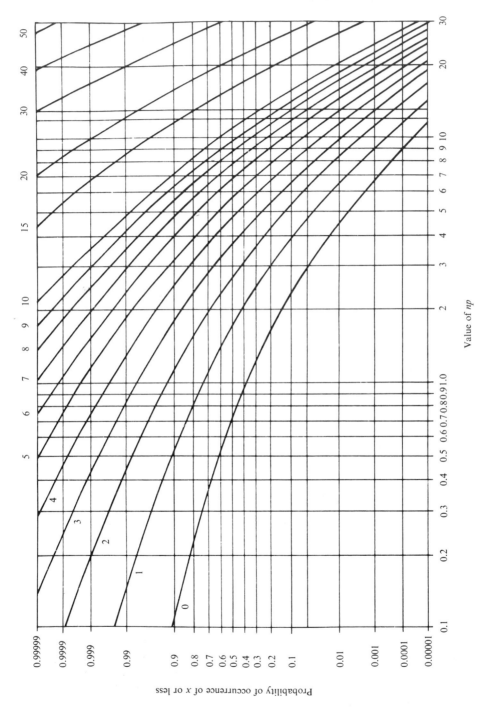

Figure 3.7. Cumulative probability curves for the Poisson distribution (modified Thorndike Chart). Reproduced, with permission, from H. F. Dodge and H. G. Romig, *Sampling Inspection Tables*, John Wiley & Sons, Inc., 1959.

42

exactly two heads is

$$P(2) = C_2^5(p)^2(1 - p)^3$$
$$= \frac{5!}{3!\,2!}(0.5)^5$$
$$= 10(0.03125) = 0.3125.$$

A probability distribution may be constructed by solving for the probability of exactly zero, one, two, three, four, and five heads in five tosses. If $p = 0.5$, as in this example, the resulting distribution would be symmetrical. If $p < 0.5$, the distribution would be skewed to the right; if $p > 0.5$, the distribution would be skewed to the left.

The binomial distribution finds frequent use as an approximation to the hypergeometric distribution because of the relative ease with which the individual probabilities may be found. It will serve as a good approximation to the extent that the lot or population is large relative to the sample size. This may be illustrated by reworking the example used to illustrate the hypergeometric distribution. Since the container of 50 items contained 3 defectives, $p = 0.06$ and $q = 0.94$. The respective probabilities are

$$P(0) = \frac{5!}{0!\,5!}(0.06)^0(0.94)^5 = (1)(0.94)^5 \qquad = 0.7339$$

$$P(1) = \frac{5!}{1!\,4!}(0.06)^1(0.94)^4 = (5)(0.06)(0.94)^4 \qquad = 0.2343$$

$$P(2) = \frac{5!}{2!\,3!}(0.06)^2(0.94)^3 = (10)(0.06)^2(0.94)^3 = 0.0299$$

$$P(3) = \frac{5!}{3!\,2!}(0.06)^3(0.94)^2 = (10)(0.06)^3(0.94)^2 = 0.0019$$

$$P(0) + P(1) + P(2) + P(3) = 1.0000.$$

The Poisson distribution. The Poisson distribution is useful as a distribution in its own right and as an approximation to the binomial. It is applicable when the opportunity for the occurrence of an event is large, but the actual occurrence is extremely unlikely. The probability of exactly x occurrences of an event of probability p in a sample n is

$$P(x) = \frac{(\mu)^x e^{-\mu}}{x!}, \qquad 0 \le x \le \infty. \tag{3.7}$$

The mean and variance of this distribution are equal and given by μ, where $\mu = np$.

Cumulative Poisson probabilities are tabulated for values of μ ranging up to 24 in Appendix A, Table A.1. Less precise values for these cumulative probabilities may be found from the modified Thorndike chart illustrated in Figure 3.7. This graph gives the cumulative probability for the occurrence of x or fewer items in a sample of n, from a population containing a proportion, p, of such items.

As an example of the application of the Poisson distribution, assume that a sample of 100 items is selected from a population of items which are 1 per cent defective. The probability of obtaining exactly three defectives in the sample is found from Equation (3.7) as

$$P(3) = \frac{(1)^3(2.72)^{-1}}{3!} = 0.062.$$

The modified Thorndike chart of Figure 3.7 may be used to find an approximate answer. The graph is entered along the abscissa at a value of $np = 1$. Reading upward until the curve $x = 3$ is reached yields an ordinate value of 0.98. The same procedure is repeated for $x = 2$, giving an ordinate value of 0.92. The probability of exactly three defectives is then $0.98 - 0.92$, or 0.06. Finally, Table A.1 in Appendix A could have been used to solve for the required probability.

The Poisson distribution may be used as an approximation to the binomial distribution. Such an approximation is good when n is relatively large, p is relatively small, and in general, $pn < 5$. These conditions were satisfied in the previous example.

3.4. CONTINUOUS PROBABILITY DISTRIBUTIONS

Continuous probability distributions are used to define the probability of the occurrence of an event that may take on values over a continuum. Under certain conditions, it may be desirable to use a continuous probability distribution to approximate a discrete probability distribution. By so doing, tedious summations may be replaced by integrals. In other instances, it may be desirable to make a continuous distribution discrete. This operation is necessary where a numerical solution is to be performed on a digital computer. This section deals with continuous probability distributions.

The rectangular distribution. The rectangular or uniform probability distribution may be either discrete or continuous. The continuous form of this simple distribution is given by

$$f(x) = \frac{1}{a}, \qquad 0 \le x \le a. \tag{3.8}$$

The discrete form divides the interval 0 to a into $n + 1$ cells over the range 0 to n with $1/(n + 1)$ as the unit probabilities. The mean and variance of the rectangular probability distribution are given as $a/2$ and $a^2/12$ for the continuous case, and as $n/2$ and $n^2/12 + n/6$ for the discrete case.

The general form of the rectangular probability distribution is shown in Figure 3.8. The probability that a value of x will fall between 0 and a is

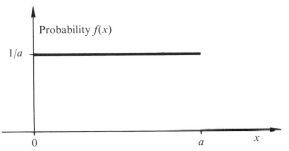

Figure 3.8. The general form of the rectangular distribution.

the area under the function $1/a$ between the limits 0 and a. This is equal to unity. One may determine the probability associated with a specific value of x, or a range of x, by integration for the continuous case. The probability associated with a specific value of x for the discrete distributions of the previous section was found from the functions given. Determination of the probability associated with a range of x required a summation of individual probabilities. This is a fundamental difference in dealing with discrete and continuous probability distributions.

Values drawn at random from the rectangular distribution with x allowed to take on values ranging from 0 through 9 are given in Appendix A, Table A.2. These random rectangular variates may be used to randomize a sample or to develop values drawn at random from other probability distributions. As such, they are a useful tool in statistical analysis.

The exponential distribution. The exponential probability distribution is given by

$$f(x) = \frac{1}{a} e^{-x/a}, \qquad 0 \leq x \leq \infty. \tag{3.9}$$

The mean and variance of this distribution are given by a and a^2 respectively. Its form is illustrated in Figure 3.9.

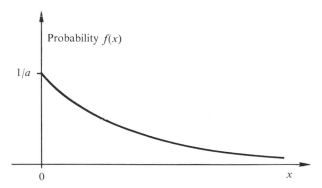

Figure 3.9. The general form of the exponential distribution.

As an example of the exponential probability distribution, consider the selection of a light bulb from a population of light bulbs whose life is known to be exponentially distributed with a mean, $\mu = 1{,}000$ hours. The probability of the life of this sample bulb not exceeding 1,000 hours would be expressed as $P(x \leq 1{,}000)$. This would be the proportional area under the exponential function over the range $x = 0$ to $x = 1{,}000$, or

$$P(x \leq 1{,}000) = \int_0^{1{,}000} f(x)\, dx$$

$$= \int_0^{1{,}000} \frac{1}{1{,}000}\, e^{-x/1{,}000}\, dx$$

$$= -e^{-x/1{,}000} \Big|_0^{1{,}000}$$

$$= 1 - e^{-1} = 0.632.$$

Note that 0.632 is that proportion of the area of an exponential distribution to the left of the mean. This implies that the probability of the occurrence of an event exceeding the mean value is only $1 - 0.632 = 0.368$.

The normal distribution. This normal or Gaussian probability distribution, is one of the most important of all distributions. It is defined by

$$f(x) = \frac{1}{\sigma\sqrt{2\pi}}\, e^{[-(x-\mu)^2/2\sigma^2]}, \quad -\infty \leq x \leq +\infty. \tag{3.10}$$

The mean and variance are μ and σ^2 respectively. Variation is inherent in nature and much of this variation appears to follow the normal distribution, the form of which is given in Figure 3.10.

The normal distribution is symmetrical about the mean and possesses some interesting and useful properties in regard to its shape. Where distances from the mean are expressed in terms of standard deviations, σ, the

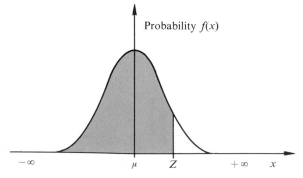

Figure 3.10. The normal probability distribution.

relative areas defined between two such distances will be constant from one distribution to another. In effect, all normal distributions, when defined in terms of a common value of μ and of σ, will be identical in form, and corresponding probabilities may be tabulated. Normally, cumulative probabilities are given from $-\infty$ to any value expressed as standard deviation units. Such probabilities are given in Appendix A, Table A.3. The table gives the probability from $-\infty$ to Z, where Z is a standard normal variate defined as

$$Z = \frac{x - \mu}{\sigma}.$$

This is shown as the shaded area in Figure 3.10.

The area from $-\infty$ to -1σ is indicated as the shaded area in Figure 3.11. From Table A.3, the probability of x falling in this range is 0.1587.

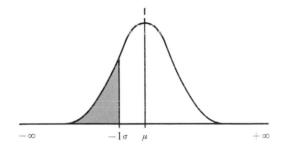

Figure 3.11. The area from $-\infty$ to -1σ under the normal distribution.

Likewise, the area from $-\infty$ to $+2\sigma$ is 0.9773. If the probability of a value falling in the interval -1σ to $+2\sigma$ is required, the following computations may be made:

$$P(\text{area} -\infty \text{ to } +2\sigma) = 0.9773$$
$$-P(\text{area} -\infty \text{ to } -1\sigma) = 0.1587$$

$$P(\text{area} -1\sigma \text{ to } +2\sigma) = 0.8186.$$

This situation is shown in Figure 3.12. The probabilities associated with any normal probability distribution can be calculated by the use of Table A.3.

Assume that the data originally given in Table 3.2 represent a sample of machined plates of indicated thickness. Also assume that these data are from a population of plates whose thicknesses are normally distributed. The mean of this sample has been calculated by Equation (3.1) and can be assumed to be a good estimate of the population mean. The sample variance

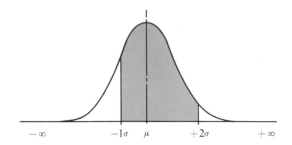

Figure 3.12. The area from -1σ to $+2\sigma$ under the normal distribution.

was calculated by Equation (3.4) and is also assumed to be an estimate of the variance of the population. These are summarized as

$$\mu \cong \bar{x} = 1.0001$$

$$\sigma^2 \cong s^2 = 0.00000365$$

$$\sigma \cong s = 0.00191.$$

It is now assumed that their properties define a specific population. The probability of a plate being smaller than 0.9990 in. can be found. Alternatively, the probability of a plate being within a set of specification limits can be calculated. In both cases, it is necessary to convert these values to the standard normal distribution for which values have been tabulated. In the first case, x_i is 0.9990 and this variation from the mean of the reference distribution is

$$Z = \frac{0.9990 - 1.0001}{0.00191} = -0.576.$$

A plate of exactly 0.9990 in. corresponds to a value lying at -0.576σ on the standard normal distribution. The probability of a plate being smaller than 0.9990 in. is the area under the normal distribution from $-\infty$ to -0.576σ, or 0.283.

The probability of a plate falling within the specification limits of 1.0000 ± 0.0040 in. is approached the same way. These two limits must first be defined as values of the standard normal distribution. For $x_1 = 0.9960$,

$$Z_1 = \frac{0.9960 - 1.0001}{0.00191} = -2.146.$$

For $x_2 = 1.0040$,

$$Z_2 = \frac{1.0040 - 1.0001}{0.00191} = +2.042.$$

The probability of a plate falling within the specification limits is calculated as

$$P(\text{area} - \infty \quad \text{to} +2.042\sigma) = 0.9794$$
$$-P(\text{area} - \infty \quad \text{to} -2.146\sigma) = 0.0160$$

$$P(\text{area} -2.146\sigma \text{ to } +2.042\sigma) = 0.9634.$$

Any probability may be similarly calculated when one assumes that the process is normally distributed and when one has obtained estimates of the population parameters.

The Poisson and normal as approximations. In most cases, the hypergeometric probability distribution would be appropriately used to describe sampling from finite populations. As an alternative, we may use the binomial distribution as an approximation if the population is relatively large. In this case the value of p does not change appreciably as items are taken from the population. The Poisson distribution may be used as an approximation to the binomial when n is relatively large, p is relatively small, and $pn < 5$. These approximations are shown in Figure 3.13.

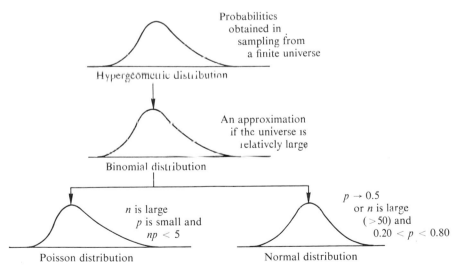

Figure 3.13. The Poisson and normal distributions as approximations.

The normal distribution may also be used as an approximation to the binomial. This approximation will usually be satisfactory if p is close to 0.5 or if n is large. If $n \geq 50$, p may be as small as 0.20 or as large as 0.80

following example: A sample of $n = 4$ is taken from a population of known mean, $\mu = 100$, and variance $\sigma^2 = 64$. The probability that the mean of that sample will exceed a value $\bar{x} = 105$ may be found by first computing

$$\sigma_{\bar{x}}^2 = \frac{\sigma^2}{n}$$

$$= \frac{64}{4} = 16.$$

The probability that a sample mean will exceed a value of $\bar{x} = 105$ is P (the area from Z to $+\infty$), where

$$Z = \frac{\bar{x} - \mu}{\sigma_{\bar{x}}} = \frac{105 - 100}{4} = +1.25.$$

P(the area from $+1.25\sigma$ to $+\infty$) $= 0.1056$.

In the preceding example, it was implicitly assumed that the variation in sample means followed a normal distribution. It might have been inferred that the universe from which these samples were obtained also follows a normal distribution. Although many real world variables are normally distributed, this latter assumption cannot be universally applied. In the preceding example, however, a relationship known as the *central limit theorem* permits one to accept the first assumption without need to accept the second. The central limit theorem states: If x has a distribution for which the moment generating function exists, then the variable $\bar{x}$ has a distribution that approaches normality as the size of the sample tends toward infinity.[1] The sample size required for any desired degree of convergence is a function of the shape of the parent distribution. Fairly good results have, however, been demonstrated with a sample of $n = 4$ for both the rectangular and triangular distributions.[2]

The central limit theorem greatly enhances the value of the normal distribution in statistical analysis. As an example, a control chart can be constructed for the means of samples and limits placed on this chart which were developed from a normal probability density function. A normal distribution is often used in the analysis of errors because it can be assumed that each individual error is the sum of many small independent errors.

Statistical errors and hypothesis testing. In logic and mathematics, a proof can be demonstrated with certainty after some procedures of proof have been defined. Thus, it is possible to state in absolute terms that the sum of the angles of a triangle is 180°. Such a proof is not possible in inferential statistics. A hypothesis must first be stated and if it is rejected as

---

[1] For a proof of this theorem see P. G. Hoel, *Introduction to Mathematical Statistics,* 3rd ed. (New York: John Wiley & Sons, Inc., 1954), p. 145.

[2] W. A. Shewhart, *Economic Control of Quality of Manufactured Product* (New York, D. Van Nostrand Company, Inc., 1931).

stated, it is rejected with a level of significance or degree of confidence that represents the chance of its being correct or in error. The level of significance is defined as a value of α, such as 0.05, and this value represents the probability that an error has been made in rejecting the hypothesis. This is referred to as *Type I error* of probability α.

In addition to the possibility of making a Type I error it is possible to accept a hypothesis when it is false. This is called a *Type II or β error*. The probability of a β error is more difficult to determine. Whereas the value of α is specified in advance, the value of β is a function of the value of α which was specified, the size of the sample which was collected, and the magnitude of the error which was not detected.

Table 3.5. OUTCOME POSSIBILITIES FOR HYPOTHESIS TESTING

Reality

		H_0 *True*	H_0 *False*
Decision	Reject H_0	Type I error (probability $= \alpha$)	Correct decision
	Do not reject H_0	Correct decision	Type II error (probability $= \beta$)

Hypothesis testing is a formal method by which statistical inferences are made. These inferences are first stated as hypotheses which are then tested through the collection of data and finally accepted or rejected, based on the results of those data. A hypothesis is usually specified as a null hypothesis, H_0, concerning the population parameter. It can then be rejected or not rejected with the consequences given in Table 3.5. Note that it is not possible to make both an α and a β error. If the decision is made to reject the null hypothesis, the probability of being in error is α and the probability of being correct is $1 - \alpha$. If the null hypothesis is not rejected, the probability of being in error is β. This cannot be quantitatively defined. This probability of a Type II error, in addition to being determined by n and α, is a function of the magnitude of the differences of that which was formulated as a hypothesis of no differences. The probability of being correct; $1 - \beta$, also cannot be calculated. This probability can, however, be defined, with α and n, as a function over a range of these differences. Such a curve is referred to as a *power function*.

The essential steps in hypothesis testing will be demonstrated with a coin-tossing example. Suppose a coin is suspected of being biased. An experiment to resolve this suspicion will require the following steps:

(1) Formulate the null hypothesis: State that there is no difference in the probability of a head and the probability of a tail, $P(H) = P(T) = 0.5$. In almost all cases the null hypothesis must be rejected to verify a conjecture.

(2) Specify the level of significance: In this example $\alpha = 0.01$ and $n = 12$ is chosen. This is an arbitrary choice and usually will be an attempt to balance the costs of sampling and the costs associated with an incorrect conclusion.

(3) Construct the statistical test: The probability of obtaining x heads or tails in n tosses is given by the binomial distribution. Assuming 4,096 trials of 12 tosses each, the expected frequencies for 0 through 12 heads or tails are given in Table 3.6.

Table 3.6. A SAMPLING DISTRIBUTION OF THE NUMBER OF HEADS IN 4,096 TRIALS

Number of Heads or Tails	Expected Frequency	Probability
12	1	0.00024
11	12	0.00293
10	66	0.01611
9	220	0.05371
8	495	0.12085
7	792	0.19336
6	924	0.22558
5	792	0.19336
4	495	0.12085
3	220	0.05371
2	66	0.01611
1	12	0.00293
0	1	0.00024

(4) Determine the rejection region: If the coin is fair, six is the most likely number of heads that will occur in 12 tosses. It is less likely but still reasonable to expect 5 or 7 heads or tails. It is, however, very unlikely for 0 or 12 heads or tails to occur unless the coin is biased. The probability of obtaining 12 heads or tails from a fair coin is $1/4,096 = 0.00024$. This is less than half the significance level, since $\alpha/2 = 0.005$. The probability of obtaining 11 or 12 heads or tails is $1/4,096 + 12/4,096 = 0.00317$, which is still less than the significance level. The probability of obtaining 10, 11, or 12 heads

or tails is $1/4{,}096 + 12/4{,}096 + 66/4{,}096 = 0.01928$. This now exceeds the value of $\alpha/2$. Thus, the rejection region will be defined as 11 or 12 heads or tails, which results in an $\alpha/2$ of 0.0032. This adjustment in the originally established level of confidence is necessary since a discrete distribution is involved.

(5) Make the decision: The final step in testing the hypothesis requires that the experiment be performed. In this case, the coin would be tossed 12 times and the results observed. If either 11 or 12 heads or tails are obtained, the null hypothesis would be rejected. This would verify the conjecture that the coin is biased.

The preceding example illustrates a two-tail test since it was not known whether the coin was biased in favor of heads or tails. A one-tail test would be used when it is known that rejection might occur in one direction. A one-tail test is more powerful; it is more likely to detect a bias if one exists because of a larger rejection region composed of the sum of the probabilities otherwise allocated to each of the two tails.

A large number of statistical tests have been designed for testing many varied hypotheses. To present even the most fundamental of these would go beyond the needs of this chapter. The basic concept of statistical testing, however, will be valuable in understanding techniques presented in future chapters.

3.6. REGRESSION AND CORRELATION

Some variables appear to be related one to another. As a variable changes and assumes different values, a second variable may also change. These two variables may be linked in a direct causal relationship; they may both be related to a third variable; or they may appear to have no known and intuitively logical relationship. Whatever the apparent existence or lack of causality, if the relationship between the paired variables follows a consistent linear pattern, this relationship can be described through linear regression. A measure of the degree of this relationship can then be obtained through correlation analysis. This section deals with the descriptive and predictive techniques of regression and correlation.

The scatter diagram. Consider the actual and observed rating data in Table 3.7. Each pair of values records a person's success in a work measurement rating exercise. The individual rates film sequences of industrial work operations and attempts to judge the speed at which a worker is accomplishing a job. If the worker is performing at a referenced normal pace he should be judged at 100 per cent. If he moves faster or slower, the rating should be judged proportionally higher or lower. It is assumed that actual

Table 3.7. ACTUAL AND OBSERVED DATA IN A WORK MEASUREMENT RATING EXERCISE

Actual	Observed	Actual	Observed	Actual	Observed	Actual	Observed
50	65	130	100	180	130	180	150
160	140	140	130	110	100	150	130
110	120	85	95	115	110	115	120
125	110	90	85	110	130	160	130
100	90	185	150	165	160	150	150
180	180	60	65	60	85	175	155
175	135	170	145	100	100	70	90
150	130	80	85	40	60	190	165
70	75	70	55	50	85	50	50
170	150	80	70	130	130	145	115

values are given for each film sequence and that the data of Table 3.7 represent these actual values plus the estimated or observed values. A perfect rating for each film sequence would require that the observed value be identical to the actual value. This has not occurred. The relative success of the individual attempting the rating can be seen from the difference in actual and observed values.

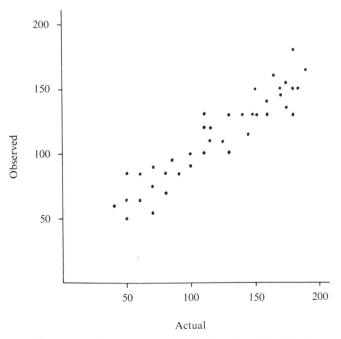

Figure 3.15. A scatter diagram for the data of Table 3.7.

Data from two variables that are related may be exhibited on a scatter diagram. One of these two variables is usually classified as the *dependent variable* and is recorded as the *ordinate*. The other variable is called the *independent* variable and it is recorded as the *abscissa*. In this framework, y is usually predicted from x, although no causal relationship is necessarily implied. Data may be recorded by plotting point values or by dividing the ordinate and abscissa into intervals and then counting and recording the number of observations falling into each cell. Figure 3.15 gives an example of plotted point values from Table 3.7.

Some assumptions are necessary for a linear regression equation and correlation coefficient to have meaning. The data are assumed to be linearly related. For a given value of an independent variable, x, the distribution of dependent values, y, is assumed to be normal. Also, the distribution of x values for a given y value is assumed normal. Actually, a two-variable normal distribution is involved. It is also assumed that the variance of y for all values of x is constant, and conversely, the variance of x for all values of y is constant. This property of the distribution is referred to as *homoscedasticity*. Finally, it is assumed that the failure of the means of y values for any given values of x to fall on a straight line is due to chance fluctuations in those means. This assumption also holds true for the mean values of x for given values of y.

Linear regression. In linear regression, we seek a straight line that passes through the data of Figure 3.15 and that minimizes the sum of the squares of the errors of estimate. The equation of a straight line for this application may be expressed as

$$y' = b + a(x - \bar{x}) \qquad (3.12)$$

where $b = y$ intercept on the $\bar{x}$ axes
$b - a\bar{x} = y'$ intercept on the y axes
$a =$ slope of the line
$\bar{x} =$ mean value of the x values
$y =$ value of the variable to be estimated
$y' =$ the corresponding linear value
$y - y' =$ the error of estimate.

The straight line, together with the associated notation, is shown in Figure 3.16.

Specific values for a and b in Equation (3.12) that minimize $\sum (y - y')^2$ are

$$b = \frac{\sum y}{n} = \bar{y} \quad \text{and} \quad a = \frac{\sum y(x - \bar{x})}{\sum (x - \bar{x})^2} = \frac{\sum xy - n\bar{x}\bar{y}}{\sum x^2 - n\bar{x}^2}.$$

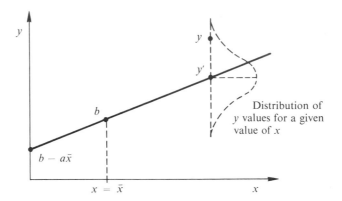

Figure 3.16. The straight line $y' = b + a(x - \bar{x})$.

Substituting the foregoing expressions into Equation (3.12) gives

$$y' - \bar{y} = a(x - \bar{x}). \tag{3.13}$$

The use of Equation (3.13) can be illustrated with the data of Table 3.7. The slope is

$$a = \frac{601,300 - 40(120.63)(113.0)}{664,425 - 40(14,550.39)} = 0.68.$$

And the value for b is

$$b = \frac{4,520}{40} = 113.$$

Therefore, $y' - 113 = 0.68(x - 120.63)$

$$y' = 0.68x + 30.97.$$

In this example, the objective of the rating exercise is for the observed values to equal the actual values. Thus, $y' = x$ is the desired line of best fit. The individual under consideration has a positive intercept and a slope less than one. He tends to rate slower workers faster than they are actually working and he tends to penalize the faster workers by not giving them due credit. He is most accurate in the middle ranges of an actual rate of 100 per cent. This equation should show him that, in future rating efforts, he should be more severe in his estimates of slower workers and more generous in his estimates of faster workers. This would tend to lower the intercept to zero and increase the slope to one.

Correlation. The correlation coefficient, r, expresses the degree of relationship between two variables and may be defined as

$$r = \frac{\sum (x - \bar{x})(y - \bar{y})}{n\sigma_x\sigma_y}. \qquad (3.14)$$

For ease of computation, this may be converted to

$$r = \frac{n \sum xy - \sum x \sum y}{\sqrt{n \sum x^2 - (\sum x)^2}\sqrt{n \sum y^2 - (\sum y)^2}}. \qquad (3.15)$$

Correlation coefficients vary from -1.00 to $+1.00$, with these two extremes representing a perfect relationship. If $r = 0$, no relationship whatsoever

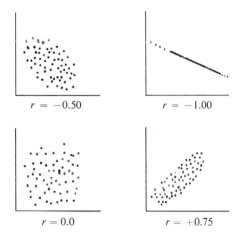

Figure 3.17. Some scatter diagrams reflecting different levels of correlation coefficients.

exists between the paired variables. In effect, r may be considered to vary from $r = 0$ to $r = +1.00$, from no predictive relationship to the case where every paired value falls on a straight line. Negative values of r indicate the same degree of relationship as corresponding positive values, except that a negative correlation coefficient indicates one value is decreasing while the other is increasing. Any linear regression equation with a negative slope will also possess a negative correlation coefficient. Some examples of correlation coefficients, and their respective scatter diagrams, are given in Figure 3.17. Note that although $r = 0.80$ implies a higher degree of relationship than $r = 0.40$, this does not mean the relationship is twice as good.

Using Equation (3.14), a correlation coefficient may be obtained for the data of Table 3.7 as

$$r = \frac{40(601,300) - (4,825)(4,520)}{\sqrt{40(664,425) - (4,825)^2}\sqrt{40(554,850) - (4,520)^2}}$$

$$= \frac{2,243,000}{2,410,984} = +0.93.$$

This is a fairly high degree of relationship but one that should be achieved in this type of exercise. Should another individual obtain a higher or lower coefficient, this would reflect a higher or lower level of consistency or precision in rating; but in rating about the equation developed in linear regression, rather than the ideal of $y = x$.

3.7. MONTE CARLO ANALYSIS

Models used to explain operational systems often incorporate probabilistic elements. This may be necessary, since the decision environment is made up of a multitude of random variables. In some cases, formal mathematical solutions are difficult or impossible to obtain from these models. Under these conditions it may be necessary to use a method known as *Monte Carlo analysis*. When applied to an operational system, Monte Carlo analysis provides a powerful means of simulation. The step-by-step procedure used in simulation by Monte Carlo is presented in this section.

Formalize the system logic. The system under study is usually assumed to operate in accordance with a certain logical pattern. Before beginning the actual Monte Carlo simulation process, it is necessary to formalize the operational procedure by the construction of a model. This may require the development of a step-by-step flow diagram outlining the logic. If the actual simulation process is to be performed on a digital computer, it is mandatory to prepare an accurate logic diagram. From this, the computer can be programed to pattern the process under study.

Consider the evaluation of the random variable A which is the result of a ratio formed by the random variable B and the random variable C. Although this may not conform to any real world situation, the model describing the process is $A = B/C$. This expression formalizes the system under study. It establishes the computational procedure required to evaluate the variable of interest.

Determine the distributions. Each random variable in the model refers to an event in the system being studied. Therefore, an important step in Monte Carlo analysis is determining the behavior of these random variables. This involves the development of empirical frequency distributions to describe the relevant variables by the collection of historical data. Once this is done, the frequency distribution for each variable may be studied statistically to ascertain whether it conforms to a known theoretical distribution.

For the example under consideration, assume that data for random variable B have been collected and studied. It is concluded that this random variable conforms to the exponential distribution with a mean of 4. This is a theoretical distribution with the functional form

$$f(x) = \tfrac{1}{4}e^{-x/4}.$$

Likewise, assume that data for random variable C have been collected. Suppose that the resulting frequency distribution is as shown in Figure 3.18.

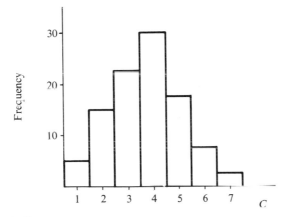

Figure 3.18. Distribution of the random variable C.

It is decided that no theoretical distribution adequately describes these data. Therefore, the empirical distribution will be used in the Monte Carlo analysis.

Develop the cumulative distributions. The probability distributions describing the random variables will be theoretical or empirical or both. Those expressed theoretically may be manipulated mathematically in order to obtain the required cumulative probability distributions. The cumulative distribution for random variable B may be expressed as

$$F(x) = \int_0^x f(x)\, dx$$

$$= \int_0^x \tfrac{1}{4}e^{-x/4}\, dx$$

$$= -e^{-x/4}\, \big|_0^x$$

$$= 1 - e^{-x/4}. \tag{3.16}$$

This cumulative exponential distribution is shown in Figure 3.19.

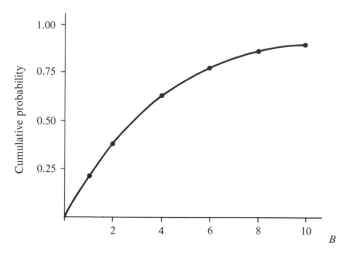

Figure 3.19. Cumulative exponential distribution of mean $a = 4$.

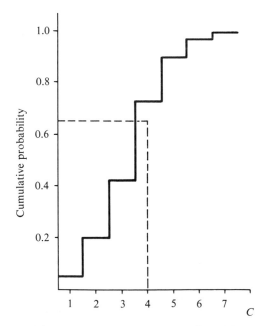

Figure 3.20. Cumulative distribution of the random variable C.

Those distributions expressed empirically cannot be converted to cumulative distributions by mathematical means. This is the case for random variable C shown in Figure 3.18. The Monte Carlo analysis, however, requires a cumulative distribution for each random variable. Therefore, graphical means must be used. Figure 3.20 exhibits the cumulative distribution corresponding to the distribution of Figure 3.18. It is developed by summing the probabilities from left to right and plotting the results. This is the same as the mathematical process used for the exponential distribution.

The cumulative distributions of Figure 3.19 and Figure 3.20 may be used to transform random rectangular variates, such as those given in Appendix A, Table A.2, to values drawn at random from the basic distributions. By this means, specific values are determined for random variable B and random variable C. Thus, a random rectangular variate with a value of 681 gives a value for the random variable B of 4.572, as is shown in Figure 3.19. Similarly, a random rectangular variate with a value of 654 gives a value for the random variable C of 4, as is shown in Figure 3.20. Use of Figure 3.19 may be bypassed since its mathematical equivalent is available. Equation (3.16) may be used to transform the random rectangular variate 681 to a random exponential variable directly. The result is

$$0.681 = 1 - e^{-x/4}$$
$$x = 4.572.$$

Perform the Monte Carlo analysis. The example under consideration requires that random variable B be divided by random variable C. This requirement is established by the model of the system under study. The result of one outcome of the random variable A. For the two values previously obtained, A is found to be $4.572/4 = 1.143$. This is the first entry in Table 3.8.

Repeated application of this process gives values for the random variable A. Twenty trials are exhibited in Table 3.8. Column A identifies the trial. Column B is a three-digit random rectangular variate taken from Appendix A, Table A.2. This random rectangular variate is converted to a value drawn at random from distribution B by the use of Figure 3.19. The result is entered in column C. Column D is the next random rectangular variate in sequence from Appendix A, Table A.2. It is converted to a value drawn at random from distribution C by the use of Figure 3.20. The result is entered in column E. Finally, column F is the value in column C divided by the value in column E. It is the random variable A.

The Monte Carlo analysis shown in Table 3.8 was continued through 100 trials. A frequency distribution of the values in column F is shown in Figure 3.21. It describes the nature of random variable A within sampling variation. There is no mathematical method for deriving the distribution of

Table 3.8. THE MONTE CARLO ANALYSIS

Trial (A)	Random Number (B)	B (C)	Random Number (D)	C (E)	$A = \dfrac{B}{C}$ (F)
1	.681	4.572	.654	4.0	1.143
2	.425	2.220	.695	4.0	0.555
3	.469	2.540	.126	2.0	1.270
4	.392	1.996	.206	3.0	0.665
5	.104	0.440	.020	1.0	0.440
6	.990	18.420	.766	5.0	3.684
7	.833	8.260	.391	3.0	2.753
8	.953	12.240	.407	3.0	4.080
9	.657	4.280	.313	3.0	1.427
10	.604	3.732	.213	3.0	1.244
11	.925	10.380	.748	5.0	2.076
12	.808	6.600	.509	4.0	1.650
13	.730	5.240	.888	5.0	1.048
14	.754	5.640	.585	4.0	1.410
15	.511	2.868	.033	1.0	2.868
16	.851	7.628	.131	2.0	3.814
17	.746	5.480	.344	3.0	1.827
18	.899	9.180	.384	3.0	3.060
19	.092	0.386	.802	5.0	0.077
20	.807	6.580	.874	5.0	1.316

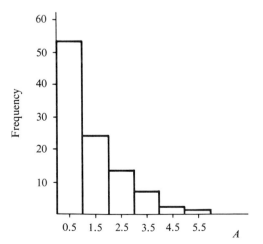

Figure 3.21. Frequency distribution of the random variable A.

random variable A from the distributions assumed for random variable B and random variable C. Therefore, the need and value of the Monte Carlo approach should be evident.

QUESTIONS

1. Describe an operational situation that would result in discrete data, in continuous data.

2. Why must continuous data be made discrete in order to construct a frequency distribution?

3. Describe a variable that would produce a skewed frequency distribution.

4. Contrast the relative frequency concept of probability with another concept for establishing the probability of occurrence of an event.

5. Give examples that illustrate each of the three probability theorems

6. Give an example of a variable that would be distributed according to the hypergeometric distribution, the binomial distribution, the Poisson distribution.

7. Give an example of a variable that would be distributed according to the rectangular distribution, the exponential distribution, the normal distribution.

8. Discuss the difference between descriptive statistics and inferential statistics.

9. Contrast the differences between a population and a sample.

10. Define the central limit theorem and explain its importance.

11. Give an example of a possible null hypothesis and describe the Type I(α) error and the Type II(β) error.

12. What is a scatter diagram?

13. Define linear regression, linear correlation.

14. What assumptions are involved in linear regression and correlation?

15. Under what conditions might the Monte Carlo method be used to derive a solution for a model?

PROBLEMS

1. The data which follow represent the pounds of metal recovered from a casting operation. Plot a frequency distribution of these data.

11.8	12.4	12.3	12.3	12.3	11.3	12.3	10.5
11.5	10.1	11.0	11.7	11.2	9.9	11.2	11.2
10.9	10.7	10.8	13.0	12.1	11.2	11.4	12.2
13.0	12.6	12.5	11.6	13.1	13.9	13.0	13.1
11.8	11.9	14.2	12.5	11.7	10.9	11.0	12.4
12.8	12.4	12.6	14.0	13.0	12.2	11.4	11.9
10.5	12.9	12.3	12.0	12.7	13.9	14.2	13.2
12.0	13.1	12.5	12.1	11.4	12.7	12.0	10.4
11.0	13.3	13.5	10.3	11.7	12.8	12.3	12.3
12.6	11.7	13.0	11.1	12.8	11.2	12.5	11.2
14.0	12.0	12.0	12.5	11.5	12.1	11.4	10.9
11.3	13.3	11.4	12.9	13.3	11.3	14.2	11.5
12.2	13.1	12.5	12.1				

2. Calculate the mean, the median, and the mode of the data in Problem 1.

3. Calculate the range and the standard deviation of the data in Problem 1.

4. If the data in Problem 1 were drawn from a normal distribution, what would be the probability of the next unit exceeding 13 lb? Falling between 10 and 13 lb?

5. If 25 random samples of size 4 from the data of Problem 13 were drawn, what would be the variance of the sample means?

6. Calculate the probability of obtaining exactly 2 heads in 5 tosses of a coin; 1 head; no heads.

7. A hungry, near-sighted giant was strolling past the Cotton Bowl one Saturday afternoon. Hearing a great noise he peered over the top of the stands onto the field to see whether he could find something to eat. On the field at the time were 12 football players in red uniforms, 11 players in white uniforms, 6 officials, 1 large dog, and a protesting coach. The giant scooped the 30 people together (the dog escaped) and randomly selected five for lunch. He knew that officials were fairly tough to eat and that if he ate two or more he would get indigestion. Find the probability that the giant got indigestion by using the hypergeometric distribution. Solve with the binomial as an approximation; the Poisson as an approximation.

8. What is the probability that the giant in Problem 7 got three or more players in red uniforms? Solve with the hypergeometric distribution. Solve with the normal as an approximation.

9. In a bridge game, in which each player has a 13-card hand from a standard 52-card deck, you have 4 hearts and your partner has 3 hearts. What is the probability that the other 6 hearts are divided evenly between your two opponents? What is the probability that they are divided 4 and 2; 5 and 1, 6 and none?

10. A manufacturing process is 0.3 per cent defective. What is the probability of finding no defectives in 100 pieces? What is the probability of finding one defective; finding two or more defective?

11. Solve Problem 10 using the Poisson distribution to obtain approximate answers.

12. Test the hypothesis that a coin is not biased by tossing it twelve times. Use an α of 0.05 and a two-tailed test. Use an $\alpha = 0.20$ and a two-tailed test.

13. As a class exercise, obtain data for the height and weight of each student in class. On the basis of these data, what is the best estimate of the weight of an individual, given his height? What correlation coefficient describes these data?

14. The following scores were achieved by a group of freshmen in the subjects of mathematics and social studies. How may the former scores predict the latter and with what degree of precision?

Mathematics	Social Studies	Mathematics	Social Studies	Mathematics	Social Studies
23	21	31	24	25	22
21	22	27	25	24	23
30	24	21	17	33	31
15	17	23	27	33	24
20	28	25	26	21	23
23	25	28	30	21	19
32	23	24	15	29	30
17	22	27	15	33	28
26	27	27	20	24	28
30	24	31	22	27	24

15. Estimate the probability of obtaining a seven or less if a pair of dice are rolled, by Monte Carlo analysis. Compare the result with the theoretically expected value.

16. Use Monte Carlo analysis to estimate the area of a circle with a 1-in. diameter. Compare the result with the actual area.

17. Convert four random rectangular variates to values drawn at random from the continuous distribution $f(x) = 0.5x; 0 \le x \le 2$.

18. If A is distributed exponentially with a mean of 2 and B is distributed as in Problem 17, find the distribution of C, where $C = A + B$.

Part II

ECONOMY OF PRODUCTION OPERATIONS

four

MODELS OF
THE PRODUCTION PROCESS

*Organizations come into existence to accomplish objectives
that individuals either cannot undertake or cannot
accomplish economically. An organization remains in
existence as long as some progress is being made toward achieving
the organizational objective and as long as each contributor
to the organization believes he receives more from it than he
contributes to it. As previously defined, an organization must
be efficient if it is to survive.*

*An industrial organization comes into being and remains
in existence while it engages in the activity of coordinating
a production process. This process alters the physical environment
to create products and services which are used to satisfy human wants.
Because of the utility which may be attached to the goods and services,
the organization receives an income from their exchange. The
organization must also provide a monetary outlay for the elements which
serve as an input to the production process. To the extent that the
income received exceeds the cost of the input, the process is operating
at an economic efficiency which exceeds 100 per cent. Thus, the altering
of the physical environment is an operation which must be pursued with
economy. This chapter examines the over-all production process and
develops simple economic models for the production
system as a whole.*

71

4.1. THE PRODUCTION SYSTEM

The *production process* may be described as a system for converting some combination of inputs to one or more forms of output. This conversion system may be quite simple or very complex. An essential feature of the process is the conversion of inputs through altering the physical environment and thus creating an output of increased utility. This section describes the inputs and outputs associated with a production system and presents the general form of decision models for production operations.

Inputs. Many thousands of distinct classes of elements serve as the input to a production process. It is not feasible to enumerate all of these. A rather broad classification is desirable at this level of examination.

An organization consists of the coordinated activities of people. The labor input must be remunerated for its contributions. Human contributions concerned with the production process can be divided into subclasses of direct labor, indirect labor, and supervision. There may also be an investigation and research group concerned with the discovery and development of new products and processes. Expenditures may also be made for promotional effort in an attempt to increase consumer demand for the goods and services. Finally, there will be a management group responsible for over-all coordination of the production system.

Many different forms of materials may be required to meet the objectives of the organization. These are usually classified into the two categories of direct material and indirect material. In the first category are the raw materials physically altered and directly converted into finished goods and services. In the second category are materials which may be employed and consumed in support of the production process.

Producer goods are a third major input to the process. These may include land and buildings as well as the equipment directly employed in physically altering the input materials. Most producer goods are consumed in the production process. This consumption, and the eventual necessity for replacement, must be treated as an input element requiring the outlay of capital. The life of equipment may vary from only a short time to a period of many years. Deterioration during this life must be estimated and included as a cost of production.

Besides the input elements of labor, material, and producer goods, it is necessary to consider capital as an input and then to consider interest charges as a cost. Most firms require the use of capital to meet operating expenses, and interest charges represent a rental for the use of this money. In addition to interest charges as an outlay, most firms pay taxes in return for government services. These services can also be considered as an input element. Interest and taxes may not have the same physical aspects as labor, material, and equipment, but they are costs of production.

Outputs. The outputs of industrial organizations are as diverse as the products and services that possess utility. Usually, the specification of an output is the first step in the formation of an organization. An existing organization may, however, search for and find an additional product or service which it may then attempt to produce and market.

Goods and services are sold in a market place that is dynamic. New opportunities continually develop while existing products and services may lose their utility. A new material or a new process may suggest an output that was previously uneconomical or technologically unfeasible. Shifting demand may end the market for an existing product and so require the development of a new product. The utility of an existing product or service, or the potential utility of a proposed product, will be of vital concern to the organization.

Once a product or service has been specified, the total income resulting from sales will depend on the price of each unit and the total number of units sold. These two factors are not independent, and a decision in regard to each must be based upon estimates that may require market surveys and other forecasting techniques.

The decision environment. A production system gives rise to a decision environment that may be viewed as an input-output process whose inputs

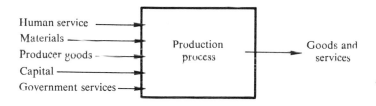

Figure 4.1. Schematic illustration of the production system.

and outputs may be summarized as in Figure 4.1. Although this representation does not include intangible inputs and outputs that are subjectively evaluated by the contributors, it provides a useful simplification of a complex system. Figure 4.1 is actually only a part of the illustration that would be required to describe the man-machine complex of organized activity discussed in Chapter 1.

If the income received for the goods and services produced exceeds the outlay for the required input elements, a profit will result. This leads to a fundamental measure of the success of an industrial organization: *Profit* equals income minus outlay. This simple measure of success permits the development of useful decision models for production operations. A more profound measure of success is the concept of economic efficiency embracing the want-satisfying power of the organization as a whole.

The following sections develop two basic models relating variables under the control of a decision maker to those not directly under his control. Each will be of the form,

$$E = f(x_i, y_j).$$

The first is concerned with the level of output as the variable under direct management control. The objective is to find the level of production output that maximizes profit. The second deals with the amounts of labor input and of capital input as variables under direct management control. The objective is finding the combination of these inputs that results in a minimum cost or a maximum profit. Before going on to develop these models, it is necessary to discuss the variables not directly under management control.

4.2. CLASSES OF PRODUCTION COSTS

A production process is an intermediate step in an input-output system. The production process acts as the converter and is responsible for the increased utility attached to the output of the system. The outlay of money in return for the input elements is considered the cost of this operation. Costs can be attributed to human service, materials, and producer goods. In addition, costs can be attached to the use of capital and government services. Each of these costs must be the subject of careful study with the objective of optimizing effectiveness.

Production costs may be classified across another pertinent dimension: that of their independence or dependence upon the level of production. In the first class are fixed costs and in the second class are variable costs. In addition, costs can be viewed in the framework of cost extensions for added levels of production. This latter view of costs leads to the concept of incremental cost analysis. Fixed, variable, and incremental costs are considered in this section.

Fixed costs. A cost thought to remain fairly constant over a complete range of operational activity is considered to be fixed. Cost items in this class are more or less fixed in amount over a time period, such as a year, regardless of the number of units produced. In general, managerial expenses as well as sales, promotional, and research inputs are independent of production levels. The cost of some indirect materials along with depreciation and rental expenses may be regarded as fixed. In addition, interest charges on capital will be constant if the capital requirements do not change with the level of production activity.

Fixed costs usually arise because of preparation for the future. A machine is bought now so that labor costs may be reduced. Materials which may never be needed are purchased in large quantities and stored in order to avoid idleness of production facilities and men. Research is carried out with no immediate benefit in view in hope that it will pay in the long run. Investments that give rise to fixed costs are made in the present with the anticipation that they will be recovered with a profit resulting from an increase in income.

Variable costs. A second classification of costs assumes that the consumption of some input elements will increase in a linear relationship with increases in production. Thus, the cost per unit of output will be a constant. Direct labor and direct material are typically considered as input elements which can be linearly related to output. Their cost will therefore vary with the production quantity. To some extent, indirect labor and supervision can be classified in this category.

Classifying costs as either fixed or variable permits a rather definitive cost-output projection. In practice many costs are not so easily defined. Some costs are a mixture of fixed and variable expenses, with the latter not linearly related to output. A production increase may require an overtime labor input at premium rates. Depreciation may be partially dependent upon time and partially dependent upon wear and tear. Obsolescence is particularly difficult to categorize. Some expenses may be expected to follow one pattern over a range of output and then change as a second range is entered. As an example, utility expenses may decrease as a lower rate is attained at a higher level of power consumption. Material costs may increase with output as less efficient production facilities are brought into operation.

Most costs should properly be considered as neither fixed nor variable. Nevertheless, they may be placed in one class or the other if the approximation does not result in a great sacrifice in accuracy. Alternatively, a cost may be prorated with a portion assigned to one class and the remainder to the other. The advantage to be gained in simple projections of cost-output relationships may warrant this dichotomous classification system.

A schematic representation of fixed and variable costs is given by Figure 4.2. Note that the fixed costs are assumed constant over the appropriate range of output, whereas the variable costs are linearly increasing over this range. In some cases, the fixed costs will be quite significant in comparison to the unit variable cost. In other cases the fixed costs may be negligible. Where these two cases will produce the same product or service output, analyses can be made and the selection of an alternative will rest upon the anticipated total cost. This will be treated in the next section.

Incremental costs. The use of incremental analysis requires that the outcome of alternative courses of action be estimated in terms of changes in revenue in comparison to changes in cost. With this reasoning, a decision

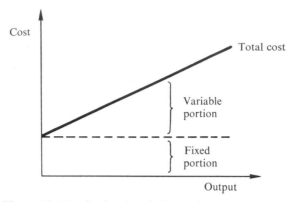

Figure 4.2. The fixed and variable portions of a total cost function.

is profitable if it increases revenue more than it increases cost. (The measurement of an incremental cost is illustrated in Figure 4.3.)

Incremental cost analysis can be useful, provided that some discretion is used in its application. Consider the following example: The total cost of producing 300 units per year is $3,600. This gives an average cost of $12 per unit. The opportunity of selling an additional 10 units for a total of $100 has presented itself. At $10 per unit this would appear to result in a loss of $2 per unit. The total cost of producing 310 units has, however, been estimated to be $3,650. Then, using the incremental cost concept, $\Delta C = \$3{,}650 - \$3{,}600$ or 50 and $\Delta Q = 110 - 100$ or 10 units. The incremental cost would be $\Delta C/\Delta Q = \$50/10$ or $5 per unit. Thus, the sale of an additional 10 units would result in a profit of $5 per unit rather than

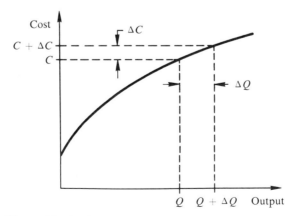

Figure 4.3. An incremental cost, ΔC, resulting from the incremental output, ΔQ.

a loss of $2 per unit. This profit would not have been realized unless the incremental cost of production had been recognized and considered.

Caution must be exercised in the use of the incremental cost concept. Although a decision is sound if it increases revenue more than cost, or reduces cost more than revenue, the total effect of the decision must be evaluated. In the preceding example, customers may learn of the dual price structure and resent paying the higher price in subsequent transactions. A second lot of 10 units may be immediately requested at the same price of $10 per unit. This added output may require additional fixed costs to add to production capacity. Alternatively, a subsequent order may have been placed at the original price and this order cannot now be met because this last sale exhausted the output capacity.

Incremental analysis is actually a method of reasoning wherein receipts and expenditures that have already occurred are considered beyond control. Subsequent receipts and expenditures are evaluated only in terms of their added amounts, and action is taken in accordance with their relative magnitudes.

4.3. THE ECONOMIC PRODUCTION CHART

The *profit* which results from production operations has been defined as the income received from the sale of the product less the cost of production. In many cases the effectiveness of production operations depends upon the level of output selected by the decision maker. When profit can be defined as a function of the level of system output, it is possible to select a level of production which will maximize profit. An economic production chart may be used to illustrate the relationship between costs, income, and level of production. It is a schematic model, although the relationships it illustrates may be expressed in algebraic terms. This section is concerned with both the graphical and the algebraic forms of this model.

Graphical analysis. A schematic representation of the economic production chart can be demonstrated with the aid of an example. Assume that varying production levels ranging from zero through 10 units of output may be produced and sold each period of time, such as a day, month, quarter, or year. The cost and income associated with these production levels are given in Table 4.1. In this example, the variable cost, given in column C, is increasing at a nonlinear rate. The income, given in column E, becomes nonlinear in the higher ranges of output. The difference between income and total cost represents the profit of the operation within the time period, at the production level indicated. This is shown in column F. Profit is maximized for an output of seven units where income less total cost is $55.

The data of Table 4.1 are illustrated schematically in Figure 4.4. This economic production chart illustrates the relationship between fixed cost, variable cost, total cost, and level of output, as well as income and level of output. The range of profitable operation occurs at that level of output where income exceeds total cost. In this example, profitable operation occurs for the range of output from six through eight units, with the maximum return at seven units.

Table 4.1. INCOME AND COST DATA FOR VARYING OUTPUT LEVELS

Production Output, Q (A)	Fixed Cost (B)	Variable Cost (C)	Total Cost (B + C) (D)	Income (E)	Profit (E − D) (F)
1	$300	$100	$400	$125	$−275
2	300	180	480	250	−230
3	300	240	540	375	−165
4	300	290	590	500	−90
5	300	345	645	625	−20
6	300	415	715	745	+30
7	300	505	805	860	+55
8	300	620	920	970	+50
9	300	765	1,065	1,065	0
10	300	945	1,245	1,135	−110

The economic production chart also identifies the break-even point, if one exists. The break-even point occurs where income first equals total cost. In Figure 4.4, this point falls between an output of five and six units. A break-even point is a useful concept giving the minimum level of production output beyond which it is possible to realize a profit. The economic evaluation of producer goods is often stated as an estimate of the level of output needed to achieve the break-even point

The data of Table 4.1 can be analyzed on an incremental basis. Table 4.2 gives a continuation of Table 4.1 with columns G and H listing the average cost and income per unit. The incremental cost and incremental income are given in columns I and J. Each of these is sketched in Figure 4.5, permitting another insight to the original problem.

Note that the average cost is initially quite high. As more units are produced, the fixed cost is distributed over a wider base and it becomes a less significant portion of the total cost. Eventually the unit variable cost may begin to increase as the production capabilities become overburdened and less efficient. Then, the sum of the diminishing average fixed cost, and average variable cost begins to increase. In this example, the average income is assumed constant through a range of five units. As the demand is assumed to drop off, the unit income diminishes and the average income drops off

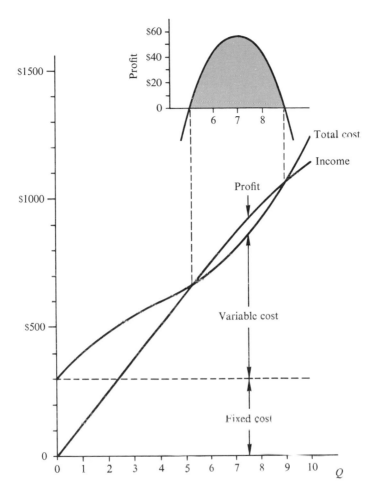

Figure 4.4. Economic production chart for the data of
Table 4.1.

to a lesser extent. At any level of production output, total profit will be
the average income less average cost times the number of units of output.

Figure 4.5 permits incremental analysis of the production situation.
Through seven units of output, the incremental income exceeds the incremental cost. The cost of producing the eighth unit, however, is more than
the revenue that will be received from its sale. Seven units is the optimum
level of production output. Producing more than seven units will result in
a reduction in total profit.

Algebraic analysis. The schematic form of the economic production
chart can be translated into an algebraic equivalent. This symbolic form

Table 4.2. AVERAGE AND INCREMENTAL VALUES FOR THE DATA OF TABLE 4.1

Production Output, Q (A)	Average Cost $(D \div A)$ (G)	Average Income $(E \div A)$ (H)	Incremental Cost $(D_Q - D_{Q-1})$ (I)	Incremental Income $(E_Q - E_{Q-1})$ (J)
1	$400	$125	—	—
2	240	125	$80	$125
3	180	125	60	125
4	148	125	50	125
5	129	125	55	125
6	119	124	70	120
7	115	123	90	115
8	115	121	115	110
9	118	118	145	95
10	125	114	180	70

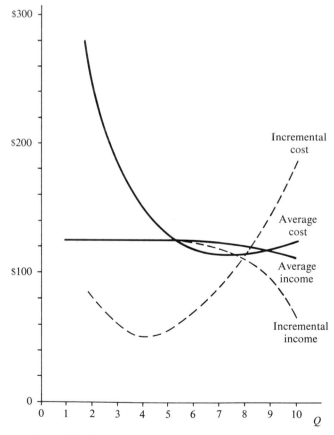

Figure 4.5. Economic production chart for the data of Table 4.2.

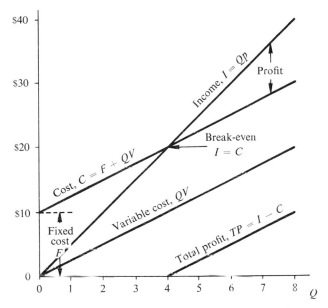

Figure 4.6. Economic production chart with linear cost and income.

facilitates mathematical manipulation of the model and permits more precision in its use. However, the ability to visualize and communicate the effects of operating at varying production levels is reduced.

If income and variable costs are assumed to be linear functions of the quantity of output, the definition and analysis of the production situation is greatly simplified. Let

Q = number of units made and sold during each time period

p = price received per unit of product

$I = Qp$, the income from Q units of product

F = fixed cost per period

V = variable cost per unit of product

$C = F + QV$, the sum of the fixed and variable costs for Q units of product

$TP = I - C$, the total profit per time period from Q units of product. A negative value of TP represents a loss.

A number of algebraic relationships can now be defined and illustrated by using the schematic model of Figure 4.6. In this case, the fixed cost, $F = \$10$; the variable cost, $V = \$2.50$ per unit; the price, $p = \$5$ per unit; and the production capacity, $N = 8$ units.

The break-even point may be defined as that value of Q where income equals cost, or $Qp = F + QV$. Solving for Q

$$Q = \frac{F}{p - V} . \qquad (4.1)$$

And, in this example,

$$Q = \frac{\$10}{\$5 - \$2.50} = 4 \text{ units.}$$

The ordinate of the break-even point may be found by substituting $F/(p - V)$ for Q in $I = Qp$ or $C = F + QV$. The value of the ordinate in dollars will be

$$I = p\left[\frac{F}{(p - V)}\right] \quad \text{or} \quad C = F + V\left[\frac{F}{(p - V)}\right]. \tag{4.2}$$

And, in this example,

$$I = \$5\left[\frac{\$10}{\$5 - \$2.50}\right] = \$20 \quad \text{or} \quad C = \$10 + \$2.50\left[\frac{\$10}{\$5 - \$2.50}\right] = \$20.$$

Since TP is the total profit per time period, it is often desirable to express TP as a function of Q, the number of units produced and sold. This relationship may be derived as

$$\begin{aligned} TP &= I - C \\ &= Qp - (F + QV) \\ &= Q(p - V) - F. \end{aligned} \tag{4.3}$$

In this example, the total profit, at an output of six units, would be $TP = 6(\$5 - \$2.50) - \$10 = \$5$. And, at an output of three units, $TP = 3(\$5 - \$2.50) - \$10 = -\$2.50$. The negative sign indicates a loss in the amount of $2.50.

Production above normal capacity. Suppose now that a production output of 10 units per time period is desired and possible, but at a variable cost of $4 per unit for the 2 units of output exceeding the normal capacity of 8 units. This can be described by letting Q' and V' represent the respective units and variable cost of output exceeding normal capacity. The schematic model of this extended example is given in Figure 4.7. The cost of production now becomes

$$C = F + QV + Q'V' \tag{4.4}$$

with Q limited to the range of the maximum normal production, $Q = 8$. The cost of producing 10 units would be $C = \$10 + 8(\$2.50) + 2(\$4) = \$38$. Equation (4.3) can be modified and profit defined as

$$\begin{aligned} TP &= I - C \\ &= Qp + Q'p - F - QV - Q'V' \\ &= p(Q + Q') - F - QV - Q'V'. \end{aligned} \tag{4.5}$$

The profits realized by producing at the rate of 10 units per period would be $TP = \$5(8 + 2) - \$10 - 8(\$2.50) - 2(\$4) = \$12$.

As long as the slope of the income function exceeds the slope of the cost function, production at extended capacity can be pursued with profit. Should this be continued, the cost of additional production would probably exceed the added revenue. This is an example of the law of diminishing returns. When the incremental cost equals incremental revenue, the level of profit has been maximized.

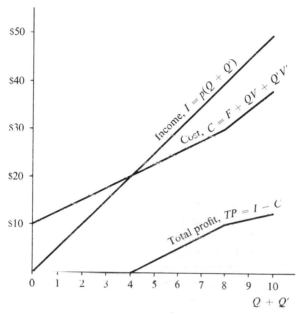

Figure 4.7. Economic production chart indicating the effect of extended production operations.

The effect of dumping. In some instances, a constant unit price can be realized for the sale of a product only over a specific range of production. At a level exceeding this value, the added units must be sold at a reduced price. This is sometimes referred to as *dumping*. Returning to the original example, assume that the price, p, can be obtained for the first six units. The next two units, Q'', must be sold at the reduced price of $p'' = \$4$. The effect of dumping can be seen in Figure 4.8. The income realized is now

$$I = Qp + Q''p'' \tag{4.6}$$

with Q limited to a value of six units. The total profit may be expressed as

$$TP = Qp + Q''p'' - F - QV - Q''V$$
$$= Q(p - V) + Q''(p'' - V) - F. \tag{4.7}$$

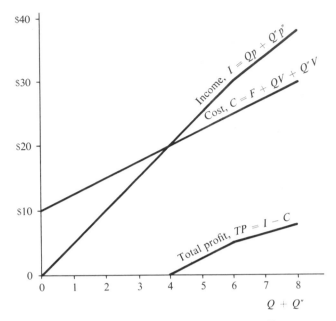

Figure 4.8. Economic production chart indicating the effect of dumping.

The total profit realized from the sale of eight units would be $TP = 6(\$5 - \$2.50) + 2(\$4 - \$2.50) - \$10 = \$8$.

The practice of dumping is profitable if the reduced price exceeds the variable cost of production. This is governed by the law of diminishing returns. As soon as the price drops below the variable cost of production, the optimum profit level has been passed and total profit will diminish.

4.4. THE PRODUCTION FUNCTION

The production process is essentially a means for converting some combination of inputs into an output of increased utility. Often, a production system can utilize varying levels of inputs to produce an identical output. When total cost or total profit can be expressed as a function of the input quantity combination, it may be possible to select that quantity combination of input elements that optimizes effectiveness. Such an expression is called a *production function* since it gives the relationship between rates and combinations of inputs and the rate of output. This section deals with the determination of the quantity combination of input elements, under direct control of a decision maker, that minimizes cost or maximizes profit.

The input-output function. A production function defines the relationship between the input and output of a production process. If Q represents the rate of output, this function can be expressed in general terms as

$$Q = f(a_1, a_2, \ldots, a_n) \tag{4.8}$$

where $a_1, a_2, \ldots, a_n$ represent continuously divisible production factors. The relationship given by Equation (4.8) is one of rates rather than simple quantities. As an example, output may be units per hour, week, or year. The inputs are not simply labor, machines, and land but rather their services measured in units per time period, such as man-hours per hour, machine hours per day, or acre years per year. Production is a time-dependent process, and a production function must incorporate this time dimension. The production function does not incorporate cost, although inputs and the output can eventually be converted to a common cost base. Also, the relationship applies to only one production process. Other processes are assumed to require separate functions. Finally, input factors not directly included in the production function are regarded as fixed over the range of output being considered.

The relationship between a single input variable and output, Q, may be described with a curve. The relationship between two input variables and output may be described with a surface oriented in three dimensions. As more input variables are included in the functional relationship, the input-output surface assumes added dimensions. In order to permit graphical analysis, production factors are often grouped into the two input classes of labor, L, and capital, C. Under this assumption, Equation (4.8) becomes

$$Q = f(L, C). \tag{4.9}$$

There is some justification for this grouping of inputs. Labor is the co-ordinated human effort required in organized activity. Capital can then be taken to include the cost of material, equipment, land, and all other physical inputs. A trade-off is then possible when equipment is utilized to replace human effort.

As various combinations of L and C are substituted into the production function, Q assumes different values. The surface thus traced is called a *production surface*. It is oriented in three dimensional space, with any point on its surface representing a specific output for a specific combination of labor and capital input. Such a production surface might assume the form illustrated by Figure 4.9. Usually Q is zero along both the L and C axes, indicating that no output is possible unless both inputs are present. As both labor and capital inputs increase, the surface usually rises. The surface may reach a peak, indicating a level has been achieved beyond which additions will result in a decrease in output. Up to this point, the surface normally increases at a decreasing rate due to the law of diminishing returns. The form of the surface will depend upon the functional relationship given by Equation (4.9).

By holding one variable constant, the surface can be described with curves on a two-dimensional plane. By holding Q constant, curves of constant product output (isoquants) may be traced as illustrated by Figure 4.10. By holding either L or C constant, the relationship between the

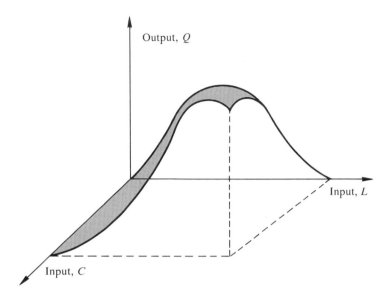

Figure 4.9. A production surface with labor and capital inputs.

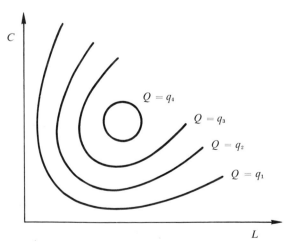

Figure 4.10. A family of constant output curves.

remaining variable and Q can be illustrated. For example, if C is held constant, the effect of L upon Q is shown in Figure 4.11.

A simple graphical analysis of output can be undertaken in two dimensions by holding one input variable constant. As an example, if the output curve $C = c_2$ from Figure 4.11 were to be studied on an average and an incremental basis, the results would be as indicated in Figure 4.12. The

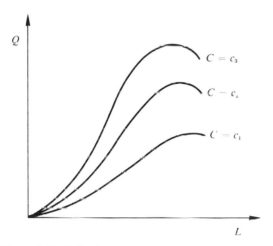

Figure 4.11. A family of output curves of constant capital inputs.

maximum output would be achieved at an input of l_2. Beyond this point the incremental output is negative. The maximum average output per unit of input would be achieved at l_1. This occurs at the point at which a line tangent to the actual output function just touches that function. An output increase beyond l_1 occurs, but at a reduction in the ratio Q/L.

The minimum cost input rate combination. Use of the production function as a decision model requires that inputs and outputs be related by a common economic measure. Dollars is the measure most frequently used. It is usually assumed that costs in dollars are known with certainty at varying rates of input, and that an optimum combination of inputs is one which either minimizes costs to achieve a desired output, or maximizes output at a specified total dollar input.

Under the assumption of two inputs, L and C, minimum cost will be achieved when the ratio of the incremental outputs of labor and capital is equal to the ratio of the price of each. Symbolically, the minimum cost occurs when

$$\frac{\Delta Q/\Delta L}{\Delta Q/\Delta C} = \frac{p_L}{p_C} \qquad (4.10)$$

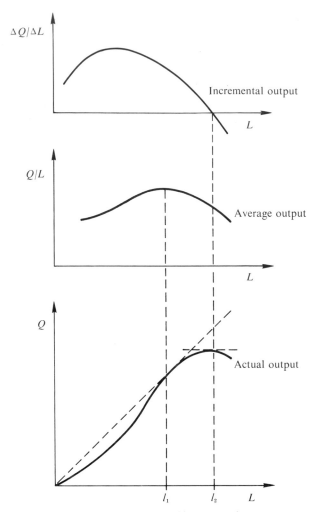

Figure 4.12. Actual, average, and incremental output curves.

where p_L and p_C are the prices of a unit of labor input and a unit of capital input respectively. Equation (4.10) may be modified by the equivalent derivative notation as

$$\frac{\partial Q/\partial L}{\partial Q/\partial C} = \frac{p_L}{p_C}.$$ (4.11)

Equation (4.10) or Equation (4.11) indicates that the cost of production is minimum when the input factors have been combined in such a fashion that the marginal or incremental cost of the marginal input of every factor is identical. Thus, factors will be added to the production process until their incremental cost per incremental unit of output exceeds other available factors. The optimum mix will be achieved when these costs are equal.

As an example of the application of Equation (4.11) consider the simple production function,

$$Q = L^{1/2}C^{1/2}.$$

The surface described by this production function is the hyperbolic paraboloid illustrated by Figure 4.13. If the cost of labor is $10 per unit, and the re-

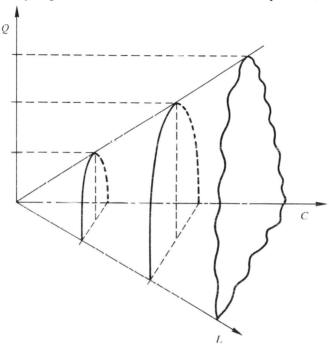

Figure 4.13. The production surface described by the function, $Q = L^{1/2}C^{1/2}$.

quired return per unit of capital is also $10, then the minimum cost combination of labor and capital may be found from Equation (4.11) as

$$\frac{C^{1/2}\frac{1}{2}L^{-1/2}}{L^{1/2}\frac{1}{2}C^{-1/2}} = \frac{\$10}{\$10}$$

$$\$10(C^{1/2}\tfrac{1}{2}L^{-1/2}) = \$10(L^{1/2}\tfrac{1}{2}C^{-1/2})$$

$$L = C.$$

As a further illustration, assume that a total of $1,000 is available to spend for labor and capital. Since the price of labor equals the price of capital, each of which is $10 per unit, this will provide 100 units of these inputs. A minimum cost output is achieved when $L = C$ thus making the optimum mix of labor and capital equal to 50 units of each. This will result in an output of

$$Q = 50^{1/2}50^{1/2} = 50 \text{ units.}$$

The maximum profit input rate combination. Consider an extension of the previous example. Assume that the price received for each unit of output, p_Q, is a function of the total output expressed as

$$p_Q = \$30 - \frac{Q}{1,000}.$$

The input rate combination of labor and capital that results in a maximum profit is sought. This requires the formulation of a total profit expression in terms of L and C. Total profit will be total revenue minus total cost, which may be expressed as

$$TP = p_Q(Q) - [p_L(L) + p_C(C)]$$

$$= \left[\$30Q - \frac{Q^2}{1,000} \right] - [\$10L + \$10C].$$

But since

$$Q = L^{1/2}C^{1/2}$$

$$TP = \left[\$30(L^{1/2}C^{1/2}) - \frac{L(C)}{1,000} \right] - [\$10L + \$10C]. \tag{4.12}$$

The maximum profit combination of L and C may be found by taking the partial derivative of total profit with respect to L, and then with respect to C, and setting the results equal to zero. This results in

$$\frac{\partial TP}{\partial L} = C^{1/2}15L^{-1/2} - \frac{C}{1,000} - 10 = 0 \tag{4.13}$$

$$\frac{\partial TP}{\partial C} = L^{1/2}15C^{-1/2} - \frac{L}{1,000} - 10 = 0. \tag{4.14}$$

From Equation (4.14),

$$C^{1/2} = \frac{15,000L^{1/2}}{L + 10,000}. \tag{4.15}$$

Substituting Equation (4.15) into Equation (4.13) gives

$$\frac{15,000L^{1/2}15L^{-1/2}}{L + 10,000} - \frac{1}{1,000}\left[\frac{15,000L^{1/2}}{L + 10,000} \right]^2 - 10 = 0.$$

Solving for L gives $L = 5,000$. Substituting into Equation (4.15) gives

$C = 5,000$. This input rate combination will result in a maximum profit and it satisfies the condition $L = C$ required for optimality.

The total profit resulting from this input combination may be found by substituting into Equation (4.12) as follows:

$$TP = \$30(5,000)^{1/2}(5,000)^{1/2} - \frac{5,000(5,000)}{1,000} - \$10(5,000) - \$10(5,000)$$

$$= \$150,000 - \$25,000 - \$100,000 = \$25,000.$$

This profit occurs at an output of

$$Q = (5,000)^{1/2}(5,000)^{1/2} = 5,000 \text{ units.}$$

Suppose that the price of capital changes from $10 per unit to $12 per unit. The optimum mix of labor and capital would be

$$\frac{C^{1/2}\tfrac{1}{2}L^{-1/2}}{L^{1/2}\tfrac{1}{2}C^{-1/2}} = \frac{\$10}{\$12}$$

$$\$12(C^{1/2}\tfrac{1}{2}L^{-1/2}) = \$10(L^{1/2}\tfrac{1}{2}C^{-1/2})$$

$$L = \tfrac{6}{5}C.$$

The total profit would be

$$TP = \left[\$30(L^{1/2}C^{1/2}) - \frac{L(C)}{1,000}\right] - [\$10L + \$12C]. \tag{4.16}$$

Taking the partial derivatives with respect to L and C and setting these equal to zero gives

$$\frac{\partial TP}{\partial L} = C^{1/2}15L^{-1/2} - \frac{C}{1,000} - 10 = 0 \tag{4.17}$$

$$\frac{\partial TP}{\partial C} = L^{1/2}15C^{-1/2} - \frac{L}{1,000} - 12 = 0. \tag{4.18}$$

From Equation (4.18),

$$C^{1/2} = \frac{15,000L^{1/2}}{L + 12,000}. \tag{4.19}$$

Substituting Equation (4.19) into Equation (4.17) gives

$$\frac{15,000L^{1/2}15L^{-1/2}}{L + 12,000} - \frac{1}{1,000}\left[\frac{15,000L^{1/2}}{L + 12,000}\right]^2 - 10 = 0.$$

Solving for L gives $L = 4,432$. Substituting into Equation (4.19) gives $C = 3,693$. This input rate combination results in a maximum profit and satisfies the condition $L = \tfrac{6}{5}C$ required for optimality.

The total profit resulting from this input combination may be found by substituting into Equation (4.16) as follows:

$$TP = \$30(4{,}432)^{1/2}(3{,}693)^{1/2} - \frac{(4{,}432)(3{,}693)}{1{,}000} - \$10(4{,}432) - \$12(3{,}693)$$

$$= \$121{,}364 - \$16{,}367 - \$44{,}320 - \$44{,}316 = \$16{,}361.$$

This profit occurs at an output of

$$Q = (4{,}432)^{1/2}(3{,}693)^{1/2} = 4{,}045 \text{ units.}$$

Thus, an increase in the price of capital caused a shift in the utilization of each input from $L = C$ to $L = \frac{6}{5}C$. The result was a reduction in total profit from \$25,000 to \$16,361.

The effect of varying labor and capital inputs from the optimum mix can be demonstrated numerically. Table 4.3 gives the total profit and the output which results from changes of 100 units in each input element. The profit which results in each case is less than that achieved with the optimum mix.

Table 4.3. LABOR AND CAPITAL INPUTS AND THEIR RESULT UPON PROFIT AND OUTPUT

Labor Input L	Capital Input C	Total Profit TP ($)	Output Q
4,432	3,693	16,361	4,045
4,332(−100)	3,593(−100)	16,349	3,945
4,532(+100)	3,793(+100)	16.354	4,146
4,332(−100)	3,793(+100)	16,353	4,054
4,532(+100)	3,593(−100)	16,331	4,035

Table 4.3 suggests a means for finding the maximum profit numerically. By a systematic series of trials it is possible to find the combination of labor and capital that will maximize profit. This procedure must be used when the total profit equation cannot be differentiated.

QUESTIONS

1. Describe the production process as an input-output system.

2. What are the three categories of physical inputs to the production process?

3. What are the two nonphysical inputs to the production process?

4. Why must the output of the production process be geared to a dynamic market place?

5. Give some examples of fixed costs.

6. Give some examples of variable costs.

7. What is an incremental cost?

8. Describe the concept of incremental reasoning.

9. What is a break-even point?

10. Discuss the economic production chart in terms of $E = f(x_i, y_j)$.

11. Discuss the production function in terms of $E = f(x_i, y_j)$.

12. What condition must be satisfied if the optimum mix of input factors to a production function has been found?

13. What difficulties might be encountered in a numerical solution to a production function?

PROBLEMS

1. Sketch the economic production chart described by $F = \$5,000$, $V - \$10$ per unit, and $p = \$15$ per unit. Indicate the break-even point.

2. Solve for the break-even point in Problem 1 by algebraic analysis. What is the profit at an output of 2,000 units?

3. If the maximum production capacity of 2,000 units in Problem 2 can be exceeded by 500 units at a variable cost of $13 per unit, solve graphically and algebraically for the additional profit.

4. If the last 200 of the 500 units in Problem 3 must be dumped at a price of $11 per unit, solve graphically and algebraically for the incremental effect of these added 500 units.

5. A market survey of towns A, B, and C, reveals that it will be possible to sell 9,000, 3,000, and 3,000 loaves of bread per day in each town, respectively, six days a week. At the present time two alternatives are under consideration to meet this demand. In the first, one plant could be located equidistant between the three towns and produce up to 20,000 loaves at a fixed cost of $1,000 per day. The variable cost would be $0.08 per loaf. Alternatively, plants of capacity 12,000, 4,000, and 4,000 loaves, respectively could be located in each of the towns. The fixed cost in each case would be $700, $325, and $325 per day. The variable cost would be only $0.06 per loaf because of the elimination of trucking costs. If the market survey proves correct, which alternative would be most desirable? If sales were to increase to production capacity, which alternative would be most desirable?

6. A firm has the capacity to produce 850,000 units per year. At present it is operating at 70 per cent of capacity. The annual income is $0.11 per unit regardless of output. Annual fixed costs are $22,500 and the variable cost is $0.068 per unit.

(a) What is the annual profit or loss at this capacity?

(b) At what percentage of capacity does the firm break even?

(c) What will be the profit or loss at 60 and 80 per cent of capacity?

7. Sketch the production function $Q = 8X - X^2$ between $X = 0$ and $X = 6$ where X is hundreds of units of input and Q is tens of units of output. Sketch the average output and marginal output curves.

8. If the price received per unit in Problem 7 were $100 and the input units cost $3 each, what is the maximum profit that can be realized? At what level of input and output does maximum profit occur?

9. Find the optimum mix of labor and capital for the production function $Q = L^{1/2}C^{1/2}$ with $p_Q = \$30 - Q/1{,}000$ and $p_L = \$15$, $p_C = \$5$. What profit is realized with this mix?

10. In the mid-1700's a number of significant breakthroughs occurred in England in the technology of the textile industry. Every school boy of today is familiar with these inventions, but in the late 1700's, the water frame, the mule-spinner, the power loom, the spinning jenny, and the flying shuttle represented a novel means of transferring skill to machines. Under these conditions, capital expenditures for equipment could be considered as a partial substitute for labor. Immediately following the War of 1812, an enterprising English aeronautical engineer, after being laid off by a defense contractor, took up employment in a textile concern. He singlehandedly developed a production function for the entire industry. By employing women and children to work 14 hours per day, the age of the machine could be implemented and output, Q, in square rods of cloth, could be represented as $Q = L^{3/4}C^{1/4}$. With $p_Q = £50 - Q/500$ and $p_L = £5$, and $p_C = £10$, what profit could be realized with the optimum quantity and mix of labor and capital? ($£ = 1$ pound sterling).

five

MANUFACTURING
PROGRESS MODELS

*An operation has been defined as a set of coordinated acts
required for accomplishing an objective. Since
many production operations are repetitive, the set of
activities involved may be accomplished with a reduction in time as the number of
units produced increases. Other industrial operations may be
characterized by improvements in the rate at which those operations are
performed. Under these conditions, the decision maker must predict the effect
of this reduction on the operations under his control. The manufacturing
progress model may assist him in this prediction.*

*The progress model is a simple graphical or analytical expression
which may be used to predict the reduction in direct labor
man-hours necessary to complete an operation as the operation is
repeated over time. A number of terms have been used to describe this forecasting
model: experience curve, improvement curve,
production acceleration curve, manufacturing progress function,
and learning curve have been employed to describe the concept of a
predicted reduction in the direct labor man-hours necessary to accomplish
a unit of work. Although these different names often produce
some confusion, the mechanics of each are almost identical.
This chapter is directed toward developing models which may
be used to explain the concept of manufacturing progress.*

5.1. MANUFACTURING IMPROVEMENTS

The manufacturing progress model is an expression of the anticipated improvement in the manufacturing process. It serves as a standard which may be used in calculating production costs and determining production schedules. The progress function is based on the following assumptions:

(1) The amount of time required to complete a given task or unit of product will be less each time the task is undertaken.

(2) The unit time will decrease at a decreasing rate.

(3) The reduction in unit time will follow a specific predictable pattern, such as an exponential function.

The empirical evidence that supports the preceding assumptions were first noted in the aircraft industry. The reduction in direct labor man-hours required to build aircraft was observed and found to be predictable. Since then, the progress function has found applications in other industries, particularly in those with low production volume, such as machine tool manufacturing and shipbuilding.

The rate of improvement. The manufacturing progress function rests on the assumption that the direct labor man-hours necessary to complete a unit of product will decrease by a constant percentage each time the production quantity is doubled. For example, a typical rate of improvement in the aircraft industry is 20 per cent between doubled quantities. This establishes an 80 per cent progress function and means that the direct labor man-hours necessary to build the second aircraft will be 80 per cent of those required to build the first. The fourth aircraft will require 80 per cent of the man-hours that the second required, the eighth will require 80 per cent of the fourth, the sixteenth will be 80 per cent of the eighth, and so forth. The rate of improvement is constant with regard to doubled production quantities but diminishes with time.

The situation described can be illustrated with an example. Suppose that the first production aircraft requires 100,000 direct labor man-hours to complete and that an 80 per cent progress function is to be used to predict subsequent improvements. Under the assumptions of the example, the second unit would require $100,000(0.80) = 80,000$ direct labor man-hours; the fourth unit would require $80,000(0.80) = 64,000$ direct labor man-hours. If this analysis is continued for doubled production units, it will be found that unit 128 will require 20,972 direct labor man-hours and unit 256 will require 16,777 direct labor hours. The foregoing shows why "follow-on" contracts in low-volume production are much more economical than the original contract and why low-volume military and commercial aircraft and space-craft production is so expensive.

Consider an example in mass production, building automobiles. For simplicity, assume that the necessary direct labor man-hours are diminishing over time because of technological improvements. Also, assume that the set of coordinated acts necessary to complete an automobile is not changing radically from one year to the next. Assume further that a manufacturer has built a total of 10,000,000 units to date, and that he will build 1,000,000 automobiles each year in the future. At this rate it will take 10 years to double production. A 20 per cent reduction in direct labor man-hours will be realized during these 10 years if an 80 per cent manufacturing progress function applies This amounts to approximately a 2 per cent per year improvement; a realistic figure for technological improvements in a mass production industry. This example has been oversimplified, but it does illustrate the relative magnitude of improvement when the production quantities are in the millions. In addition, it illustrates why the rate of improvement in relation to time or from one unit to the next, may be so small as to appear negligible.

Manufacturing improvements and learning. The manufacturing progress curve is sometimes referred to as a *learning curve*. This is unfortunate since it implies that all improvements are a result of direct labor learning. Actually, the contribution of the direct labor employee may be only a part of the total reduction in the time required to complete a production unit. Other improvements will come from management and, in large part, from supporting staff organizations. It is difficult to quantify the contributions of each group since they vary over time and from one industrial environment to another. It is possible, however, to describe these contributions in qualitative terms.

The production employee's performance will improve as he become familiar with the task. This improvement should be evident in the completion of more units of product per increment of time. The employee's learning may take the form of increased familiarity with the correct method or assembly technique, familiarity with the tooling, or with the inspection requirements and workpiece specifications. The employee may also acquire a better understanding of the proper position of his task in relation to the total production process. The learning of the individual worker will have an immediate effect, in terms of manufacturing improvement. This learning, however, will probably not result in significant improvements over a long period of time, particularly in repetitive and short cycle operations.

Improvement resulting from management or direct labor supervision will be felt only through staff functions and production employees, respectively. These improvements will depend upon managerial capabilities and, in particular, upon the attention given a specific product when more than one product is being produced. A major portion of the improvement will result from the efforts of personnel in supporting staff organizations. These contributions will be as diverse as the staff functions themselves, although all have as an objective, and should contribute to, the reduction in direct labor man-hours necessary to complete a cycle of work.

The extent to which tooling is established before production and the tooling refinements made during production will influence the magnitude of manufacturing improvement. Modifications in tool design and the correction of tooling errors will reduce the unit production time. Increased or supplementary production requirements may result in more elaborate tooling which should in turn, reduce the unit production time.

The degree to which manufacturing methods have been developed and specified prior to production, together with the emphasis placed on improving these methods during production, will affect manufacturing improvements. In a broader sense, this work simplification includes revisions in plant layout and materials handling which should also influence the unit production time.

Production control personnel may facilitate improvement through better planning, routing, scheduling, dispatching, and follow-up. This will result in an increased utilization of machines, tools, and labor and should ultimately produce a reduction in the direct labor man-hours per unit.

The materials management organization deals with the purchase of raw materials and component parts, as well as with the control and storage of preproduction, in-process, and finished inventory. As this function is improved, material shortages and the resulting disruption of production should be reduced or eliminated.

The engineering department is responsible for product design and testing. The manner in which this function is accomplished before and during production will affect total manufacturing improvement. Contributions, such as the correction of specification errors, the simplification of product design, and the incorporation of requested design changes, will be an important factor in manufacturing improvement after production has begun.

How far a quality assurance program can reduce the number of rejects and thus reduce losses and/or the necessity for rework and repair will influence the total manufacturing improvement. An especially important function of the quality control program is serving as a feedback mechanism in notifying operating personnel of deviations or shifts in the manufacturing process. The extent and rapidity with which this mechanism acts will influence manufacturing improvement.

Many other factors might reduce unit production time. The installation and maintenance of a wage incentive system may affect productivity. An employee suggestion system might produce some improvements. Intangibles which raise morale, such as a program of noise reduction, an employee newsletter, or various fringe benefits, may serve to reduce unit manufacturing time. It may also be desirable to inform production employees of the present and projected production rates. If these are realistic, employees may concertedly attempt to meet them. The degree to which the foregoing factors influence manufacturing improvement largely depends upon the amount of available improvement remaining immediately after the first unit has been completed, and also upon the subsequent attempt to accomplish as much improvement as possible.

The shape of the progress function. The manufacturing progress function is assumed to describe a constant percentage improvement as the production quantities double. All progress functions rest on this assumption and differ only in the percentage improvement between doubled production quantities and in the direct labor man-hours required to complete the first production unit. Therefore, all progress functions will have the same general shape. Any function may be defined if the number of direct labor hours required to complete the first unit is established, and if the subsequent rate of improvement is specified.

The number of direct labor hours required to complete the first production unit depends upon three major factors: First, previous experience and the relevance of this experience; a firm with extensive, directly applicable experience will require fewer direct labor man-hours for the first unit than will a firm with little experience. Second, the amount of effort that the organization expends in preparation for production will influence the time to complete the first unit; the firm may expend extensive time and energy in tooling-up for the required manufacturing process. Hence the first unit will require less manufacturing time. Third, the characteristics of the unit itself will affect first-unit manufacturing time. The complexity and the size of the unit will have a direct bearing on its manufacturing time.

The rate of improvement that will be experienced as additional units are produced is also a function of the preceding factors. Two additional related factors will also influence this rate: (1) the effort that the organization puts forth to improve or reduce manufacturing times should affect the ultimate rate of improvement; (2) the opportunity for improvement will also determine the improvement rate. If the time required to manufacture the first unit is high, subsequent improvement may come rather easily. If the reverse is true, subsequent improvement will be difficult. This latter case may be the more desirable even though the reduction in manufacturing time may be less striking than a higher first unit with more improvement. An important aspect of this is that the man-hours required for unit number one and the rate of improvement must be considered simultaneously in assessing production performance.

5.2. THE GRAPHICAL FUNCTION

One reason for the initial acceptance and popularity of the manufacturing progress function is the relative ease with which it can be applied. The relationship between direct labor man-hours and units produced, can be expressed as a curve on graph paper from only a few plotted points. Thus, the information needed for a specific unit of production can be taken directly from this graph. On log–log paper the progress function will result in a straight line. This is the usual method of expressing the relationship between the unit number and the direct labor hours. Before proceeding to the log–log representation, however, the function will be exhibited on arithmetic graph paper.

The function on arithmetic paper. Consider the previous example of an aircraft model which requires 100,000 direct labor man-hours to produce the first unit. Assume that in producing subsequent units a reduction of

Table 5.1. UNIT, CUMULATIVE, AND CUMULATIVE AVERAGE DIRECT LABOR MAN-HOURS REQUIRED FOR AN 80 PER CENT PROGRESS FUNCTION WITH UNIT NUMBER ONE AT 100,000 HOURS

Unit Number	Unit Direct Labor Man-hours	Cumulative Direct Labor Man-hours	Cumulative Average Direct Labor Man-hours
1	100,000	100,000	100,000
2	80,000	180,000	90,000
4	64,000	314,210	78,553
8	51,200	534,591	66,824
16	40,960	892,014	55,751
32	32,768	1,467,862	45,871
64	26,214	2,392,453	37,382
128	20,972	3,874,395	30,269
256	16,777	6,247,318	24,404

20 per cent in the direct labor man-hours between doubled production units can be expected. This establishes an 80 per cent progress function expressed in tabular form for movements of doubled production quantities in Table 5.1. The cumulative values shown in the table were computed after first finding the unit times for all units.

The cumulative average direct labor man-hours shown in Table 5.1 were obtained by dividing the cumulative values by the unit number. Thus, the first eight aircraft will require a total of 534,591 direct labor man-hours. The average direct labor man-hours per aircraft is therefore 534,591/8 = 66,824. Units and cumulative average values for this example are illustrated in Figure 5.1 for units 1–16 and in Figure 5.2 for units 1–2,048.

By interpolation in Figure 5.1 it is possible to determine any unit values or cumulative average value through unit number 16. Thus, aircraft number 11

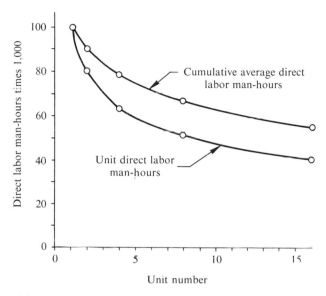

Figure 5.1. An eighty per cent progress curve with unit number one at 100,000 hours.

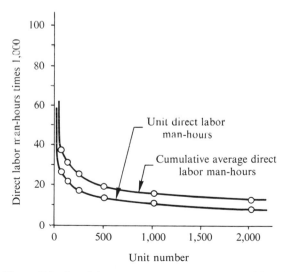

Figure 5.2. An eighty per cent progress curve with unit number one at 100,000 hours.

should require 46,000 direct labor man-hours. The first 11 aircraft should require a total of 11(61,500) or 676,500 man-hours. Figure 5.2 shows that unit number 700 will require approximately 12,000 direct labor man-hours. The first 800 aircraft will require 800(17,000) or 13,600,000 direct labor man-hours. Thus, with these two graphs it is possible to plot the given unit and cumulative average values, sketch in a curve to connect these points, and then read off any other required value from the curves. There are some difficulties in this method. First, it is not easy to draw in accurately a smooth curve which connects the given points. Secondly, it is possible to obtain only an approximate reading from the curve The first objection can be eliminated and the second partially overcome by using log–log rather than arithmetic graph paper.

The function on log–log paper. On arithmetic graph paper, equal numerical differences are represented by equal distances. For example, the linear distance between 1 and 3 will be the same as between 8 and 10. On logarithmic graph paper, the linear distance between any two quantities is dependent upon the ratio of those two quantities. Two pairs of quantities having the same ratio will be equally spaced. For example, the distance from 2 to 4 will be the same as from 30 to 60 or from 1,000 to 2,000.

If the progress function is plotted on double logarithmic paper, both the abscissa and the ordinate are represented logarithmically. This permits the progress function to be plotted as a straight line. A power function may be plotted as a straight line on log–log paper. Hence the progress function can be plotted either from two points or one point and the slope, such as unit number one and the per cent improvement. Also, by using log–log paper, the values for a large quantity of units can be presented on a single graph. Arithmetic graph paper, on the other hand, generally requires more values to define a curve. Either two separate graphs or one extremely large graph is required to present the curve over a wide range of units. Extrapolation or projection from a few points is difficult.

Figure 5.3 exhibits the same unit and cumulative average values that were used to construct the function on arithmetic paper, except that these are plotted on log–log paper. Reading from Figure 5.3, unit number 300 will require 16,000 direct labor man-hours. A total of 300 units should require 300(23,000) or 6,900,000 hours. Note that the function in Figure 5.3 representing the cumulative average direct labor man-hours is above, and nearly parallel to, the unit function, after the first few units.

The relative ease of using a double logarithmic graphical representation of the progress function should be evident from the preceding example. In practice, this representation is extensively used. The progress curve, representing a projection or a forecast, is first established. Then, as production units are completed, the actual values are recorded on the graph. This

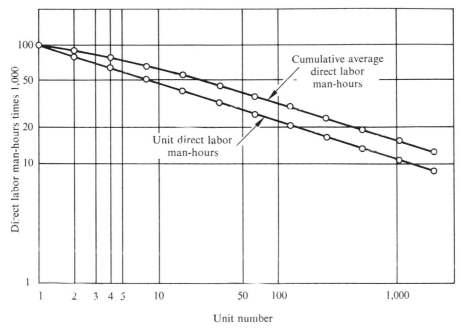

Figure 5.3. An eighty per cent progress curve with unit number one at 100,000 hours.

provides a current exhibit of the actual production progress compared to the planned progress. If the actual progress deviates significantly from the planned progress function, the forecast must be revised or corrective action must be applied to the production process.

5.3. THE ANALYTICAL MODEL

The manufacturing progress model has been described as an empirical concept. It has been suggested that the relationship between direct labor man-hours and units produced will follow a predictable pattern. If this is true, the relationship can be defined with a mathematical function. This section is concerned with analytical methods of determining the unit, the cumulative, and the cumulative average values of direct labor man-hours for various production quantities.

Development of the unit formula. An analytical expression for the manufacturing progress function will be developed from the assumption that the number of direct labor man-hours required to produce doubled production units is reduced by a constant percentage. Let

x = the unit number
Y_x = the number of direct labor hours required to produce the xth unit
K = the number of direct labor hours required to produce the first unit
ϕ = the slope parameter of the manufacturing progress function.

From the assumption of a constant percentage reduction in direct labor hours for doubled production units,

$$Y_x = K\phi^0 \qquad \text{where} \quad x = 2^0 = 1$$
$$Y_x = K\phi^1 \qquad \text{where} \quad x = 2^1 = 2$$
$$Y_x = K\phi^2 \qquad \text{where} \quad x = 2^2 = 4$$
$$Y_x = K\phi^3 \qquad \text{where} \quad x = 2^3 = 8$$

Therefore,

$$Y_x = K\phi^d \qquad \text{where} \quad x = 2^d.$$

Taking the common logarithm gives

$$\log Y_x = \log K + d \log \phi \qquad \text{where} \quad \log x = d \log 2.$$

Solving for d gives

$$d = \frac{\log Y_x - \log K}{\log \phi}, \quad \text{and} \quad d = \frac{\log x}{\log 2}.$$

From which

$$\frac{\log Y_x - \log K}{\log \phi} = \frac{\log x}{\log 2}$$

$$\log Y_x - \log K = \frac{\log x(\log \phi)}{\log 2}.$$

Let

$$n = \frac{\log \phi}{\log 2}.$$

Therefore,

$$\log Y_x - \log K = n \log x.$$

Taking the antilog of both sides gives

$$\frac{Y_x}{K} = x^n$$

$$Y_x = Kx^n. \tag{5.1}$$

Application of Equation (5.1) can be illustrated by reference to the example of an 80 per cent progress function with unit number 1 at 100,000 direct labor man-hours. Solving for Y_8, the number of direct labor man-hours required to build the eighth unit gives

$$Y_8 = 100,000(8)^{\log 0.8/\log 2}$$
$$= 100,000(8)^{-0.322}$$
$$= \frac{100,000}{(8)^{0.322}}$$
$$= \frac{100,000}{1.9535} = 51,200.$$

As an additional example, consider the situation with unit number 1 at 120,000 direct labor hours and a 90 per cent progress function. The number of direct labor hours required for unit number 50 is

$$Y_{50} = 120,000(50)^{\log 0.9/\log 2}$$
$$= 120,000(50)^{-0.152}$$
$$= \frac{120,000}{50^{0.152}} = 66,211.$$

The cumulative and cumulative average formulas. The cumulative number of direct labor man-hours required to produce N units may be expressed as

$$T_N = Y_1 + Y_2 + \cdots + Y_N = \sum_{x=1}^{N} Y_x. \tag{5.2}$$

A fairly good approximation for Equation (5.2) is possible by integrating from 0.5 to $N + 0.5$. Thus,

$$T_N \cong \int_{0.5}^{N+0.5} Y_x \, dx = K \int_{0.5}^{N+0.5} x^n \, dx$$
$$\cong \frac{K}{1+n} [(N+0.5)^{(1+n)} - (0.5)^{(1+n)}]. \tag{5.3}$$

As an example of the use of Equation (5.3) suppose that the approximate cumulative direct labor hours required to build four units, T_4, under an 80 per cent progress function with unit number one at 100,000 hours is needed.

$$T_4 \cong \frac{100,000}{1 + (\log 0.8/\log 2)}$$
$$\times \{(4 + 0.5)^{[1+(\log 0.8/\log 2)]} - (0.5)^{[1+(\log 0.8/\log 2)]}\}$$
$$\cong \frac{100,000}{0.678} [(4.5)^{(0.678)} - (0.5)^{(0.678)}]$$
$$\cong 147,493[2.772 - 0.625] = 316,667.$$

Application of Equation (5.2) would give a value for T_4 of 314,210 direct labor man-hours. Thus, the approximation method gives an error of $+0.78$ per cent. This error would be even less for larger values of N.

The cumulative average direct labor man-hours required to produce N units may be expressed as

$$V_N = \frac{Y_1 + Y_2 + \cdots + Y_N}{N} = \frac{\sum_{x=1}^{N} Y_x}{N}. \tag{5.4}$$

By substituting Equation (5.3) a fairly good approximation for Equation (5.4) is obtained. Thus,

$$V_N \cong \frac{K}{N(1+n)} [(N + 0.5)^{(1+n)} - (0.5)^{(1+n)}]. \tag{5.5}$$

An example of the application of Equation (5.5) can be illustrated with a 90 per cent progress function with unit number 1 at 120,000 direct labor man-hours. The cumulative average direct labor man-hours required to build a total of 50 units may be calculated as

$$V_{50} \cong \frac{120{,}000}{50[1 + (\log 0.9/\log 2)]}$$

$$\times [(50 + 0.5)^{[1+(\log 0.9/\log 2)]} - (0.5)^{[1+(\log 0.9/\log 2)]}]$$

$$\cong \frac{120{,}000}{42.4} [(50.5)^{0.848} - (0.5)^{0.848}]$$

$$\cong 2{,}830(27.825 - 0.556) = 77{,}174.$$

Equation (5.3) and Equation (5.4) were based on the substitution of an integral for a summation with a change of limits. The validity of this substitution is illustrated in Figure 5.4. Note that the area under the step function is nearly the same as the area under the integral. And the lined area (the excess of the integral over the step function) is approximately equal to the cross-hatched area (the excess of the step function over the integral).

Consider another approximation for the cumulative direct labor man-hours given by the integral

$$T_N \cong \int_0^N Y_x \, dx$$

$$\cong K \int_0^N x^n \, dx$$

$$\cong K \left(\frac{N^{n+1}}{n+1} \right). \tag{5.6}$$

Dividing Equation (5.6) by N gives an approximation for the cumulative average number of direct labor man-hours expressed as

$$V_N \cong \frac{1}{n+1}(KN^n). \tag{5.7}$$

Inspection of Equation (5.7) indicates that the cumulative average number of direct labor man-hours can be obtained by multiplying the unit value by the factor $1/(n+1)$.

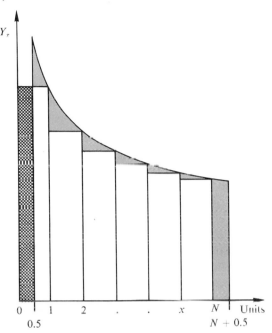

Figure 5.4. The step function $\sum_1^N Y_x$ and the integral $\int_{0.5}^{N+0.5} Y_x \, dx$.

The validity of this approximation is illustrated in Figure 5.5. The shaded area represents the error due to integration. The error will be sizable for small values of x. As x becomes large, however, the incremental error is small and the initial error is spread over more units. The percentage error in the approximation may be expressed as

$$\frac{\left(\frac{1}{1+n}\right)Kx^n - \dfrac{\sum\limits_1^N Y_x}{N}}{\dfrac{\sum\limits_1^N Y_x}{N}}.$$

Consider the following example using an 80 per cent curve with unit 1 at 1

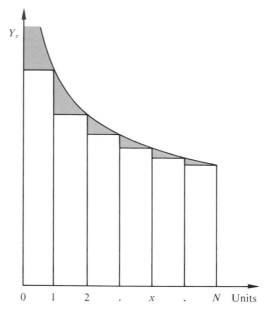

Figure 5.5. The step function $\sum_{1}^{N} Y_x$ and the integral $\int_{1}^{N} Y_x\, dx$.

direct labor man-hour. The percentage error at 20 units will be

$$\frac{0.5623 - 0.5242}{0.5242} = +7.27.$$

The percentage error at 200 units will be

$$\frac{0.2679 - 0.2636}{0.2636} = +1.63.$$

Thus, the factor $1/(1 + n)$ does not yield a value for the cumulative direct labor man-hours that is as accurate as the previous approximation. It is simple to use, however, and gives fairly good results for large values of x.

The use of tabular values. Application of the manufacturing progress function is facilitated by the use of tabular values. Appendix B gives unit and cumulative values for selected slope parameters with unit 1 at 1 direct labor man-hour. The unit values in Table B.1 were obtained from $Y_x = Kx^n$. The cumulative values in Table B.2 were obtained by summing the unit values of Table B.1. Cumulative average values can be found from Table B.2 by dividing the cumulative value by the number of units involved.

Solutions to specific values require multiplying the tabular values that apply by K. For example, if $K = 65$ direct labor hours, multiply the tabular value by 65. This is necessary since the tables are based on a K value of unity.

Interpolation may be employed for either x or ϕ or both if the small loss of accuracy is relatively unimportant. If the loss of accuracy is important, the formulas may be used directly, or a table with the required parameters may be constructed.

5.4. DEFINING THE PROGRESS FUNCTION

It has been empirically demonstrated that improvements in manufacturing operations can often be described by a constant percentage improvement between doubled production quantities. Thus, the manufacturing progress function is based upon empirical evidence. This does not mean that the progress curve cannot be a good forecasting device. It does mean that the curve must be supported in each case through the collection and analysis of data from this or a similar operation or product to determine whether the manufacturing progress function is appropriate. Then, the member of the family of functions which is applicable can be specified. Once this has been done, the progress function may serve as the basis for forecasting in manufacturing operations.

Determining a specific function from production standards. Direct labor hours for the first production unit and a subsequent rate of improvement must be estimated for each application of the manufacturing progress function. There are two common production standard methods of approach in obtaining these estimates. The first requires development of a work standard from a system of elemental standard data. The second requires use of data from similar, but already completed jobs. In either case, the rate of improvement is considered to be constant and dependent upon the general production capabilities of the company. It is assumed not to vary over time, or from one job to another. Then, all that needs to be defined is the direct labor man-hours necessary to complete the first production unit.

In using elemental standard data, a detailed study is made of the operation, and a standard time is set under the assumption that most of the improvement has already been realized. Then, either of two alternatives is followed: (1) A constant may be applied to modify this standard time to obtain an estimate for the first production-unit man-hours. For example, a given production facility may be approximately and repeatedly 35 per cent efficient on the first production unit. The standard time is then divided by 0.35 to obtain the time for the first production unit. This constant would be determined by the preproduction effort expended and would rarely vary from one job to another. If it did, it would have to be estimated with each new job.

(2) The standard time would be estimated as the time to complete some specific unit of production some time in the future. As before, this information would be obtained from previous experience. For example, the standard direct labor man-hours could be attained by production-unit number one thousand. Then the time for the first production unit would be estimated by calculating from this reference point using the estimated slope.

A second method for defining the progress function also rests upon the assumption that the rate of improvement is constant for a given production facility. It is only required that the number of direct labor hours needed for the first production unit be estimated. This may be established from comparison with similar jobs. In the aircraft industry it is common practice to estimate the time for the first unit from the basic airframe weight. The weight of the aircraft less engines, instruments, and auxiliary gear is multiplied by a constant obtained from previous experience in building similar aircraft. This estimate for the number of direct labor man-hours, together with the assumed rate of improvement, specifies a progress function for any new model under consideration.

Fitting the progress function to two points. In some instances, data are collected and it is desired in retrospect to determine the progress function that fit that data. Such information could then be used in predicting future analogous operations. In other instances, a progress function may be forecast through an estimate of only two points, for example, the time needed to complete the first and the tenth unit. In considering the case where only two points are specified, it may therefore be desirable to determine the progress curve that extends through them. The two given points may be specified as x_i, Y_i, and x_j, Y_j. Then, at each point

$$Y_i = Kx_i^n \qquad Y_j = Kx_j^n.$$

Dividing the second equation into the first gives

$$\frac{Y_i}{Y_j} = \left(\frac{x_i}{x_j}\right)^n.$$

Taking the log of both sides yields

$$\log \frac{Y_i}{Y_j} = n \log \frac{x_i}{x_j}$$

$$n = \frac{\log Y_i - \log Y_j}{\log x_i - \log x_j}. \qquad (5.8)$$

A value for K may be determined by substituting n into the equation $Y_i = Kx_i^n$ or the equation $Y_j = Kx_j^n$. This may be illustrated with an example: Suppose that the first production unit required 12 direct labor man-hours. It is estimated that the one-hundredth unit will take 6 man-hours. The manufacturing progress function that will describe this improvement can be found from Equation (5.8) as

$$n = \frac{\log 12 - \log 6}{\log 1 - \log 100}$$

$$= \frac{1.0792 - 0.7782}{0 - 2.000} = -0.1505.$$

Therefore,

$$\log \phi = n \log 2$$
$$= (-0.1505)(0.3010)$$
$$= 9.9547 - 10.$$

Taking the antilog of both sides gives a value for ϕ of 0.901. Therefore, the progress function passing through these two points is

$$Y_x = 12x^{-0.1505}.$$

Fitting the progress function to more than two points. In some applications, we have a set of data for which a specific progress function must be specified. This can be done most simply by plotting the data on log–log graph paper and sketching a straight line that appears to fit these data. When more than two values are plotted, it is unlikely that there exists a straight line that will pass through all these values. The method of least squares may be used to specify the line of best fit for such data.

The general progress function, $Y_x = Kx^n$, when expressed in logarithmic form, is the straight line $\log Y_x = \log K + n \log x$. Log K is the intercept at $\log x = 0$ or $x = 1$, and n is the slope of the line. Thus, the general progress function can be defined by specifying n and $\log K$. The method of least squares will yield

$$n = \frac{\sum [\log Y][\log x - (\sum \log x / M)]}{\sum [\log x - (\sum \log x / M)]^2} \qquad (5.9)$$

$$\log K = \frac{\sum \log Y - n \sum \log x}{M}. \qquad (5.10)$$

The number of data points is designated M.

The development of a line of best fit by specification of the parameters n and $\log K$ can be illustrated with an example. Assume that data have been collected on production item 10, 20, 30, 40, and 50. It is desired to determine the general progress function that best fits these data in order to make predictions about future production rates. Five unit numbers and the direct labor man-hours for each of these units are given. These data can be expressed

Table 5.2. CALCULATIONS LEADING TO A LINE OF LEAST SQUARES

Unit Number			Direct Labor Man-Hours		
(x)	$(\log x)$	$\log x - \dfrac{\Sigma \log x}{M}$	(Y)	$(\log Y)$	$\log Y \left(\log x - \dfrac{\Sigma \log x}{M} \right)$
10	1.000	-0.41584	59.2	1.7723	-0.73699
20	1.3010	-0.11484	48.5	1.6857	-0.19359
30	1.4771	$+0.06126$	46.1	1.6637	$+0.10192$
40	1.6021	$+0.18626$	42.0	1.6232	$+0.30234$
50	1.6990	$+0.28316$	40.1	1.6031	$+0.45393$
	7.0792			8.3480	

$$\Sigma \left(\log x - \frac{\Sigma \log x}{M} \right)^2 = +0.30474$$

$$\Sigma \left[\log Y \left(\log x - \frac{\Sigma \log x}{M} \right) \right] = -0.07239$$

in tabular form as shown in Table 5.2. The parameters can be calculated from the completed table and Equations (5.9) and (5.10) as

$$n = \frac{-0.07239}{0.30474} = -0.2375.$$

Since $\log \phi = n \log 2$

$$\log \phi = -0.2375(0.3010) = 9.9285 - 10.$$

Taking the antilog gives $\phi = 0.848$. Thus, an 84.8 per cent progress function describes these data. Also,

$$\log K = \frac{8.3480 - (-0.2375)(7.0792)}{5} = 2.0058.$$

Taking the antilog gives $K = 101.3$ hr. Therefore, the manufacturing progress function is defined as

$$Y_x = 101.3x^{-0.2375}.$$

5.5. APPLICATIONS OF THE PROGRESS FUNCTION

The manufacturing progress function may form the basis for decision making in the procurement, production, and financial aspects of a manu-facturing enterprise. In procurement the function can be used to determine the item cost for manufacturing, and as a basis for the manufacture or purchase decision. In production, the progress function may be used to determine equipment loading and manpower schedules. In finance, decisions related to bidding, pricing, and capital requirements may be based on the manufacturing progress function. In each of these applications, the progress model would act as a forecasting device against which actual performance could be measured. This section presents selected applications of the progress function.

Procurement applications. Once a specific manufacturing progress function has been selected, it may be used to determine the average item cost for manufacturing over a given production run. Item cost per unit is expressed in terms of the direct labor cost, the direct material cost, and the factory burden cost. Direct labor cost will require computation of the average number of direct labor hours per unit. Direct material cost will be a constant charge per unit of product. Factory burden cost will be related to direct labor cost by the use of a percentage. Let

lr — direct labor hourly rate
dm = direct material cost per unit
fb = factory burden rate expressed as a decimal fraction of the direct labor hourly rate.

Item cost per unit, C_i, can be expressed as

$$C_i = V_N(lr) + dm + V_N(lr)(fb).$$

Substituting Equation (5.7) for V_N gives

$$C_i = \frac{KN^n}{n+1}(lr) + dm + \frac{KN^n}{n+1}(lr)(fb)$$

$$= \frac{KN^n}{n+1}(lr)(1+fb) + dm. \tag{5.11}$$

As an example of the application of Equation (5.11) consider a situation in which 50 units are to be manufactured. The direct labor hourly rate is $3 per hour, the direct material cost per unit is $210, and the factory burden rate is 0.70. It is estimated that the first unit will require 100 direct labor man-hours to produce and that a 90 per cent progress function is applicable. The item cost per unit is

$$C_i = \frac{100(50)^{\log 0.9/\log 2}}{(\log 0.9/\log 2) + 1}(\$3.00)(1 + 0.70) + (\$210.00)$$

$$= \frac{55.1846}{0.848}(\$5.10) + (\$210.00) = \$541.30.$$

If C_i' is the item cost per unit for a purchased item, the number of units that must be produced for a break-even item cost may be expressed as

$$C_i' = \frac{KN^n}{n+1}(lr)(1+fb) + dm$$

$$\frac{KN^n}{n+1} = \frac{C_i' - dm}{lr(1+fb)}$$

$$N = \left[\frac{(C_i' - dm)(n+1)}{lr(1+fb)K}\right]^{1/n} \tag{5.12}$$

Suppose that the item of the previous example can be purchased for $510 per unit. The number of units that must be produced in order that the manufacturing alternative be as attractive as purchasing can be found from Equation (5.12) as

$$N = \left[\frac{(\$510 - \$210)(0.848)}{\$3.00(1.70)100}\right]^{-1/0.152}$$

$$= (0.4988)^{-6.58} = 97.$$

Production applications. The manufacturing progress function can be used as the basis for production scheduling. The curve provides information concerning the anticipated time required to perform an operation or a series of operations. Such information is a prerequisite to many production decisions. Information extracted from the curve may be used to establish requirements for manpower, floor space, machinery, and tools. If the size of the work force is constant, the reduction in time required to process one unit should result in a reduction in flow time, and an increase in the rate of delivery. Materials and purchased components must arrive on this schedule. The quality assurance program must be geared to meet the increasing flow of the product. Thus, all manufacturing operations which support production must be geared to production and the manufacturing progress function.

As an example of the application of the manufacturing progress function to the determination of manpower requirements consider the following situation. A supervisor has shown a consistent performance improvement in his department. Production to date has involved a total of 150 units. The average number of man-hours per unit was 7.0. Production is to be increased over the next four weeks and the supervisor wishes to determine the number of men required to produce 40 units in the first week, 60 in the second, 90 in the third, and 140 in the fourth.

Without considering the effect of a reduction in direct labor man-hours, the supervisor would multiply the number of units required each week by 7.0 and divide by 40. This would give a projected manpower requirement of 7 men in the first week, 11 in the second, 16 in the third, and 25 in the fourth.

By scheduling a predicted improvement in performance, however, a more realistic manpower requirement can be established.

Suppose that analysis of the direct labor man-hours associated with the initial 150 units of production gives an estimated first unit value of 12.8 man-hours with a 90 per cent progress function. Then, from Table B.1 of Appendix B it can be determined that the first 190 units will require a total of 1,285 man-hours. The first 150 units required a total of 1,050 man-hours, giving a projected man-hour requirement for the first week of 235. This should require 6 men for a 40-hr week. Adding the units required in the second week gives a total man-hour requirement of 1,619 for the production of 250 units. The projected man-hours for the second week is 1,619 less 1,285 or 334. For a 40-hr week this will require 9 men. Proceeding in this manner gives a projected manpower requirement of 13 men in the third week and 20 men in the fourth week.

The analysis presented is based on two assumptions: (1) that a 90 per cent progress function will apply for the future production schedule, (2) that the new personnel needed each week will be just as productive as those carried over from previous weeks. Note that in the fourth week only 5.6 man-hours will be required per unit produced. Because of this reduction in direct labor man-hours, it was possible to reduce the projected manpower requirement from that established without consideration of manufacturing improvement.

Financial applications. With the manufacturing progress model as a statement of manufacturing capabilities, one can use the function for preparing bids, for setting prices for new products, or for extending existing contracts. Alternatively, the function can be used to check the reasonableness of subcontracted bids or purchase prices in some situations. Once a financial decision has been made, the curve may be used to maintain financial control. The starting load costs of the product can be calculated, forecasts of capital requirements can be made, budgets can be prepared, and financial control can be implemented. After the product is in production, financial control can be maintained and deviations or cost trends can be analyzed and questioned.

Assume that a plant has produced a total of 790 units and that 2,765 man-hours have been expended to date at an average rate of $2 per hour. The number of units manufactured each month has steadily increased, but so has the number of man-hours. The plant manager wishes to determine whether the increased number of man-hours will raise the average unit labor cost above the $4.35 originally estimated for a run of 2,000 units.

Production data for this situation are given in columns A and C of Table 5.3. The plant manager is interested in estimating the cumulative average man-hours per unit when 2,000 units are completed. More specifically, he wishes to project the cumulative average costs to determine whether they will

Table 5.3. MONTHLY PRODUCTION DATA AND MAN-HOURS EXPENDED PER MONTH

Month	Units per Month (A)	Cumulative Units (B)	Man-Hours per Month (C)	Cumulative Man-Hours (D)	Cumulative Average Man-Hours per Unit (E)
1	—	—	258.0	258.0	—
2	92	92	340.0	598.0	6.50
3	103	195	373.1	971.1	4.98
4	115	310	402.2	1,373.3	4.43
5	133	443	407.6	1,780.9	4.02
6	152	595	450.4	2,231.3	3.75
7	195	790	533.7	2,765.0	3.50

reach $4.35 per unit at 2,000 units. This will be accomplished graphically under the assumption that the cumulative average curve is a straight line on log–log paper after 20 units.

Columns B, D, and E of Table 5.3 are completed as indicated. The monthly units and monthly man-hours are accumulated to complete the cumulative units and cumulative man-hours columns. Then, the values in column D are divided by those in column B to obtain the cumulative average man-hour values of column E. These values are recorded on log–log graph paper as indicated in Figure 5.6. It is noted that the cumulative average trend line shows a constant improvement after unit number 195. When 2,000 units are reached, the average labor hours per unit will have declined to 2.75. At a labor rate of $2 per hour, the average labor cost per unit for the run of 2,000 units will be $5.50 rather than the original estimate of $4.35. Thus, the original

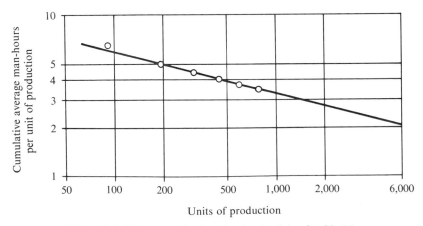

Figure 5.6. The cumulative function for the data of Table 5.3.

estimate was in error. It might then be asked, how many units must be produced to reduce the average unit cost to $4.35? This amounts to the average unit man-hour rate of 2.175 units per hour ($4.35 per unit divided by $2 per hour). From Figure 5.6, it appears that it would be necessary to produce 6,000 units in order to reduce the average cost to $4.35 per unit.

This problem could be approached analytically. A line of least squares could be fitted to the given data and the intercept (the man-hours for the first unit) and the slope (the percentage improvement) calculated. Then, the approximation formula could be used to answer the original question. With the data as given in this problem, however, it is not possible to specify the unit man-hours for any specific unit. Hence, it would be necessary to find the line of best fit for the cumulative average curve, realizing that a straight line is appropriate on log–log paper only after about 20 units of production. This approach would be satisfactory in solving for the cumulative average value at unit 2,000.

5.6. OTHER FORMS OF THE PROGRESS FUNCTION

The manufacturing progress function developed and illustrated in the previous sections was based on the assumption that the number of direct labor hours per unit decreased by a constant percentage for doubled production quantities. Although this is the most popular model, a number of other forms have been used in specific instances. Some of these are presented in this section. Finally, this section will discuss the relationship of manufacturing progress data to the progress function.

The linear cumulative average model. The first application of a progress model used a cumulative average function that was proportional to a power of the cumulative production. It was originally proposed that the *cumulative average time* required to manufacture a product would reduce by a constant percentage as production quantities were doubled. Thus,

$$V_N = Kx^n \quad \text{and} \quad T_N = xKx^n \quad \text{or} \quad Kx^{(n+1)}.$$

Also, the unit formula can be approximated by

$$Y_N \cong (n + 1)(Kx^n), \qquad N \geq 20.$$

This progress function when plotted on log–log graph paper would result in the cumulative average curve as a straight line as indicated in Figure 5.7.

With this distinction between the linear cumulative average model and the linear unit model, it is appropriate to discuss the relative merits of each. Neither model can be substantiated on the basis of logic; as has already been mentioned, the progress function (either interpretation) is intuitively sound but its only support has been empirical evidence. This empirical evidence is far from sufficient to establish the superiority of one model over the other. Under either interpretation, the unit and the cumulative average functions are nearly parallel after 20 units of production, and the superiority of one interpretation over the other would have to be established during the very early stages of production. This has not been done. The only remaining basis for selecting one model over the other, is the preference of the people using

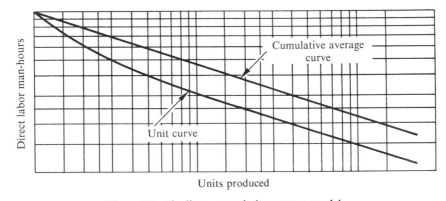

Figure 5.7. The linear cumulative average model.

the model and the use to which the model will be put. Note, however, that the unit interpretation and use of the unit curve will permit a more sensitive control of the process. The cumulative average formulation on the other hand, will not be as sensitive to a change in the production rate due to averaging of the data. The curve may have a smoother appearance but this will be deceiving. Hence, the unit model is suggested unless there are other specific issues involved which outweigh this loss of sensitivity in control.

Refinements of the progress function. It has been assumed that the manufacturing progress function (the unit or cumulative average models) is linear when plotted on log–log graph paper. The graphical and analytical solutions, and the examples given in the preceding sections, rest on the assumption that the direct labor man-hours required to complete a unit of product will decrease according to an exponential function that is linear when expressed on logarithmic grids. It has been suggested that there is no logical or analytical proof of this relationship; only empirical evidence can be developed. The characteristic of linearity on logarithmic grids, however, and the resulting ease with which the curve can be applied seems to account in a large measure for the general acceptance and continued popularity of the concept of the manufacturing progress function.

Almost since its initial use, suggestions have been made for refinements to the manufacturing progress function. Since the assumption of linearity rests on only empirical evidence, it would be logical to assume that attempts would be made to choose a nonlinear curve. Such a choice would be an improvement if it were to "fit" empirical data better than the classical linear formulation. Most refinements have started with the premise that the linear function on logarithmic grids, $Y_x = Kx^n$, does not describe empirical data as well as could be expected. Examples have been offered to illustrate the magnitude of the error in specific situations. Refinements have been proposed and developed. The Stanford "B" curve, the "S" curve, the Rand Modified Progress curve, and the Boeing Modified Progress curve are such refinements. Both the Stanford "B" curve and the "S" curve deviate from the linear hypothesis in that they have an initial humped or arched segment which is concave downward when plotted on logarithmic grids. The Stanford "B" curve approximates linearity; the "S" curve, as the name implies, calls for a convex segment before becoming linear. The Rand Modified Progress curve assumes linearity for the initial portion of the curve followed by a convex segment which eventually brings the curve into a flat and constant standard of production. The Boeing Modified Progress curve is an attempt to account for and predict irregularities in the curve due to major design changes in the product. That curve seeks to describe a particular situation more precisely rather than to redefine the linear function, as is done in the first three cases.

The reliability of data. At least two questions concerning the reliability of progress data should be considered. First, consider the situation where a manufacturing progress curve is specified and the resulting production conforms to this curve. It appears that a desirable situation exists as this is what was originally intended. Once a control or quantitative objective is imposed upon an operation, however, strong forces are created to make performance conform to the objective. This would be desirable if the progress curve represented a valid standard, one that could just be attained through diligence on the part of all employees. If this standard is very easily attained, then in all probability, the standard is all that will be attained. Eventual conformance to a progress curve is not evidence that the specified curve was the correct curve. Rather, evidence must be gathered as to the relative effort expended in conforming to the specified curve. Using a certain progress function for all work is not only dangerous but is indefensible on the basis of empirical evidence if, during the same period of time, the function was used as a control device.

The second issue concerning the reliability of manufacturing progress data, is the definition of the data itself. If direct labor man-hours are recorded and charged against a product there will be a strong temptation to classify questionable work as indirect labor. Thus, if direct labor man-hours are decreasing while indirect labor man-hours are on the rise, no real progress has been attained. Similarly it may even be difficult to obtain an accurate production count. Where a simplified design change is introduced, one must use judgment to decide whether this is an improvement contributed from a supporting staff organization or a new model which should be treated with a new progress function. The issues just described are not insurmountable in the use of the manufacturing progress model, but they should be recognized and considered during its application.

QUESTIONS

1. Describe the manufacturing progress function.

2. Describe the three classes or types of contributions which may lead to manufacturing improvements.

3. How may the shape of a specific progress curve be defined? What factors might contribute to this relative shape?

4. What are some of the disadvantages of expressing the progress curve on arithmetic graph paper?

5. Give the unit, the cumulative, and the cumulative average formulas for the progress function.

6. Describe the two classes of methods that are used to determine a specific progress function.

7. Why is it sometimes desirable to fit a progress function to two or more data points?

8. What criterion may be used in fitting a line of least squares to data?

9. What are the three areas of application of the progress curve?

10. What is the linear cumulative average model of the progress function?

11. Under what justification have refinements to the progress function been made?

PROBLEMS

1. Sketch the progress curve $K = 10$ hr, $\phi = 0.90$, on arithmetic graph paper through 16 units. How long should unit numbers 6 and 12 take to complete?

2. Solve Problem 1 using the unit formula.

3. Solve for the cumulative average number of hours to complete both 10 units and 100 units under the progress curve $K = 10$ hr, $\phi = 0.90$, using the two

approximation formulas. Compare these answers with the tabular values given in Appendix B.

4. A poor but honest tenant farmer, Dudley Forthumbs, was experiencing some difficulty in keeping flying creatures out of the kitchen of his home. The insects and small birds were not consuming too much food, but some of the larger birds were often able to make off with the best portion of the family meal. At the insistence of his wife, Dud set out to build the 10 screens necessary to cover the 10 windows in the kitchen. After some set-up time, he was finally able to complete the first screen in 48 hr. He then became discouraged and was about to go fishing. His wife, however, reminded him that manufacturing improvements could be expected and the last screen would probably be accomplished in half the time the first one took. If Dud's wife was correct, how much total time would be required to build the total of 10 screens?

5. If this same home owner in Problem 4 were to continue his project and build 10 additional screens, what is the best estimate of the average time to complete each of the second batch of 10 screens?

6. If the following data were collected on alternate production units,

Unit Number	Direct Labor Man-hours
2	90
4	70
6	65
8	60
10	55

what is the best estimate of the cumulative average time to complete a total of 50 such units?

7. The following cost data apply to Problem 6:

Direct labor rate .... $3.00 per hour
Factory burden 0.60
Direct material cost........ $2.50 per piece

What is the average unit cost of the 50 units? What would be the average unit cost of a follow-on contract for a second 50 units?

8. A product can be manufactured under a direct labor hourly rate of $4 per hour, a direct material cost of $19 per unit, and a factory burden rato of 1.10. The first production unit will require four man-hours to complete. Improvements of 20 per cent between doubled quantities can be expected. The product could also be purchased for $40. At what total quantity are the two alternatives equal in cost?

9. Under the assumptions of the linear cumulative average model, if the first production unit took 40 days to complete and $\phi = 0.80$, how long would it take to complete five units?

10. In Problem 9, how long would the fifth unit take to complete?

11. The validity of $K \int_{0.5}^{N+0.5} x^n \, dx$ and $[1/(1 + n)]KN^n$ as approximations for $\sum_1^N Y_x$ are illustrated in Figures 5.4 and 5.5 respectively. Graphically illustrate the validity of $K/2 + K \int_1^N x^n \, dx + \frac{1}{2}Kx^n$ as an approximation for $\sum_1^N Y_x$.

six

INTEREST, DEPRECIATION,

AND EQUIVALENCE

*Objectives of organized activity are usually achieved by implementing
one or more alternatives selected from an available set.
Each member of the set may contribute differently
to the effectiveness with which the organizational objectives are
achieved. It is easier to select a specific alternative if the available
alternatives are reduced to a common basis
for comparison.*

*Many operational alternatives may be described in terms
of their receipts and disbursements over time. When this is
the case, reducing these economic values to a common base
is essential in decision making. This chapter deals with
the specific procedures useful in calculating economic equivalence.[1]
The time value of money is explained through the development
of interest formulas. Depreciation models are presented as a
means for finding the equivalent annual cost of physical assets.
Finally, the common methods for comparing alternatives on an equivalent
economic basis are illustrated.*

---

[1] Much of the material presented in this chapter was adapted from H. G. Thuesen and
W. J. Fabrycky, *Engineering Economy*, 3rd ed. (Englewood Cliffs, N.J.: Prentice-Hall,
Inc., 1964).

6.1. THE TIME VALUE OF MONEY

Fundamentally, the rent paid for the use of a building is essentially the same as interest paid for the use of capital. The ethics and economics of charging a rent for the use of money have been discussed by philosophers and economists throughout the ages. Regardless of the ethics of the practice, its economic aspect must be considered in selecting operational alternatives that involve receipts and disbursements over time. This section deals with the time value of money, expressed as an interest rate, together with its impact on decision making.

Interest rate and interest. The interest rate is the ratio of the rent either paid or received for the use of money to the amount of money itself, over a period of time, usually one year. This ratio is generally expressed as a percentage. For example, if $6 is paid for the use of $100 for one year, then the interest rate is 6 per cent. The lender may consider interest received as a result of investing funds as a gain or profit. The borrower may consider interest as a charge or cost.

A person who owns a sum of money has a number of choices regarding its use. One of these involves lending this money on condition that the borrower repay the initial sum plus interest at some future date. If this is the choice, a number of factors should be considered in specifying an interest rate: First, the probability that the borrower will not repay the loan; this will depend upon his integrity as well as on the security granted to the lender. If the chances are 1 in 50 that the loan will not be repaid, then the lender is justified in charging 2 per cent of the sum to compensate for the risk of loss. This reasoning is most appropriate in the case of a lender who is lending many such sums of money. Then, in the long run, with a constant 2 per cent risk of loss, a 2 per cent charge on each loan will compensate for those loans which are not repaid. A second consideration in lending money is the cost of investigating the borrower, together with the administrative costs of monitoring the actual disbursement and receipt of money. If this cost is $1 per $100 loan for one year, then a 1 per cent administrative charge might be included. Finally, the net amount which will compensate the lender for being deprived of the use of the money for the time period is important. This charge might be considered as pure gain and might amount to $3 for a $100 loan. On the basis of the preceding analysis, a total interest rate of 6 per cent might be charged.

To the borrower, the interest charge represents an expense for the use of money. He will evaluate the magnitude of the interest charge by considering the use to which the money will be put. If he borrows to finance an operation which will result in some expected gain, then this gain must exceed the interest charge. Most production operations are partially financed with borrowed money. Thus, the charge for the use of money should be considered along with the charges for materials, labor, and producer goods. The sum of these charges should be less than the receipts for the products or services. The net difference represents the profit of the operation. The use of borrowed money to finance the cost of production with the expectation of making a profit is sometimes referred to as the *earning power of money*. The opportunity to use money to earn a profit will be considered by a prospective borrower of money in evaluating an interest rate.

Simple interest. The rent for a sum of money is usually expressed as the rate for the use of the money for a period of one year. The amount of interest charged on repayment of a loan is proportional to the duration of the loan expressed in years.

In simple interest, money is earned only on the principal sum. With P as the principal sum, n as the number of years, and i as the interest rate, simple interest can be expressed as

$$I = Pni. \tag{6.1}$$

As an example, consider a sum of $10,000 borrowed for four years at an interest rate of 7 per cent per annum. The interest earned may be calculated from Equation (6.1) as

$$I = \$10,000(4)(0.07) = \$2,800.$$

The amount of simple interest earned or charged would be $2,800. At the end of the four-year period, the principal sum of $10,000 would be returned together with this $2,800.

Compound interest. In compound interest, the money earned at the end of each interest period either becomes due at that time or earns interest upon itself. In the example just given the total interest of $2,800 could be paid in four equal payments of $700, one at the end of each year of the loan. This would satisfy the requirement of compound interest.

Alternatively, the interest earned during the life of the loan would earn interest upon itself and would be paid at the end of the four-year period. The total amount of money paid at the end of the loan of the previous example with compound interest is shown in Table 6.1. When the interest

Table 6.1. THE CALCULATION OF COMPOUND INTEREST AND PRINCIPAL WHEN INTEREST IS PERMITTED TO COMPOUND

Year	Amount Owed at Beginning of Year (A)	Interest Added at End of Year (B)	Amount Owed at End of Year (A + B)	Amount Paid at End of Year
1	$10,000.00	$10,000.00 × 0.07 = $700.00	$10,000(1.07) = 10,700.00	$0
2	10,700.00	10,700.00 × 0.07 = 749.00	$10,000(1.07)^2$ = 11,449.00	0
3	11,449.00	11,449.00 × 0.07 = 801.43	$10,000(1.07)^3$ = 12,250.43	0
4	12,250.43	12,250.43 × 0.07 = 857.53	$10,000(1.07)^4$ = 13,107.96	13,107.96

earned each year is added to the amount of the loan for the purpose of calculating interest charges, interest is said to be compounded annually. Formulas useful in dealing with compound interest are presented in the next section.

6.2. INTEREST FORMULAS

In compound interest, the interest earned at the end of an interest period is either paid at that time or earns interest upon itself. Formulas for the latter case are developed in this section. Let

$i =$ Nominal annual rate of interest
$n =$ Number of interest periods, usually annual
$P =$ Principal sum, at a time regarded to be the present
$R =$ Single payment in a series of n equal payments, made at the end of each interest period
$S =$ Sum, n interest periods hence, equal to the compound amount of a principal sum, P, or the sum of the compound amounts of the payments, R, at the interest rate i.

Single-payment compound-amount factor. When interest is permitted to compound as in Table 6.1, the interest earned during each interest period is

Table 6.2. THE SINGLE-PAYMENT COMPOUND-AMOUNT FACTOR

Year	Amount at Beginning of Year	Interest Earned during Year	Compound-Amount at End of Year
1	P	Pi	$P + Pi = P(1 + i)$
2	$P(1 + i)$	$P(1 + i)i$	$P(1 + i) + P(1 + i)i = P(1 + i)^2$
3	$P(1 + i)^2$	$P(1 + i)^2 i$	$P(1 + i)^2 + P(1 + i)^2 i = P(1 + i)^3$
n	$P(1 + i)^{n-1}$	$P(1 + i)^{n-1} i$	$P(1 + i)^{n-1} + P(1 + i)^{n-1} i = P(1 + i)^n$ $= S$

added to the principal sum at the beginning of the next interest period. By substituting general terms in Table 6.1, the relationship between S, P, n, and i can be developed as shown in Table 6.2. The resulting factor, $(1 + i)^n$, is known as the single-payment compound-amount factor and is designated ($\overset{SP\ i-n}{\quad}$). This factor may be used to express the equivalence between a present sum, P, and a future sum, S, at an interest rate i for n years. This relationship is

$$S = P(1 + i)^n$$

or

$$S = P(\overset{SP\ i-n}{\qquad}). \tag{6.2}$$

Values for this factor and those which follow are tabulated in Appendix C, Tables C.1–C.9.

The compound amount of $1,000 in six years at 5 per cent interest compounded annually may be found from Equation (6.2) as

$$S = \$1,000(1 + 0.05)^6$$
$$= \$1,000(1.340) = \$1,340.00.$$

Or, by use of the factor designation and its associated tabular value,

$$\overset{SP\ 5-6}{S = \$1,000(1.340)} = \$1,340.00.$$

The single-payment compound-amount factor may be used to solve for the interest rate i, or the number of interest periods, n, as required. Consider the following example: An individual is willing to loan $100 for a period of five years if he can earn $25 interest. The annual interest rate required in order to receive the compound amount of $125 after five years can be found from Equation (6.2) as

$$\overset{SP\ i-5}{\$125 = \$100(\qquad)}$$

$$\overset{SP\ i-5}{(1.250)} = \frac{\$125}{\$100}.$$

But since $\overset{SP\ 4-5}{(1.217)}$ and $\overset{SP\ 5-5}{(1.276)}$, linear interpolation gives

$$i = 4 + (1)\frac{1.250 - 1.217}{1.276 - 1.217} = 4 + \frac{0.33}{0.59} = 4 + 0.56.$$

The interest rate he must receive is 4.56 per cent, compounded annually.

Single-payment present-worth factor. The single-payment compound-amount relationship may be solved for P and expressed as

$$P = S\left[\frac{1}{(1 + i)^n}\right].$$

The resulting factor, $1/(1 + i)^n$, is known as the single-payment present-worth factor and is designated ($\overset{PS\ i-n}{\qquad}$). This factor may be used to express the equivalence between a future sum, S, and a present sum, P, at an interest rate i for n years. This relationship is

$$\overset{PS\ i-n}{P = S(\qquad)}. \qquad (6.3)$$

As an example, assume that it is desired to accumulate $1,000 four years from now. If the interest rate is 5 per cent, the amount of money that must be deposited is found from Equation (6.3) as

$$\text{PS } 5-4$$
$$P = \$1,000(0.8227) = \$822.70.$$

If required, solution in terms of i or n can be effected as with the previous formula.

Equal-payment series compound-amount factor. In some situations, a series of receipts or disbursements occurring uniformly at the end of each year may be encountered. The sum of the compound amounts of this series may be calculated by reference to Figure 6.1.

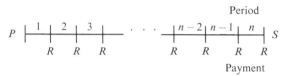

Figure 6.1. An equal payment series.

The R dollars deposited at the end of the nth year will earn no interest and contribute only R dollars to S. The R dollars deposited at the end of period $n - 1$ will earn interest in the amount of Ri, and $R(1 + i)$ will be contributed to the sum. The payment made at the end of $n - 2$ will contribute $R(1 + i)^2$. The sum of this series will be

$$S = R(1) + R(1 + i) + R(1 + i)^2 + \cdots + R(1 + i)^{n-2} + R(1 + i)^{n-1}$$
$$= R[1 + (1 + i) + (1 + i)^2 + \cdots + (1 + i)^{n-2} + (1 + i)^{n-1}].$$

Multiplying this series by $(1 + i)$ gives

$$S(1 + i) = R[(1 + i) + (1 + i)^2 + (1 + i)^3 + \cdots + (1 + i)^{n-1} + (1 + i)^n].$$

Then, subtracting the first equation from the second gives

$$S(1 + i) - S = R[(1 + i)^n - 1]$$
$$iS = R[(1 + i)^n - 1]$$
$$S = R\left[\frac{(1 + i)^n - 1}{i}\right].$$

The resulting factor $[(1 + i)^n - 1]/i$, is known as the equal-payment series compound-amount factor and is designated ($\overset{\text{SR } i-n}{\quad}$). This factor may be used to express the equivalence between an equal payment series, R, and a future sum, S, at an interest rate i for n years. This relationship is

$$S = R(\overset{SR\ i-n}{\quad}). \tag{6.4}$$

Consider an example of \$500 payments invested at the end of each year for four years at 6 per cent interest. The amount which will be received at the end of the four-year period may be found from Equation (6.4) as

$$S = \overset{SR\ 6-4}{\$500(4.375)} = \$2,187.50.$$

Consider a second example of an annual year-end investment of \$100 deposited in an account which pays 4 per cent compounded annually. Equation (6.4) may be used to determine the number of years required to accumulate \$2,000 as

$$\$2,000 = \$100(\overset{SR\ 4-n}{\quad})$$

$$\overset{SR\ 4-n}{(20.000)} = \frac{\$2,000}{\$100}.$$

But since $\overset{SR\ 4-14}{(18.292)}$ and $\overset{SR\ 4-15}{(20.024)}$, linear interpolation gives

$$n = 14 + (1)\frac{20.000 - 18.292}{20.024 - 18.292} = 14 + \frac{1.708}{1.732} = 14 + 0.99.$$

The investment program would take 14.99 years or in effect, in 15 years the desired \$2,000 would be accumulated.

Equal-payment series sinking-fund factor. The equal-payment series compound-amount factor may be solved for R and expressed as

$$R = S\left[\frac{i}{(1 + i)^n - 1}\right].$$

The resulting factor, $i/[(1 + i)^n - 1]$, is known as the equal-payment series sinking-fund factor and is designated ($\overset{RS\ i-n}{\quad}$). This factor may be used to express the equivalence between a future sum, S, and an equal-payment series, R, at an interest rate i for n years. This relationship is

$$R = S(\overset{RS\ i-n}{\quad}). \tag{6.5}$$

As an example, suppose that it is desired to deposit a series of uniform, year-end payments over 10 years in order to provide a total of \$5,000 at the end of that period. The amount that should be deposited each year at an interest rate of 6 per cent is found from Equation (6.5) as

$$R = \overset{RS\ 6-10}{\$5,000(0.07587)} = \$379.35.$$

Solution for i or n can be effected, if required.

Equal-payment series capital-recovery factor. The substitution of $P(1 + i)^n$ for S in the equal-payment series sinking-fund factor results in

$$R = P(1 + i)^n \left[\frac{i}{(1 + i)^n - 1} \right]$$
$$= P \left[\frac{i(1 + i)^n}{(1 + i)^n - 1} \right].$$

The resulting factor, $i(1 + i)^n / [(1 + i)^n - 1]$, is known as the equal-payment series capital-recovery factor and is designated ($\overset{RP\ i-n}{\quad}$). This factor may be used to express the equivalence between a present amount, P, and an equal-payment series, R, in the future at an interest rate i for n years. This relationship is

$$R = P(\overset{RP\ i-n}{\quad}). \tag{6.6}$$

As an example of the use of this factor, assume a company borrowed \$100,000 at 6 per cent interest which it must repay in equal end-of-year amounts over the next eight years. The amount which must be repaid at the end of each year may be found from Equation (6.6) as

$$R = \overset{RP\ 6-8}{\$100,000(0.16104)} = \$16,104.00.$$

If required, solution can be effected in terms of i or n.

Equal-payment series present-worth factor. The equal-payment series capital-recovery factor can be solved for P and expressed as

$$P = R \left[\frac{(1 + i)^n - 1}{i(1 + i)^n} \right].$$

The resulting factor, $[(1 + i) - 1] / i(1 + i)^n$, is known as the equal-payment series present-worth factor and is designated ($\overset{PR\ i-n}{\quad}$). This factor may be used to express the equivalence between future equal-payment series, R, and a present amount, P, at an interest rate i for n years. This relationship is

$$P = R(\overset{PR\ i-n}{\quad}). \tag{6.7}$$

As an example of this formula, assume that a machine will save \$4,000 per year in operating costs over the next 10 years. If an interest rate of 10 per cent is used, the present worth of these savings may be found from Equation (6.7) as

PR 10–10
$$P = \$4,000(6.14457) = \$24,578.28.$$

Summary of interest formulas. The interest formulas derived in the previous paragraphs express relationships between P, R, S, i, and n. In any given application an equivalence between S and P, P and S, S and R, R and S, P and R, or R and P is required for an interest rate i and a number of years n. Table 6.3 may be used to select the interest factor needed in a given

Table 6.3. SUMMARY OF INTEREST FORMULAS

Single-payment compound-amount	Given P, find S	$S = P(1 + i)^n$	$S = P(\overset{SP\ i\ -\ n}{})$
Single-payment present-worth	Given S, find P	$P = S\dfrac{1}{(1 + i)^n}$	$P = S(\overset{PS\ i\ -\ n}{})$
Equal-payment series compound-amount	Given R, find S	$S = R\left[\dfrac{(1 + i)^n - 1}{i}\right]$	$S = R(\overset{SR\ i\ -\ n}{})$
Equal-payment series sinking-fund	Given S, find R	$R = S\left[\dfrac{i}{(1 + i)^n - 1}\right]$	$R = S(\overset{RS\ i\ -\ n}{})$
Equal-payment series present-worth	Given R, find P	$P = R\left[\dfrac{(1 + i)^n - 1}{i(1 + i)^n}\right]$	$P = R(\overset{PR\ i\ -\ n}{})$
Equal-payment series capital-recovery	Given P, find R	$R = P\left[\dfrac{i(1 + i)^n}{(1 + i)^n - 1}\right]$	$R = P(\overset{RP\ i\ -\ n}{})$

situation. The factor designation scheme summarized in the last column makes it possible to set up a problem symbolically before determining the value of the factor.

Numerical values corresponding to each of the factor designations for the most frequently used ranges of i and n are given in Appendix C, Tables C.1–C.9. Individual tabular values are given to a number of decimal places sufficient for most applications. Linear interpolation may be used for either i or n with fairly accurate results. If results with a degree of accuracy beyond that which may be obtained by the use of tabular values are required, it will be necessary to use the formulas directly, together with logarithmic operations.

Effective interest rates. An interest rate quoted for an interest period of one year is called a *nominal annual rate*. Each interest formula derived in the previous paragraphs was based on the assumption of annual compounding interest. Sometimes, however, interest may be compounded more frequently. The result of this more frequent compounding will be an effective interest rate that will be higher than the nominal annual rate.

As an example, consider a nominal annual interest rate of 8 per cent which is to be compounded every six months. This is equivalent to an actual rate of 4 per cent compounded each half year. The compound amount can be found as $(1.04)^2 = 1.0816$. Thus, the effective interest rate is 8.16 per cent. The effective interest rate may be expressed as

$$\left(1 + \frac{\phi}{c}\right)^c - 1 \tag{6.8}$$

where c is the number of interest periods per year and ϕ is the nominal annual interest rate. This effective interest rate may be used with the formulas derived previously for situations involving more frequent compounding.

As an example, consider the following situation: The compound amount of $1,000 in six years at 5 per cent compounded semiannually first requires application of Equation (6.8) to find the effective interest rate. This rate is

$$\left(1 + \frac{0.05}{2}\right)^2 - 1 = 0.050625.$$

Then, application of Equation (6.2) gives the compound amount as

$$S = \$1,000(1.050625)^6 = \$1,344.89.$$

6.3. THE CONCEPT OF DEPRECIATION

The production of goods and services is directly dependent upon the employment of large quantities of producer goods which require considerable investment. Although this investment results in high worker productivity, this economy must be sufficient to absorb the reduction in value of these facilities as they are consumed in the production process. Alternative operational proposals may involve different programs of capital investment; hence it is essential that the cost of capital consumed be considered in evaluating these alternatives.

Classifications of depreciation. With the possible exception of land, physical assets are likely to lessen in value with the passage of time. This reduction in value may be due to physical depreciation, functional depreciation, or accident.

Physical depreciation results from the physical impairment of an asset.

Commonly referred to as *wear-and-tear* or *deterioration*, physical impairment may manifest itself as corrosion, abrasion, or cracking. This type of depreciation lowers the ability of the physical asset to perform its intended service.

Functional depreciation rests not upon a reduction in the ability of the asset to perform its intended service, but rather on a change in the demand for the service rendered by the asset. This reduction in demand for the product or service produced by the asset may be due to obsolescence resulting from the discovery of a second asset that makes it uneconomical to continue to use the first asset. Another form of functional depreciation occurs when the asset can no longer meet the demands placed upon it. The service has not changed. Rather, the demand for the service has changed, making it no longer feasible for this particular asset to satisfy demand. Finally, an asset that is no longer needed becomes obsolete with a resulting reduction in value.

Accidents may result in a sudden reduction in the value of an asset. Although insurable losses are usually not classified as depreciation, minor losses which are not insured do reduce the value of the asset and may be treated as depreciation.

The value-time function. The capital that should be recovered over the life of a depreciable asset is equal to the first cost less its salvage value at the time of retirement. In addition to this recovery of investment, interest should be earned on the unrecovered balance during the life of the asset. Understanding the concept of depreciation is complicated because two aspects must be considered: First, the actual lessening in value of the asset with use and the passage of time. Thus, the bearings on a machine may wear and structural elements may deteriorate. A building may become functionally obsolete. This is actual depreciation. The second aspect is accounting for this lessening in value. These two aspects are usually identical when the asset is first obtained. There are some advantages to these being identical when the asset is finally removed, either at the end of its estimated life or some time earlier or later than this estimated date. This is not always possible, however, since accounting for the lessening in value of a physical asset requires an estimate of the future.

In considering depreciation as a cost of production, it is necessary to predict the pattern of future value of an asset. It is customary to assume that the value of an asset decreases yearly in accordance with one of several mathematical functions. The choice of a particular depreciation model is not an easy task. This choice involves an estimate of the effective life of the asset, its salvage value at the end of this life, and the form of the mathematical function. Once a value-time function has been selected, it is chosen to represent the value of the asset at any point in time. A general value-time function is illustrated in Figure 6.2.

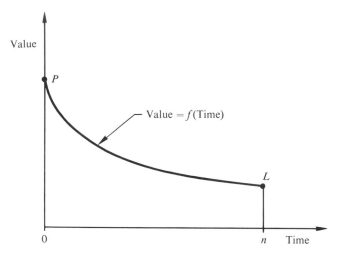

Figure 6.2. A general value-time function.

The calculated amount of decrease in value from one point in time to the next depends upon the initial cost of the asset, the method of depreciation selected, and the estimated salvage value. Once these estimates have been made, they are acted upon as if they represent actual facts until another decision is made. When a new decision is made, it is based upon the facts as they exist at that time.

Capital recovery plus return. Capital assets are purchased with the belief that they will earn more than they cost. One part of the anticipated earnings is considered to be *capital recovered*. The capital invested in an asset is recovered in the form of earnings resulting from the sale of products or services produced by the asset. Additional capital may be recovered in the form of the final sale of the asset at the end of its useful life. If a machine provided services in the amount of $1,800 during its useful life, and if it was finally sold at a salvage value of $200, then a total of $2,000 would be considered to be recovered capital. If the asset initially cost $2,000, then the capital invested in it would have been fully recovered.

A second part of the prospective earnings of an asset will be considered to be *return*. Since capital invested in an asset is recovered in small increments over time, it is necessary to consider the interest on the undepreciated balance as a cost of ownership. An investment in an asset is expected to return not only the capital invested in the asset, but also provide for interest earnings on the diminishing investment remaining. These two forms of earnings are collectively referred to as *capital recovery plus return*.

Depreciation is a cost of production. If the cost of capital consumption is neglected, profits will appear higher by the amount equal to the capital consumed. Then, at the end of the life of the asset there may have been no financial provision made for its replacement.

6.4. DEPRECIATION MODELS

One aim in accounting for the depreciation of an asset is to have a monetary measure of the capital worth of the enterprise. A more immediate aim is to arrive at the physical expenditure of physical capital, in monetary terms, that has been occasioned by each unit of product produced. This aim permits an accounting for the cost of the goods or service. The accounting objective is difficult because the physical depreciation per unit of product depends upon the total depreciation and the number of units produced, neither of which can be known until after the asset has been consumed. Nevertheless, an estimate of these must be made in advance. This section is concerned with depreciation models which may be used in accounting for the consumption of capital assets.

The straight-line model. The straight-line depreciation model assumes that the value of an asset decreases at a constant rate. Expressions for capital recovered, capital unrecovered, return, and capital recovered plus return may be developed for each year of the asset's life. Let

$$P = \text{the first cost of the asset}$$
$$L = \text{estimated salvage value}$$
$$n = \text{estimated life}$$
$$i = \text{interest rate.}$$

The capital recovered each year by the straight-line model may be expressed as $(P - L)/n$.

As an example of the application of the straight-line model assume that an asset has a first cost of \$7,000, an estimated life of six years, and an estimated salvage value of \$1,000. The total depreciation will be \$7,000 $-$ \$1,000 $=$ \$6,000 over a period of six years. The depreciation each year will be \$1,000.

For the conditions assumed, the investment in the asset during the first year is \$7,000; during the second year \$6,000; during the third year \$5,000, and so forth. If the desired rate of return on the investment is 8 per cent, the return for the first year should be \$7,000 $\times$ 0.08 $=$ \$560; for the second year \$6,000 $\times$ 0.08 $=$ \$480; for the third year \$5,000 $\times$ 0.08 $=$ \$400, and so forth. The capital recovered, capital unrecovered, return, and capital recovered plus return for each year of the assets life are given in Table 6.4. General expressions for these terms may be developed from the numerical example as exhibited in Table 6.5.

Table 6.4. AN EXAMPLE OF THE STRAIGHT-LINE METHOD OF DEPRECIATION

Year	Capital Recovered	Capital Unrecovered Beginning of Year	Return on the Capital Unrecovered	Capital Recovered Plus Return
1	$1,000	$7,000	$560	$1,560
2	1,000	6,000	480	1,480
3	1,000	5,000	400	1,400
4	1,000	4,000	320	1,320
5	1,000	3,000	240	1,240
6	1,000	2,000	160	1,160

The equivalent end-of-service value of capital recovered plus return may be found by multiplying the capital recovered plus return for the rth year by the compound-amount factor for the rth year, and summing over all r years. Let S equal the equivalent end-of-service-life value of capital recovered plus return, then

$$S = \sum_{r=1}^{n} \left\{ \frac{P-L}{n} + \left[P - (r-1)\left(\frac{P-L}{n}\right) \right] i \right\} (1+i)^{n-r}$$

$$= \sum_{r=1}^{n} \left[\frac{P-L}{n} + Pi + \frac{P-L}{n} i \right] (1+i)^{n-r} - \sum_{r=1}^{n} i\left(\frac{P-L}{n}\right) r(1+i)^{n-r}$$

$$= \left[\frac{P-L}{n}(1+i) + Pi \right] \sum_{r=1}^{n} (1+i)^{n-r} - i\left[\frac{P-L}{n} \right] \sum_{r=1}^{n} r(1+i)^{n-r}.$$

But

$$\sum_{r=1}^{n} (1+i)^{n-r} = (1+i)^{n-1} + (1+i)^{n-2} + \cdots + (1+i) + 1$$

$$= \frac{(1+i)^n - 1}{i}$$

Let

$$\rho = \sum_{r=1}^{n} r(1+i)^{n-r}$$

$$= (1+i)^{n-1} + 2(1+i)^{n-2} + \cdots + (n-1)(1+i) + n$$

$$(1+i)\rho = (1+i)^n + 2(1+i)^{n-1} + \cdots + n(1+i) + 1 - 1.$$

Subtracting ρ from $(1+i)\rho$, term by term

$$i\rho = (1+i)^n + \sum_{r=1}^{n} (1+i)^{n-r} - (n+1)$$

$$= (1+i)^n + \frac{(1+i)^n - 1}{i} - (n+1).$$

Table 6.5. GENERAL EXPRESSIONS FOR THE STRAIGHT-LINE METHOD OF DEPRECIATION

Year	Capital Recovered	Capital Unrecovered Beginning of Year	Return on Capital Unrecovered	Capital Recovered plus Return
1	$\dfrac{P-L}{n}$	P	Pi	$\dfrac{P-L}{n} + Pi$
2	$\dfrac{P-L}{n}$	$P - \left(\dfrac{P-L}{n}\right)$	$\left[P - \left(\dfrac{P-L}{n}\right)\right]i$	$\dfrac{P-L}{n} + \left[P - \left(\dfrac{P-L}{n}\right)\right]i$
3	$\dfrac{P-L}{n}$	$P - 2\left(\dfrac{P-L}{n}\right)$	$\left[P - 2\left(\dfrac{P-L}{n}\right)\right]i$	$\dfrac{P-L}{n} + \left[P - 2\left(\dfrac{P-L}{n}\right)\right]i$
r	$\dfrac{P-L}{n}$	$P - (r-1)\left(\dfrac{P-L}{n}\right)$	$\left[P - (r-1)\left(\dfrac{P-L}{n}\right)\right]i$	$\dfrac{P-L}{n} + \left[P - (r-1)\left(\dfrac{P-L}{n}\right)\right]i$
n	$\dfrac{P-L}{n}$	$P - (n-1)\left(\dfrac{P-L}{n}\right)$	$\left[P - (n-1)\left(\dfrac{P-L}{n}\right)\right]i$	$\dfrac{P-L}{n} + \left[P - (n-1)\left(\dfrac{P-L}{n}\right)\right]i$

Substituting these evaluations into the expression for S, gives

$$S = \left[\frac{P-L}{n}(1+i) + Pi\right]\frac{(1+i)^n - 1}{i}$$

$$- i\left(\frac{P-L}{n}\right)\left[\frac{(1+i)^n}{i} + \frac{(1+i)^n - 1}{i^2} - \frac{n+1}{i}\right]$$

$$= Pi\frac{(1+i)^n - 1}{i} + \frac{P-L}{n}\left[\frac{(1+i)^n - 1}{i} + (1+i)^n - 1\right.$$

$$\left. - (1+i)^n - \frac{(1+i)^n - 1}{i} + n + 1\right]$$

$$= P(1+i)^n - P + \frac{P-L}{n}(n) = P(1+i)^n - L.$$

An expression for the equivalent annual cost of capital recovered plus return may be derived by multiplying the equivalent end-of-service-life value of capital recovered plus return by the sinking fund factor as follows:

$$[P(1+i)^n - L]\left[\frac{i}{(1+i)^n - 1}\right]$$

$$P\left[\frac{i(1+i)^n}{(1+i)^n - 1}\right] - L\left[\frac{i}{(1+i)^n - 1}\right]$$

$$P\left[\frac{i(1+i)^n}{(1+i)^n - 1}\right] - L\left[\frac{i(1+i)^n}{(1+i)^n - 1} - i\right]$$

$$(P - L)\left[\frac{i(1+i)^n}{(1+i)^n - 1}\right] + Li$$

$$\overset{\text{RP } i-n}{(P - L)(\quad\quad) + Li.} \qquad\qquad (6.9)$$

The sinking-fund model. The sinking-fund depreciation model assumes that the value of an asset decreases at an increasing rate. One of a series of equal amounts is assumed to be deposited into a sinking fund at the end of each year of the asset's life. The sinking fund is ordinarily compounded annually and, at the end of the estimated life of the asset, the amount accumulated equals the total depreciation of the asset. Thus, if an asset has a first cost of $7,000, an estimated life of six years, an estimated salvage value of $1,000, and if an interest rate of 8 per cent is used, the amount deposited into the sinking fund at the end of each year would be

$$\overset{\text{RS } 8-6}{(\$7,000 - \$1,000)(0.13632) = \$817.92.}$$

The capital recovered during any year is the sum of the amount deposited into the sinking fund at the end of the year and the amount of interest earned on the sinking fund during the year. For the foregoing example, the capital recovered during the first year would be \$817.92; during the second year, \$817.92 + \$817.92 × 0.08 = \$883.35; during the third year, \$817.92 + \$1,701.27 × 0.08 = \$954.02, and so forth. These values are given in the first section of Table 6.6.

Table 6.6. AN EXAMPLE OF THE SINKING-FUND METHOD OF DEPRECIATION

Year	Capital Recovered	Capital Unrecovered Beginning of Year	Return on the Capital Unrecovered	Capital Recovered plus Return
1	\$817.92	\$7,000.00	\$560.00	\$1,377.92
2	883.35	6,182.08	494.57	1,377.92
3	954.02	5,298.73	423.90	1,377.92
4	1,030.35	4,344.61	347.57	1,377.92
5	1,112.78	3,314.26	265.14	1,377.92
6	1,201.80	2,201.48	176.12	1,377.92

The investment in the asset during the first year is \$7,000; during the second year, \$6,182.08; during the third year, \$5,298.73, and so forth. The return for the first year would be \$7,000 × 0.08 = \$560; for the second year, \$6,182.08 × 0.08 = \$494.57; for the third year, \$5,298.73 × 0.08 = \$423.90, and so forth. The capital recovery plus return would be a constant \$1,377.92 each year, as indicated in Table 6.6.

From Table 6.6, general expressions for the sinking-fund method of depreciation can be developed and expressed as for the straight-line method in Table 6.5. It can then be shown that by multiplying the capital recovery plus return term by the compound amount factor and summing over all years, the equivalent annual capital recovered plus return may also be reduced to

$$(P - L)(\overset{\text{RP }i-n}{}) + Li.$$

The fixed-percentage model. The fixed-percentage depreciation model assumes that the reduction in the value of an asset decreases at a decreasing rate. In effect, the depreciation during any year is equal to the undepreciated amount at the beginning of that year times D, where $D \times 100$ is the fixed percentage rate of depreciation. The undepreciated balance remaining at the end of any year equals the unrecovered balance at the beginning of that year times $(1 - D)$. The unrecovered capital at the end of the first, second, and nth year is then $P(1 - D)$, $P(1 - D)^2$, and $P(1 - D)^n$, respectively, with $P(1 - D)^n = L$. The general expression for determining D, given P, L, and n is then

$$D = 1 - \left(\frac{L}{P}\right)^{1/n}, \qquad L > 0. \tag{6.10}$$

In the previous example, where $P = \$7,000, L = \$1,000.$ and $n = 6$ years,

$$D = 1 - \left(\frac{1,000}{7,000}\right)^{1/6} = 1 - 0.723 = 0.277.$$

The capital recovered during the first year would be $\$7,000.00 \times 0.277 = \$1,939.00$; during the second year $(\$7,000.00 - 1,939.00) \times 0.277 = \$1,401.90$; during the third year $(\$7,000.00 - 1,939.00 - 1,401.90) \times 0.277 = \$1,013.57$, and so forth. These values are given in the first section of Table 6.7.

Table 6.7. AN EXAMPLE OF THE FIXED PERCENTAGE METHOD OF DEPRECIATION

Year	Capital Recovered	Capital Unrecovered Beginning of Year	Return on the Capital Unrecovered	Capital Recovered plus Return
1	$1,939.00	$7,000.00	$560.00	$2,499.00
2	1,401.90	5,061.00	404.88	1,806.78
3	1,013.57	3,659.10	292.73	1,306.30
4	732.81	2,645.53	211.64	944.45
5	529.82	1,912.72	153.02	682.84
6	382.84	1,382.10	110.57	493.41

The investment in the asset during the first year would be $\$7,000.00$; for the second year, $\$5,061.00$; for the third year, $\$3,659.10$, and so forth. With an interest rate of 8 per cent, the return for the first year would be $\$7,000.00 \times 0.08 = \$560.00$; for the second year, $\$5,061.00 \times 0.08 = \$404.88$; for the third year, $\$3,659.10 \times 0.08 = \$292.73$, and so forth. The capital unrecovered, return, and capital recovery plus return are given in Table 6.7 for each year of the asset's life. From this table, general expressions can be developed as with the straight-line method of depreciation. From these, the equivalent annual capital recovery plus return can also be shown to equal

$$(P - L)(\overset{\text{RP } i-n}{\quad\quad}) + Li.$$

The sum-of-the-years-model. The sum-of-the-years model of depreciation also assumes that the value of an asset decreases at a decreasing rate. The sum of the numbers from 1 to n is used as the denominator for a series of fractions, n in number, used to calculate annual depreciation. The numerator of the fraction for any specific year is the life expectancy as of that year. The depreciation allocation for any year is found by multiplying the specific fraction times the depreciable amount.

Returning to the example of $P = \$7,000, n = 6$, and $L = \$1,000$, then $1 + 2 + 3 + 4 + 5 + 6 = 21$, and the depreciation during the first year would be

$$(P - L)\frac{n}{\sum n} \tag{6.11}$$

$$(\$7,000 - 1,000)\left(\frac{6}{21}\right) = \$1,714.29.$$

During the second year, the depreciation would be $(\$7,000 - 1,000)(5/21) = \$1,428.57$; during the third year $(\$7,000 - 1,000)(4/21) = \$1,142.86$, and so forth. These values are given in the first section of Table 6.8.

Table 6.8. AN EXAMPLE OF THE SUM-OF-THE-YEARS METHOD OF DEPRECIATION

Year	Capital Recovered	Capital Unrecovered Beginning of Year	Return on the Capital Unrecovered	Capital Recovered plus Return
1	$1,714.29	$7,000.00	$560.00	$2,274.29
2	1,428.57	5,285.71	422.86	1,851.43
3	1,142.86	3,857.14	308.57	1,451.43
4	857.14	2,714.28	217.14	1,074.28
5	571.43	1,857.14	148.57	720.00
6	285.72	1,285.71	102.86	388.58

The unrecovered capital would be $7,000 during the first year; $7,000 − 1,714.29 = $5,285.71, during the second year; $5,285.71 − $1,428.57 = $3,857.14, during the third year, and so forth. With an 8 per cent interest rate, the return for the first year should be $7,000 × 0.08 = $560.00; for the second year, $5,285.71 × 0.08 = $422.86; for the third year, $3,857.13 × 0.08 = $308.57, and so forth. The capital unrecovered plus return for each year of the asset's life is given in Table 6.8. As with the previous depreciation models, general expressions could now be developed. With these, the capital recovery plus return term can be multiplied by the compound amount factor and summing over all years, the equivalent annual capital recovered plus return would be

$$(P - L)(\overset{RP\ i-n}{\qquad}) + Li.$$

Equivalence of depreciation models. In economy analysis it is often necessary to compute the equivalent annual cost of capital recovered plus return so that alternatives involving competitive assets may be compared on an equivalent basis. Whatever the depreciation model chosen to represent the value of the asset over time, the equivalent annual cost of capital recovered and return is

$$(P \quad L)(\overset{RP\ i-n}{\qquad}) + Li.$$

Table 6.9. EXPRESSIONS FOR DEPRECIATION AND INTEREST ON UNDE-PRECIATED BALANCE

End of Year	Depreciation at End of Year	Interest on Undepreciated Balance at End of Year
0	0	0
1	A	$Ai + Bi + \cdots + Ni + Li$
2	B	$Bi + \cdots + Ni + Li$
n	N	$Ni + Li$

As long as the retirement of an asset takes place at the age and salvage value for which capital recovered and interest on the unrecovered balance were calculated, it can be shown that the sum of capital recovered plus return will be equivalent for any model of depreciation. If $(P - L) = A + B + \cdots + N$, where $A, B, \ldots, N$ are capital recovered amounts for successive years, then the depreciation and interest on the undepreciated balance is shown in Table 6.9.

The interest, Li, on the salvage value will be equal for all methods of depreciation and need not be considered further. The quantity $B + Bi$ as of the end of the second year is equivalent to

$$(B + Bi)\left[\frac{1}{(1 + i)}\right] = B$$

as of the end of the first year. Addition of this amount, B, to Bi results in a total $(B + Bi)$ as of the end of the first year. This sum is in turn equivalent to B as of the end of year 0. By similar calculations, quantities involving symbols A to N inclusive can be shown to have a worth of $A, B, \ldots, N$ as of the end of year 0 respectively. Since $(A + B + \cdots + N)$ equals $(P - L)$,

Table 6.10. PRESENT WORTH OF CAPITAL RECOVERY PLUS RETURN FOR STRAIGHT-LINE METHOD OF DEPRECIATION

Year	Capital Recovered plus Return	Single-payment Present-worth Factor	Present Worth
1	$1,560	PS 8−1 (0.9259)	$1,444.40
2	1,480	PS 8−2 (0.8573)	1,268.80
3	1,400	PS 8−3 (0.7938)	1,111.32
4	1,320	PS 8−4 (0.7350)	970.20
5	1,240	PS 8−5 (0.6806)	843.94
6	1,160	PS 8−6 (0.6302)	731.03

and since A, B, ..., N may be chosen to represent depreciation by any model, it may be concluded that the present worth of the depreciation calculated by any model plus the interest on the undepreciated balance is equal to the total depreciation at the beginning of the depreciation period.

As a numerical example of the equivalence of depreciation methods, consider the example used in this section. The present worth of capital recovered plus return for each year from the straight-line model of Table 6.4 is given in Table 6.10. The total present worth is $6,369.69. Likewise, the

Table 6.11. PRESENT WORTH OF CAPITAL RECOVERY PLUS RETURN FOR SINKING-FUND METHOD OF DEPRECIATION

Year	Capital Recovered plus Return	Present-worth Factor	Present Worth
1	$1,377.92	PS 8−1 (0.9259)	$1,275.82
2	1,377.92	PS 8−2 (0.8573)	1,181.29
3	1,377.92	PS 8−3 (0.7938)	1,093.79
4	1,377.92	PS 8−4 (0.7330)	1,012.77
5	1,377.92	PS 8−5 (0.6806)	937.81
6	1,377.92	PS 8−6 (0.6302)	868.37

present worth of capital recovered plus return for each year from the sinking-fund model of Table 6.6 is given in Table 6.11. The total present worth is $6,369.85. The slight difference is due to the use of tabular values with too few decimal places.

There are usually only two real transactions in an asset's depreciation. These are its purchase and its sale for salvage. In the previous example, these two transactions can be expressed in terms of present worth as

$$\overset{PS\ 8-6}{\$7{,}000 - (1{,}000)(0.6302)} = \$6{,}369.80.$$

This value agrees with that obtained for the two methods of depreciation illustrated earlier.

6.5. EVALUATING A SINGLE ALTERNATIVE

The economic evaluation of alternatives involving receipts and disbursements over time may be accomplished by reducing these alternatives to a common economic base. It is necessary to reduce alternatives to a common base in order that apparent differences become real differences, with the time value of money considered. When expressed in terms of a common base, real differences become directly comparable and may be used in decision-making. The most common bases for comparison are the present-worth amount, the equivalent annual amount, the capitalized amount, the rate of return, and the service life.

In most cases, a decision must be reached by selecting one alternative from among two or more available alternatives. Sometimes, however, the decision is limited to acceptance or rejection of a single alternative. In such a case the decision will be based on the relative merit of the alternative and other opportunities believed to exist, even though none of the latter have been crystallized into definite proposals. When only one specified alternative exists, it should be evaluated within a framework that will permit its desirability

Table 6.12. DISBURSEMENTS AND RECEIPTS FOR A SINGLE ALTERNATIVE

Item	Date	Disbursements	Receipts
Cost	1-1-19x0	$28,000	—
Rental, first year	1-1-19x1	—	$7,500
Rental, second year	1-1-19x2	—	7,500
Overhaul	1-1-19x2	2,500	—
Rental, third year	1-1-19x3	—	7,500
Rental, fourth year	1-1-19x4	—	7,500
Salvage	1-1-19x4	—	6,000

to be compared to other opportunities that may exist, but unspecified. The following example illustrates the several bases of evaluation when the decision to accept or reject a proposal must be made and there is no specific alternative proposed for comparison.

The purchase of a bulldozer is contemplated for rental to construction contractors who need and use such equipment on a temporary basis. The anticipated receipts and disbursements of this alternative are given in Table 6.12. With the exception of the initial cost, these transactions and dates are only estimates of what will occur in the future. For convenience, the disbursements and receipts which may occur during the year are assumed due and payable at the end of that year or the start of the next year, considered to be the same point in time. There is some small error in the practice of considering receipts and disbursements as year-end payments. This error is insignificant, however, in comparison to the usual errors in estimates, except under extremely high interest rates. In the foregoing example, consider an interest rate of 6 per cent as the charge on money and consider January 1, 19x0 to be the present.

Present-worth comparison. The present worth of future receipts and disbursements is easily computed and understood. In this example, the present worth of receipts as of January 1, 19x0 is

$$\overset{PR\ 6-4}{\$7,500(3.465)} + \overset{PS\ 6-4}{\$6,000(0.7921)} = \$30,740.10.$$

And the present worth of disbursements as of January 1, 19x0 is

$$\$28,000(1) + \overset{PS\ 6-2}{\$2,500(0.8900)} = \$30,225.00.$$

The present worth of receipts less disbursements is \$30,740.10 less \$30,225.00 or \$515.10.

If these estimates prove to be correct, the significance of this analysis is that if the \$28,000 is invested, a return of 6 per cent will be received in addition to an equivalent receipt of \$515.10 at the present time. To decide whether to purchase the bulldozer, this anticipated gain must be compared with or against a feeling or opinion regarding nonspecified opportunities which may present themselves.

Equivalent annual comparison. This method of analysis is similar to the present-worth method except that the difference between receipts and disbursements is now expressed as an equivalent annual amount. Using the same interest rate, the equivalent annual amount of receipts is

$$\overset{RS\ 6-4}{\$7,500(1)} + \$6,000(0.22859) = \$8,871.54.$$

And the equivalent annual amount of disbursements is

$$\overset{RP\ 6-4}{\$28,000(0.28859)} + \overset{PS\ 6-2}{\$2,500(0.8900)}\overset{RP\ 6-4}{(0.28859)} = \$8,722.63.$$

The equivalent annual amount of receipts less disbursements is \$8,871.54 less \$8,722.63 or \$148.91. As a verification, the equivalent annual amount of the present-worth difference between receipts and disbursements is

$$\overset{RP\ 6-4}{\$515.10(0.28859)} = \$148.65.$$

This result means that if \$28,000 is invested on January 1, 19x0, a 6 per cent return will be received plus the equivalent of receipts of \$148.65 on January 1, 19x1, 19x2, 19x3, and 19x4.

Capitalized comparison. The capitalized basis of comparison is sometimes used for long-term opportunities, or assets of long life. This method would not be appropriate for the bulldozer example and is developed only as an illustration. More typical of alternatives that might be reviewed under this method would be a highway, a railway embankment, a sewerage treatment plant, or a warehouse. With the capitalized comparison, the income and disbursements are treated as if they will continue all but forever.

The capitalized basis of evaluation consists of finding the single amount in the present whose return at a given rate of interest will be equivalent to the net difference of receipts and disbursements, assuming that these receipts and disbursements are repeated over time. In the example, this could take place only if a new bulldozer were purchased at the end of every fourth year in the future and the pattern of receipts and disbursements repeated itself.

Calculations for a capitalized evaluation could begin with the equivalent annual receipts and disbursements of $8,871.54 and $8,722.63 respectively. These are assumed to continue through the purchase of a new bulldozer every four years. To capitalize these amounts, it is necessary to determine amounts in the present whose annual return at 6 per cent will be $8,871.54 and $8,722.63. The capitalized receipts as of January 1, 19x0 are

$$\frac{\$8,871.54}{0.06} = \$147,859.00.$$

Similarly, the capitalized disbursements as of January 1, 19x0 are

$$\frac{\$8,722.63}{0.06} = \$145,377.17.$$

The capitalized receipts less capitalized disbursements are $147,859.00 less $145,377.17, or $2,481.83. This means that an investment of $28,000, followed by renewals of this investment each four years (provided that this pattern of receipts and disbursements remains constant), will yield the equivalent of an investment of $28,000 at 6 per cent interest forever, plus the receipt of $2,481.83 on January 1, 19x0.

Rate-of-return comparison. This is probably the best method for comparing a specific proposal with other opportunities believed to exist but not delineated. The rate of return is a universal measure of economic success. Rates of return from different classes of opportunities are usually well established and generally known. This permits comparison of an alternative against accepted norms. Thus, this characteristic makes the rate-of-return comparison well adapted to the situation where the choice is to accept or reject a single alternative.

The bulldozer proposal can be evaluated on the basis of the rate of return that would be secured from the invested funds. In effect, a rate of interest will be specified that makes the receipts and disbursements equivalent. This can be done either in terms of present worth or equivalent annual amount. In this case a present-worth evaluation will be established. For an interest rate of 6 per cent the present worth of receipts less the present worth of disbursements is $30,740.10 less $30,225.00, or $515.10. For an interest rate of 7 per cent the present worth of receipts less the present worth of disbursements is $29,979.90 less $30,183.50 or − $203.60.

To find the value of i, it is necessary to make the present worth of receipts less the present worth of disbursements equal to zero. Thus, by linear interpolation

$$i = 6 + (1)\frac{515.10 - 0}{515.10 - (-203.60)} = 6.72 \text{ per cent.}$$

This result means that the investment of $28,000 in the bulldozer should yield a 6.72 per cent return on the amount of money invested for the length of time it is invested.

Service life comparison. Often, a proposed asset is evaluated in terms of how long it will take the asset to pay for itself. Assets which tend to pay for themselves quickly are desirable in that there is less uncertainty associated with estimates of short duration. This comparison also directs attention to the life embraced by an alternative.

Service life is usually determined at an interest rate of zero, although positive interest rates may be used. The *service life* is that period of time required for the difference between operating receipts and disbursements to equal the capital cost of the asset. In other words, the service life is the period of time required for an asset to pay for itself from the net revenue.

The amount of money that the bulldozer will accumulate to pay for itself at no interest may be calculated for a three-year service life as

$$3(\$7,500) + \$6,000 - \$2,500 = \$26,000.$$

And, for a four-year service life

$$4(\$7,500) + \$6,000 - \$2,500 = \$33,500.$$

The bulldozer should pay for itself after

$$3 + (1)\frac{28,000 - 26,000}{33,500 - 26,000} = 3.27 \text{ years.}$$

It will take longer for an asset to pay for itself under an interest rate and the time will increase as the rate of interest increases. Consider the same example with an interest rate of 6 per cent. The amount of money that will have been accumulated under a three-year service life, at 6 per cent interest, will be

$$\overset{\text{PR } 6-3}{\$7,500(2.6730)} + \overset{\text{PS } 6-3}{\$6,000(0.8396)} - \overset{\text{PS } 6-2}{\$2,500(0.8900)} = \$22,860.10.$$

And, for a four-year service life

$$\overset{\text{PR } 6-4}{\$7,500(3.4651)} + \overset{\text{PS } 6-4}{6,000(0.7921)} - \overset{\text{PS } 6-2}{\$2,500(0.8900)} = \$28,515.00.$$

Therefore, the bulldozer should pay for itself after

$$3 + (1)\frac{28,000.00 - 22,860.10}{28,515.10 - 22,860.10} = 3.91 \text{ years.}$$

The bulldozer will pay for itself in less than the four-year anticipated service life.

6.6. EVALUATING MULTIPLE ALTERNATIVES

Where a number of available alternatives provide service of equal value, it is desirable to compare them directly against each other. Where service of unequal value is provided by multiple alternatives, each alternative must be evaluated as a single alternative and accepted or rejected on the basis of one or more of the comparisons suggested in the preceding section. In many cases, however, the available alternatives do provide outputs which are identical or equal in value. Under this condition, the objective is to select the alternative that provides the desired service at least cost.

Assume that a company is considering the purchase of a new lathe. A semiautomatic lathe will cost $10,000 and can be expected to last 10 years with a salvage value of $1,000. Operating cost will be $6,000 per year. A fully automatic lathe will cost $17,000, should also last 10 years, and will have a salvage value of $2,000. Operating cost will be $5,000 per year. The service provided by each machine will be identical. With a desired interest rate of 6 per cent, the alternative that meets the criterion of least cost should be selected.

Present-worth comparison. Under this method, the two alternatives may be compared in equivalent costs at a time taken to be the present. The present-worth cost of the semiautomatic lathe would be

$$\overset{\text{PR 6--10}}{\$10,000 + \$6,000(7.36009)} - \overset{\text{PS 6--10}}{\$1,000(0.55839)} = \$53,601.60.$$

The present-worth cost of the fully automatic lathe would be

$$\overset{\text{PR 6--10}}{\$17,000 + 5,000(7.36009)} - \overset{\text{PS 6--10}}{2,000(0.55839)} = \$52,683.20.$$

This comparison shows the present-worth cost of the fully automatic lathe to be less than the present-worth cost of the semiautomatic lathe by $53,601.60 less $52,683.20 or $918.40.

Equivalent annual cost comparison. The equivalent annual costs are taken as an equal cost series over the life of the assets. The equivalent annual cost of the semiautomatic lathe would be

$$\overset{\text{RP } 6-10}{\$10,000(0.13587)} + \$6,000 - \overset{\text{RS } 6-10}{\$1,000(0.07587)} = \$7,282.83.$$

And the equivalent annual cost of the fully automatic lathe would be

$$\overset{\text{RP } 6-10}{\$17,000(0.13587)} + \$5,000 - \overset{\text{RS } 6-10}{\$2,000(0.07587)} = \$7,158.05.$$

The equivalent annual difference of $7,282.83 less $7,158.05 or $124.78 is the equivalent annual cost superiority of the fully automatic lathe. As a verification, the equivalent annual amount of the present-worth difference is

$$\overset{\text{RP } 6-10}{\$918.40(0.13587)} = \$124.78.$$

Capitalized cost comparison. The capitalized basis of evaluation has been indicated as the single amount in the present whose return will yield the equivalent difference between the receipts and disbursements of an asset. On a cost comparison basis, it is the amount whose return will yield the equivalent annual cost. The capitalized cost of the semiautomatic lathe would be

$$\frac{\$7,282.83}{0.06} = \$121,380.50.$$

The capitalized cost of the fully automatic lathe would be

$$\frac{\$7,158.05}{0.06} = \$119,300.83.$$

On the basis of the foregoing, the second alternative would require $121,380.50 less $119,300.83 or $2,079.67 less capitalization.

Rate-of-return comparison. The previous three cost comparisons have indicated that the fully automatic lathe was more desirable at an interest rate of 6 per cent. At some higher interest rate, however, the two alternatives will be identical in costs and beyond that interest rate, the semiautomatic lathe will be less expensive because of its lower initial cost.

The interest rate at which the costs of the two alternatives are identical can be determined by setting the alternatives equal to each other and solving for the interest rate, i. Thus,

$$\$10,000 + \$6,000(\overset{\text{PR } i-10}{\quad}) - \$1,000(\overset{\text{PS } i-10}{\quad})$$
$$= \$17,000 + \$5,000(\overset{\text{PR } i-10}{\quad}) - \$2,000(\overset{\text{PS } i-10}{\quad})$$

$$\$1,000(\overset{\text{PR } i-10}{\quad}) + \$1,000(\overset{\text{PS } i-10}{\quad}) = \$7,000$$

$$(\overset{\text{PR } i-10}{\quad}) + (\overset{\text{PS } i-10}{\quad}) = 7.$$

For $i = 8$ per cent,

$$\underset{\text{PR 8--10}}{(6.71008)} + \underset{\text{PS 8--10}}{(0.46319)} = 7.1732.$$

For $i = 10$ per cent,

$$\underset{\text{PR 10--10}}{(6.14457)} + \underset{\text{PS 10--10}}{(0.38554)} = 6.5295.$$

Then, by interpolation

$$i = 8 + (2)\frac{7.1732 - 7.0000}{7.1732 - 6.5295} = 8.54 \text{ per cent.}$$

When funds are considered to earn less than 8.54 per cent, the fully automatic lathe will be the most desirable. When funds earn more than 8.54 per cent, the semiautomatic lathe will be preferred.

Service life comparison. The service life of 10 years for each of the two lathes is only the result of estimates and may be in error. If the services are needed for shorter or longer periods of time and the assets are capable of providing the service for a longer period of time, then the advantage may pass from one alternative to the other. Just as there is an interest rate at which two alternatives may be equal, there may be a service life at which the equivalent cost may be identical. This service life may be obtained by setting the alternatives equal to each other and solving for the life, n. Thus, for an interest rate of 6 per cent,

$$\$10,000 + \$6,000(\underset{\text{PR 6--}n}{\quad}) - \$1,000(\underset{\text{PS 6--}n}{\quad})$$

$$= \$17,000 + \$5,000(\underset{\text{PR 6--}n}{\quad}) - \$2,000(\underset{\text{PS 6--}n}{\quad})$$

$$(\underset{\text{PR 6--}n}{\quad}) + (\underset{\text{PS 6--}n}{\quad}) = 7.$$

For $n = 8$ years,

$$\underset{\text{PR 6--8}}{(6.2098)} + \underset{\text{PS 6--8}}{(0.6274)} = 6.8374.$$

For $n = 9$ years

$$\underset{\text{PR 6--9}}{(6.8017)} + \underset{\text{PS 6--9}}{(0.5919)} = 7.3939.$$

Then, by interpolation

$$n = 8 + (1)\frac{7 - 6.8374}{7.3939 - 6.8374} = 8.29 \text{ years.}$$

Thus, if the desired service were to be used less than 8.29 years, then the semiautomatic lathe would be the most desirable.

QUESTIONS

1. Define interest; interest rate.

2. From the viewpoint of the lender, what three factors might be considered in specifying an interest rate?

3. Define simple interest; compound interest.

4. What is a nominal interest rate; an effective interest rate?

5. Discuss the difference between functional and physical depreciation.

6. Why should capital consumption be included as a cost of production?

7. Name the essential components of the value-time function.

8. What is meant by capital recovery and return?

9. List the five bases of evaluating alternatives.

10. Under what condition will the evaluation of multiple alternatives be conducted as if each were a single alternative?

PROBLEMS

1. If an investment of $1,100 earns $30 in 9 months, what is the annual rate of interest?

2. How long must $2,000 be invested to amount to $2,100 if 4 per cent simple interest per annum is earned?

3. What amount will be accumulated by each of the following investments?
   (a) $3,500 at 3 per cent compounded annually over 10 years.
   (b) $42,500 at 6 per cent compounded annually over 5 years.
   (c) $800 at 4 per cent compounded quarterly over 10 years.
   (d) $400 at 10 per cent compounded semiannually over 12 years.

4. What is the present worth of the following?
   (a) A year-end series of payments of $500 compounded annually at 5 per cent for 5 years.
   (b) $2,000 every 6 months for 5 years at 6 per cent compounded semiannually.
   (c) A sum of $500 to be received in 10 years at 5 per cent compounded annually.
   (d) A sum of $1,000 to be received in 2 years at 4 per cent compounded semiannually.

5. How much money must be invested to accumulate the following future amounts?
   (a) $1,000 in 10 years at 5 per cent compounded semiannually.
   (b) $850 in 9 years at 4 per cent compounded semiannually.

6. What interest rate compounded annually is involved if $5,000 results in $6,000 in 5 years?

7. How many years will it take $5,000 to reach a sum of $7,000 at an interest rate of 6 per cent compounded semiannually?

8. What interest rate is necessary for a sum of money to double itself in 20 years?

9. What effective interest rate corresponds to the following:
   (a) Nominal interest rate of 8 per cent compounded semiannually.
   (b) Nominal interest rate of 6 per cent compounded quarterly.

10. What is the effective annual interest rate of 1/2 per cent interest per week compounded weekly?

11. How much can a man afford to pay for a $1,000 bond that pays 4 per cent interest annually and will mature in 10 years if he wishes to realize 5 per cent on his investment?

12. How much can be paid for a $10,000, 5 per cent bond with interest paid semi-annually, if the bond matures 10 years hence? Assume the purchaser is satisfied with a $4\frac{1}{2}$ per cent return.

13. An asset has a first cost of $9,000 and an estimated salvage value of $1,000 at the end of 4 years. The interest rate is 10 per cent. Graph capital recovery and tabulate capital recovery plus return for each year by the straight-line method of depreciation, the sinking-fund method of depreciation, the fixed-percentage method of depreciation, the sum-of-the-years method of depreciation.

14. An asset was bought for $4,800. It was estimated that it would last for 12 years and be worth $200 as scrap. After 5 years of operation the unit was sold for $1,000. The interest rate is 6 per cent.
    (a) What was the anticipated equivalent annual cost of capital recovery and return?
    (b) What was the actual cost?

15. A drill press was purchased 10 years ago for $2,400. It is being depreciated to no salvage value over a life of 20 years by the straight-line method of depreciation. With an interest rate of 6 per cent, what would be the difference in present book value had the sinking-fund method of depreciation been used?

16. A cement mixer is purchased for $2,400 and has an estimated salvage value of $300 and an expected life of 3 years. Approximately 25 cu yd of concrete per month will be produced by the mixer.
    (a) Calculate the annual cost of capital recovery plus return with the interest rate of 5 per cent.
    (b) Calculate the cost of capital recovery plus return per cubic yard of concrete at an interest rate of 8 per cent.

17. An asset is purchased for $1,000 and has an estimated life of 2 years and a salvage value of $200. With an interest rate of 10 per cent, what will be the book value after one year under the straight-line, sinking-fund, sum-of-the-years, and fixed-percentage methods of depreciation?

18. Develop the general expression for the fixed-percentage methods of depreciation. Multiply the capital recovery plus return term by the compound amount factor and sum over all years to obtain an expression for the equivalent annual capital recovered plus return.

19. In preparation of an attempted invasion of England by Spain in the late 1580's a collection of ships was needed to transport the invading army. In 1586, this collection was undertaken and accomplished under the direction of the Duke of Medina Sidonia. The ships were paid for under a loan floated upon the royal jewels. The cost of the invasion fleet amounted to 1 million pesos. For income tax purposes, the Duke was required to establish a depreciation schedule. He estimated the life of ships at 5 years with a salvage value to poor Gallican fishermen of 10 per cent of their original cost. For morale reasons, the sinking-fund method of depreciation was not considered.

   In 1588, this Spanish Armada was effectively destroyed by the English. Compare the sunk cost that might have been incurred under the three remaining methods of depreciation.

20. A prospective venture is described by the following receipts and disbursements:

Year End	Receipts	Disbursements
0	$0	$800
1	200	0
2	400	200
3	1,000	0

For an interest rate of 6 per cent describe the desirability on the basis of the present-worth comparison; the equivalent-annual-cost comparison; the capitalized-cost comparison.

21. A warehouse can be built for $80,000 and will have no salvage value. The annual value of storage space less maintenance and operating costs is estimated at $12,600.
    (a) What rate of return is in prospect if the warehouse is used 8 years?
    (b) For what life will the warehouse result in a return of 10 per cent?

22. A firm can purchase a machine for $20,000. A down payment of $2,000 is required and the balance may be paid in five equal year-end installments plus 4 per cent on the unpaid balance. As an alternative the machine can be purchased for $18,000 cash. At what interest rate are the two plans equivalent?

23. The heat lost through the exterior walls of a building has been estimated to cost $206 per year. Insulation should reduce this loss by 93 per cent and can be installed for $116. Insulation that should reduce the loss by 89 per cent can be installed for $90. Determine which insulation is most desirable if the building is to be used for 8 years and an interest rate of 10 per cent is applicable.

seven

MODELS FOR

EQUIPMENT REPLACEMENT

Mass production has been found to be an economical means for satisfying human wants. This process requires a complex industrial organization together with a huge investment in producer goods. These producer goods are employed to alter the physical environment and create consumer goods. As a result, they are consumed or become obsolete, inadequate, or otherwise candidates for replacement.

Replacement models fall into two categories, depending upon the life pattern of the equipment under study. The first portion of this chapter deals with models for replacing equipment that deteriorates with time. Choice between an existing asset and its potential replacement will be based on analysis directed to reducing the differences in future receipts and disbursements to an equivalent basis for comparison. The last portion of the chapter presents replacement models that may be used to establish replacement policy for equipment that does not deteriorate appreciably with time, but fails instantaneously and completely. Replacement models for items that fail require the use of probabilistic concepts and the statistics of failure data.

7.1. CONSIDERATIONS LEADING TO REPLACEMENT

When replacement is being considered, two assets must be evaluated: The present asset and its potential replacement. Since the success of an industrial organization depends upon profit, replacement should generally occur if an economic advantage will result. Replacing an asset before it is completely worn out contradicts the concept of thrift held by many decision makers. Part of the reluctance to replace physically satisfactory but economically inferior equipment arises because a decision to replace is much more binding than a decision to continue with the present asset. Continuing production with the existing asset is a course of action that may be reviewed at any time, whereas a decision to replace is a commitment for a longer period into the future. Caution in this respect is justified. This section provides a background for those which follow by discussing the primary considerations leading to replacement.[1]

Replacement because of inadequacy. A machine may be incapable of meeting the changing demand required of it. This is often manifested by equipment of fixed capacity, and a requirement which sometimes exceeds this capacity. A machine tool may not be capable of handling larger workpieces. A motor may not be able to meet an increased load. In each case the usable piece of equipment may be in excellent condition, with consideration of its replacement being forced by the need for greater capacity.

As an example of replacement because of inadequacy, consider the following example: Two years ago an ore-crushing unit was installed at a mine for a cost of $110,000. Annual operating costs of this unit are $7,500, exclusive of interest and depreciation charges, and the unit has an estimated life of 20 years with no salvage value. Because of a recent and unexpected increase in demand for the ore, it is decided to double the mining operations. Either an additional and identical ore-crushing unit will be necessary, or the existing unit will be disassembled and sold for an estimated $30,000 and a new unit of double the capacity installed at a cost of $195,000. This new unit may be operated for $9,500 per year and also has an estimated life of 20 years with no salvage value. The interest rate is 6 per cent.

The equivalent annual cost of adding an identical ore-crushing unit would be

$$\overset{\text{RP 6-20}}{\$30{,}000(0.08718)} + \overset{\text{RP 6-20}}{\$110{,}000(0.08718)} + 2(\$7{,}500) = \$27{,}204.20.$$

The equivalent annual cost of purchasing the new unit with double the

---

[1] Many concepts presented in the first half of this chapter may be found in H. G. Thuesen and W. J. Fabrycky, *Engineering Economy*, 3rd ed. (Englewood Cliffs, N.J.: Prentice-Hall, Inc., 1964).

existing capacity would be

$$RP\ 6-20$$
$$\$195,000(0.08718) + \$9,500 = \$26,500.10.$$

On the basis of this analysis, the equivalent annual cost advantage of obtaining the unit with double the capacity of the existing unit is $27,204.20 less $26,500.10, or $704.10.

A sunk cost equal to the book value of the existing ore-crushing unit less $30,000 is incurred. This sunk cost has been revealed and not caused by the analysis. The present value of the existing unit is $30,000, and this amount will be realized from its sale. An "outsider" who needs the services of an ore-crushing unit would make the analysis as just given. This "outsider" viewpoint is not biased by the past and results in an analysis based on the true differences.

Replacement because of obsolescence. New equipment is continually being developed that will perform the same operations as existing equipment but at substantial savings. When this is true, the existing asset may be replaced because of this technological obsolescence. The existing asset may still be capable of meeting the production demands placed upon it, without excessive maintenance cost and at a satisfactory level of operating efficiency. If, however, an economic advantage can be gained by replacement, the existing asset should be retired.

Consider a proposal to replace three engine lathes with a special-purpose automatic lathe for the duration of a five-year production contract. The automatic lathe can be purchased at a cost of $15,000 and it will serve for the duration of the contract. It will have an estimated resale value of $5,000 at the end of that time. The three engine lathes have a book value in accordance with their original depreciation schedule. At present, however, they can be sold for $750 each and should be worth $500 in five years. Operating expenses for the automatic lathe are estimated to be $3,000 per year. The engine lathes are operated at a cost of $2,850 per year per machine. Neglecting taxes and insurance, and using an interest rate of 8 per cent, the equivalent annual cost of retaining the engine lathes is

$$RP\ 8-5$$
$$3[(\$750 - \$500)(0.25046) + \$500(0.08) + \$2,850] = \$8,857.85.$$

The equivalent annual cost of the automatic lathe will be

$$RP\ 8-5$$
$$(\$15,000 - \$5,000)(0.25046) + \$5,000(0.08) + \$3,000 = \$5,904.60.$$

Based on this analysis, the engine lathes should be replaced although they can still perform their intended function.

Replacement because of excessive maintenance. Machines and other complex equipment rarely incur uniform wear. Some elements or components are likely to deteriorate faster and fail before others. Under these conditions it is often economical to repair the component to extend the useful life of the asset. Some repairs are minor; others are quite extensive. Some may follow an unpredictable pattern; others are periodic and can be planned. A piece of equipment may become a candidate for replacement when it needs repair. Equipment is more likely to be replaced when the needed repairs are extensive

Table 7.1. ANALYSIS OF THE COSTS OF MAINTENANCE

Year (A)	Cost of Maintenance for Year (B)	Present Worth PS 6—n B( ) (C)	Sum of Maintenance Cost to End of Year ΣC (D)	Total Cost of n Years of Service $\$48{,}000 + D$ (E)	Equivalent Average Annual Cost to End of Year RP 6—n E( ) (F)
1	$2,600	$2,453	$2,453	$50,453	$53,481
2	8,400	7,476	9,929	57,929	31,597
3	12,800	10,747	20,676	68,676	25,692
4	22,300	17,664	38,340	86,340	24,917
5	30,200	22,578	60,918	108,918	25,857

and when it appears that additional and excessive repairs will soon be needed.

As an example, consider a piping system in a chemical plant which was installed at a cost of $48,000. The system lasted only five years before it was replaced. Salvage value of the system was nil. Deterioration due to corrosion during the service period caused extensive repair. The maintenance costs for each year are given in column B of Table 7.1. Column C gives the present-worth cost of maintenance for each year. The cumulative present-worth cost of maintenance is given in column D. Column E gives the accumulative present-worth cost of service up to the year designated. Finally, column F gives the equivalent average annual cost of service that would have resulted from scrapping the system at the end of any year. Thus, if the system had been scrapped at the end of the second year, the two years of service would have resulted in an equivalent average annual cost of $31,597.

The lowest equivalent average annual cost occurred after a four-year life. Had the system been replaced at this time, the average equivalent annual cost would have been a minimum. It does not necessarily follow, however, that the greatest economy would occur if the system were scrapped after four years. This would depend upon the characteristics and cost of the replacement system. A decision to replace the existing system should be made after analyzing the costs of the present system and its proposed replacement.

Replacement because of declining efficiency. Equipment sometimes operates at an initial peak efficiency which declines with time and use. The reduction in efficiency may require increased power consumption and longer use to accomplish the same operation. This, in turn, may result in increased costs of operation which will make the equipment a candidate for replacement. As with the case of increasing maintenance costs, increasing costs of

Table 7.2. ANALYSIS OF THE COSTS OF DECLINING EFFICIENCY

Year	Efficiency at Beginning of Year	Average Efficiency during Year	Extra Hours of Operation $6,000\left(\dfrac{1-C}{C}\right)$	Present Worth of Extra Hours PS 8−n $\$1.00 D($ $)$	Cost of n Years of Service $\$450 + \Sigma E$	Equivalent Average Annual Cost RP 8−n $F($ $)$
(A)	(B)	(C)	(D)	(E)	(F)	(G)
1	1.00	0.99	61	$56	$506	$516
2	0.98	0.97	186	159	665	372
3	0.96	0.94	250	198	863	335
4	0.92	0.89	742	545	1408	425
5	0.86	—	—	—	—	—

operation can be analyzed with a tabular review of equivalent average annual cost of service. This leads to the identification of the minimum equivalent average annual cost.

Consider the following example: A certain system of pipes in a chemical plant is used to transport a chemical mixture which adds scale to the pipe walls. As a result, the inside diameter available for flow is restricted and the efficiency is reduced, as in column B of Table 7.2. When the system is in new condition, the associated pumping equipment must operate 6,000 hr per year. As the efficiency declines, owing to scaling of the pipes, the pumps must operate additional hours to transport the chemical. These extra hours are given in column D.

When operating, the pumping equipment costs $1.00 per hour. The piping system has a first cost of $450 and the interest rate is 8 per cent. With these costs, the equivalent average annual cost is tabulated for each life span of the system in column G. From this, it is evident that the piping should be replaced after three years of operation if the replacement is to have the same cost and characteristics as the existing system.

Replacement due to a combination of causes. In most situations, an asset is replaced for more than one cause. An asset may begin to require more maintenance, and/or it may begin to operate at a reduced level of efficiency. It may not always be capable of meeting the demands placed upon it. The availability of a potential replacement which may have a higher initial cost but which is more economical to operate, may result in an analysis of the economic feasibility of replacing the existing asset.

Whatever the reasons leading to the consideration of replacement, the analysis and decision must be based upon estimates of what will occur in the future. The past is irrelevant in replacement analysis and must not be allowed to influence the replacement decision.

7.2. REPLACEMENT UNDER UNEQUAL SERVICE LIFE AND SUNK COST

When equipment deteriorates, the decision to replace will depend upon the cost of new equipment and the cost of maintaining the efficiency of the old. The basic equipment replacement model is a simple economic comparison of the desirability of retaining an asset against that of replacing it with a proposed asset. These alternatives are usually delineated as present and future receipts and disbursements and compared on an equivalent-cost basis. This comparison is sometimes difficult, however, because aspects of the assets use or life may not be directly comparable. These differences may not be easily reduced to economic terms. Also, the future of a present asset is less cause for concern because of its shorter remaining life and lower value. In addition, a decision not to replace the existing asset can be reviewed and reversed at any time in the future. This section presents two situations frequently encountered in replacement analyses: The treatment of alternatives of unequal service life, and some correct and incorrect methods of dealing with sunk costs.

The treatment of unequal service life. An existing and a proposed asset should be compared, as far as possible, on an equivalent-cost basis. If the remaining life of an existing asset and the expected life of a proposed asset are identical, a direct comparison can be made if other aspects of their service are similar. Normally, however, the life of the proposed asset will extend beyond the remaining years of the present asset. The following paragraphs present a general method for placing alternatives on a comparative basis by the selection of a study period. Under this procedure, comparison is made on the basis of receipts and disbursements occurring during the selected period. The effect of receipts or disbursements occurring after the study period is either ignored or included in the analysis depending upon the situation.

Consider the following example utilizing an interest rate of 6 per cent: At the present time Machine A is being used to perform a certain operation. This machine has a present market value of $500 and an estimated remaining life of two years with no anticipated salvage value. Operating costs are $1,000 per year. It is presently planned to replace Machine A in two years with Machine B. This replacement will have an acquisition cost, an estimated service life, salvage value, and yearly operating expense of $20,000, eight years, none, and $600, respectively.

The opportunity of replacing Machine A immediately with Machine C has presented itself. Machine C will have an acquisition cost, an estimated service life, salvage value, and yearly operating expense of $11,000, six years,

Table 7.3. MACHINE REPLACEMENT ANALYSIS OVER A SELECTED STUDY PERIOD

Year End	Retain Existing Asset		Replace Existing Asset	
	Investment Cost	Operating Costs	Investment Cost	Operating Costs
0	$ 500 (A)		$11,000 (C)	
1		$1,000		$800
2	20,000 (B)	1,000		800
3		600		800
4		600		800
5		600		800
6		600		800
7		600		
8		600		
9		600		
10		600		

(Study Period indicated for years 0–6; column label "Study Period" with arrows spanning years 0 through 6.)

none, and $800 respectively. The two alternatives are exhibited in Table 7.3. Because these alternatives have unequal service lives, an arbitrary time period will be selected for their comparison. Since it is difficult to make forecasts, an arbitrary study period will be specified as six years, the life of Machine C.

If Machine A is retained for two years and replaced by Machine B, this asset will have a life of four years within the study period and four years extending beyond the study period. Under an equitable allocation of costs, the equivalent annual cost for Machine B during its life is

$$\overset{\text{RP } 6-8}{\$20,000(0.16104)} + \$600 = \$3,820.80.$$

The present-worth cost of the six years of service in the study period is

$$\overset{\text{PR } 6-2}{\$500} + \$1,000(1.83339) + \overset{\text{PR } 6-4 \quad \text{PS } 6-2}{\$3,820.80(3.46510)(0.89000)} = \$14,116.50.$$

If the existing asset is replaced with Machine C, the present-worth cost of the six years of service is

$$\overset{\text{PR 6-6}}{\$11,000 + \$800(4.91732)} = \$14,933.86$$

On the basis of this comparison, the existing asset and plan for its replacement would be retained.

Had the value of Machine B at the end of the selected study period been disregarded, the other alternative might have been selected. This assumes that the asset will be retired at the end of the study period for analysis. The equivalent annual cost of Machine B would be calculated as

$$\overset{\text{RP 6-4}}{\$20,000(0.28859) + \$600} = \$6,371.80.$$

And, the present-worth cost of six years of service in the study period would be

$$\overset{\text{PR 6-2}}{\$500} + \overset{}{\$1,000(1.83339)} + \overset{\text{PR 6-4 \quad PS 6-2}}{\$6,371.80(3.46510)(0.89000)} = \$21.983.67.$$

Thus, retaining Machine A and purchasing Machine B in two years exceeds the cost of replacing Machine A immediately with Machine C. As a result, the latter alternative would probably be selected.

The erroneous practice of disregarding value remaining in an asset introduces error equivalent to that value actually remaining. The practice of ignoring the remaining value in an asset is difficult to defend because it does not greatly reduce the burden of calculations nor does it lean toward a policy of conservation in machine replacement.

The treatment of sunk costs. When an asset is purchased and placed into operation, a depreciation model is usually selected to reflect the changing value of the asset. This is done for a number of reasons, one of which is to reflect the cost of the consumption of that asset. When the asset is eventually replaced either before, at, or after its estimated life, there may be some discrepancy existing between the value of the asset as reflected in the depreciation schedule and the actual price received for it. If more money is received for the asset than the worth established by the depreciation schedule, a capital gain is realized because of this difference. If the reverse is true and the asset is sold for less than its depreciated value, a sunk cost has occurred. In evaluating replacements, especially where an asset is being considered for replacement sooner than its intended life, it is likely that a sunk cost will be encountered.

Consider the following example as an illustration of the correct and incorrect treatment of sunk costs: Machine A was purchased six years ago for $22,000. It was intended to have a life of 10 years and a salvage value after 10 years of $2,000. The depreciation schedule, using the straight-line model of depreciation, indicates that the asset is presently worth $22,000 − 6($2,000) = $10,000. The operating expenses of the machine average $8,000 per year. Machine B, presently being considered as a replacement, is being offered for $30,000. It will have an estimated life of 10 years with no salvage value and an annual operating cost of $3,000. If the proposed asset is purchased, Machine A can be sold for $4,000. With an interest rate of 10 per cent, should Machine B be purchased?

The proper decision in this example rests upon the treatment of the sunk cost. The following analysis is based on the "outsider" viewpoint which assumes that a party exists who owns neither Machine A nor Machine B and needs the service that can be provided by one of these two assets. The equivalent annual cost of Machine A to this "outsider" would be

$$\overset{RP\ 10-4}{(\$4,000 - \$2,000)(0.31547)} + \$2,000(0.10) + \$8,000 = \$8,830.96.$$

Machine B would be obtained and operated for

$$\overset{RP\ 10-10}{(\$30,000)(0.16275)} + \$3,000 = \$7,882.50.$$

Under these conditions, the "outsider" would select machine B with an equivalent annual saving of $8,830.96 − $7,882.50 = $948.46 over the next four years. The savings or loss over the six years following these four cannot be ascertained because no information is available concerning a replacement for Machine A had it been kept for the next four years.

Another method of demonstrating the correctness of the "outsider" viewpoint in selecting replacement alternatives is to calculate the value of the machine to be replaced which will result in an annual cost identical to the annual cost of operation of the replacement. In this example, let x equal the value of Machine A such that its equivalent annual cost is the same as Machine B. Then,

$$\overset{RP\ 10-4}{(x - \$2,000)(0.31547)} + \$2,000(0.10) + \$8,000$$
$$\overset{RP\ 10-10}{-\ \$30,000(0.16275)} + \$3,000.$$

Solving for x gives

$$x = \frac{\overset{RP\ 10-10}{\$30,000(0.16275)} - \$5,200}{\underset{(0.31547)}{RP\ 10-4}} + \$2,000 = \$993.57.$$

Machine A has an apparent value of only $993.57 if the alternative of retaining Machine A is to be equivalent to obtaining Machine B. Thus, if Machine A can be sold for more than this amount a savings would be realized by replacement. In this example, the selection of Machine B would result in a savings of $4,000 less $993.57 or $3,006.43. The equivalence of these solutions is illustrated by the fact that

$$\overset{RP\ 10-4}{\$3,006.43(0.31547)} = \$948.44.$$

Even though a sunk cost cannot be recovered, it is natural to attempt to charge the sunk cost to the contemplated replacement. This practice is fallacious because it reduces the possibility of selecting this alternative and of realizing the potential savings. Even if the replacement is selected, the actual savings would be incorrectly reported. A sunk cost must be recognized as such and removed from consideration in the analysis of machine replacements. This requires accepting the fact that a sunk cost is revealed and not caused by replacement.

7.3. THE MINIMUM COST REPLACEMENT INTERVAL

Although it is mathematically attractive to forecast the minimum cost life of an asset when it is installed, this is more of an ideal than a reality. The decision to replace an asset is almost always made just before the actual replacement and is the result of the analysis of factors that exist at that time. There are a number of reasons for this: Rarely are the future cost data of an asset, and particularly the maintenance cost, available when the asset is purchased. In addition, the decision to replace an asset depends upon the economic advantage of the proposed replacement. It is equally unlikely that the characteristics and cost of an asset's replacement are available in a meaningful form when the original asset is purchased. Nevertheless, the treatment of the minimum cost replacement interval of an asset will be proposed in this section.

It will be assumed that the future costs of an asset can be predicted with some reasonable degree of accuracy at the time the asset is purchased. In order to simplify the development, only maintenance costs will be treated. It will also be assumed that the replacement is identical in cost and characteristics to the original asset.

Patterns of maintenance costs. The decision to replace an asset is dependent upon the pattern of costs which must be incurred to maintain that asset properly through its service life. For classification, these costs may be considered to be sporadic, relatively constant, or increasing over the life of the asset. It will be demonstrated that only increasing costs are grounds for equipment replacement.

Consider the example of a machine purchased for $600 with no anticipated salvage value. An interest rate of zero is assumed for simplicity. The pattern of maintenance costs is shown in Table 7.4. Averaging these costs as shown in Column D tends to smooth their sporadic occurrence. The average yearly capital costs decrease as the number of years increases. Replacement with a minimum average yearly cost is more likely just before a large maintenance expenditure, since there is no clearly defined minimum cost point.

Under constant maintenance costs, there will never be justification for

Table 7.4. ECONOMIC HISTORY OF A MACHINE UNDER SPORADIC MAINTENANCE COSTS

End of Year (A)	Maintenance Cost at End of Year (B)	Summation of Maintenance Costs ΣB (C)	Average Cost of Maintenance $C \div A$ (D)	Average Capital Cost $\$600 \div A$ (E)	Average Total Cost $D + E$ (F)
1	$100	$100	$100	$600	$700
2	400	500	250	300	550
3	100	600	200	200	400
4	100	700	175	150	325
5	400	1,100	220	120	340
6	100	1,200	200	100	300
7	400	1,600	229	86	315
8	100	1,700	213	75	288

replacement. Extending the life of the asset will reduce the average capital cost and the average yearly cost. Only under increasing maintenance costs will there be justification for replacement. This will hold true with or without interest charges.

Consider a modification of the preceding example involving maintenance costs which begin at zero and increase $100 each year. The pattern of average total costs is given in Table 7.5. With the rising average maintenance costs counterbalanced by the diminishing average capital costs, a year will be reached where the sum of these costs is a minimum. In this example, the minimum cost of $300 is achieved after either three or four years. Retaining the asset longer than four years or disposing of it before three years will result in a cost penalty.

Finding the minimum cost replacement interval. When there exists a predictable and rising trend in maintenance costs, it is possible to formulate

Table 7.5. ECONOMIC HISTORY OF A MACHINE UNDER INCREASING MAINTENANCE COSTS

End of Year (A)	Maintenance Cost at End of Year (B)	Summation of Maintenance Costs ΣB (C)	Average Cost of Maintenance $C \div A$ (D)	Average Capital Cost $\$600 \div A$ (E)	Average Total Cost $D + E$ (F)
1	$ 0	$ 0	0	$600	$600
2	100	100	50	300	350
3	200	300	100	200	300
4	300	600	150	150	300
5	400	1,000	200	120	320
6	500	1,500	250	100	350

Table 7.6. ECONOMIC HISTORY OF A MACHINE UNDER INCREASING MAINTENANCE COSTS WITH INTEREST

End of Yerv (A)	Maintenance Cost at End of Year (B)	Present-worth Factor PS 6−n (C)	Present Worth of Maintenance B × C (D)	Summation of Present Worths Σ D (E)	Capital Recovery Factor RP 6−n (F)	Equivalent Annual Cost of Maintenance (E × F) (G)	Equivalent Annual Cost of Capital Recovery F($600) (H)	Total Equivalent Annual Cost (G + H) (I)
1	$ 0	0.9434	$ 0	$ 0	1.06000	$ 0	$636	$636
2	100	0.8900	89	89	0.54544	49	327	376
3	200	0.8396	168	257	0.37411	96	224	320
4	300	0.7921	238	495	0.28859	143	173	316
5	400	0.7473	299	794	0.23740	188	142	330
6	500	0.7050	353	1,147	0.20336	233	122	355

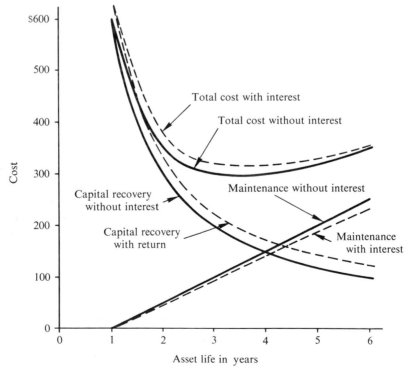

Figure 7.1. Minimum cost replacement intervals for the data of Table 7.5 and Table 7.6.

a model that may be used to find the minimum cost replacement interval. If interest is neglected, the average annual total cost of an asset under increasing maintenance costs can be expressed as

$$TC = \frac{P}{n} + O + (n-1)\frac{m}{2} \qquad (7.1)$$

where P = initial cost of the asset

O = annual operating costs plus constant portion of maintenance costs
m = the amount by which maintenance costs increase each year
n = life of the asset in years.

If Equation (7.1) is differentiated with respect to n, set equal to zero, and solved for n, the minimum cost replacement interval will result. This gives

$$\frac{dTC}{dn} = -\frac{P}{n^2} + \frac{m}{2} = 0$$

$$n = \sqrt{\frac{2P}{m}}. \qquad (7.2)$$

Using Equation (7.2), the minimum cost life of the example given by Table 7.5 is

$$n = \sqrt{\frac{2(\$600)}{\$100}} = 3.46 \text{ years.}$$

The average annual total cost may be found from Equation (7.1) as

$$TC = \frac{\$600}{3.46} + 2.46\left(\frac{\$100}{2}\right) = \$296.$$

As an illustration of the effect of interest consider a modification of the example above. Table 7.6 exhibits the same information as Table 7.5 except for the consideration of an interest rate of 6 per cent. The minimum cost replacement interval is close to that found without interest. This is illustrated graphically in Figure 7.1 together with the effect of interest on the cost components. Since the total cost function is flat in the region of its minimum, Equation (7.2) may be used as an approximation for the minimum cost replacement interval for cases involving interest, but the tabular approach can always be used when an exact solution is required.

7.4. THE MAPI REPLACEMENT ALGORITHM

The MAPI algorithm is a computational procedure developed by the Machinery and Allied Products Institute for evaluating investments or for analyzing replacement opportunities.[2] The algorithm provides an adjusted,

---

[2] A complete treatment of the MAPI procedure is given by George Terborgh, *Business Investment Policy* (Washington, D.C.: Machinery and Allied Products Institute, 1958).

after-tax rate of return criterion which the decision maker may use in replacement analyses or in selecting one investment opportunity from among many. The MAPI algorithm is simple to apply, yet quite comprehensive in its treatment of the decision variables. These attributes account for its widespread use.

Elements in the MAPI procedure. Application of the MAPI replacement algorithm requires the estimation of five elements. They are used to calculate a rate of return for the next year based upon a net investment related to conditions that might prevail without the project for the specified time period. These elements are:

(1) Net investment, expressed as the installed cost of the project minus any investment released or avoided.

(2) Next-year operating advantage, expressed as the sum of the increase in revenue and the reduction in costs brought on by the investment. These are relative to those which would be incurred over the next year in the absence of the investment.

(3) Next-year capital consumption avoided, expressed as the reduction in salvage value of assets retired by the proposed project because of retaining them an additional year. Added to this are the capital additions for the next year that would be required in the absence of the project.

(4) Next-year capital consumption incurred, measured as the reduction in value of the asset over the next year. In effect, this is that portion of the asset consumed under the depreciation schedule.

(5) Next-year income tax adjustment, measured as the net increase in income tax resulting from the project.

The foregoing elements may be used to find the rate of return without considering income tax as

$$\left[\frac{(2) + (3) - (4)}{(1)}\right] 100.$$

The effect of income tax can be considered by computing the rate of return as

$$\left[\frac{(2) + (3) - (4) - (5)}{(1)}\right] 100.$$

In either case, item (4) is found from a MAPI chart, one of which is illustrated by Figure 7.2. The chart of Figure 7.2 is applicable when the asset decreases in value at a decreasing rate. Charts are available for the cases where the value of the asset decreases at a constant rate and where the value of the asset decreases at an increasing rate.

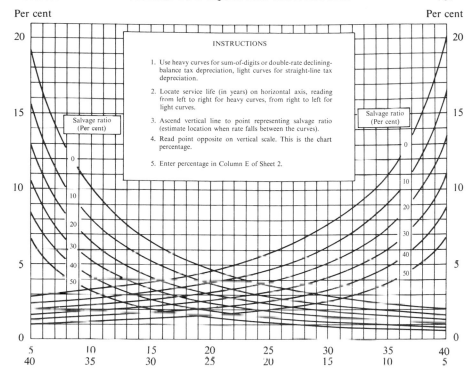

Figure 7.2. A depreciation schedule. Reproduced with permission from George Terborgh, *Business Investment Policy*, Machinery and Allied Products Institute, Washington, D.C., 1958.

The MAPI algorithm differs from the methods presented previously in that the first-year rate of return is used as a basis for decision. If a one-year planning period is inadequate for the replacement situation under consideration, the MAPI approach should not be used.

An example of the MAPI procedure. As an example of the MAPI algorithm consider the replacement of a machine by a newer model which will result in a savings due to machine time, spoilage, maintenance, and down time.[3]

A complete overhaul is required for a 38-year-old screw machine. The equipment analyst recommends the purchase of a newly designed automatic screw machine with a vertical slide and feeding arrangement as a better alternative. The installed cost of the project will be $16,705. Buying the equipment will avoid an investment of $4,220 in a complete overhaul of the present equipment, which is prorated over 10 years. In addition, it is estimated that the disposal value of the present equipment is $300.

---

[3] This example was adapted with permission from George Terborgh, *Business Investment Policy* (Washington, D.C.: Machinery and Allied Products Institute, 1958), pp. 158–60.

PROJECT NO.   2   SHEET I

SUMMARY OF ANALYSIS
(SEE ACCOMPANYING WORK SHEETS FOR DETAIL)

I. REQUIRED INVESTMENT

I	INSTALLED COST OF PROJECT	$ 16,705	I
2	DISPOSAL VALUE OF ASSETS TO BE RETIRED BY PROJECT	$ 300	2
3	CAPITAL ADDITIONS REQUIRED IN ABSENCE OF PROJECT	$ 4,220	3
4	INVESTMENT RELEASED OR AVOIDED BY PROJECT (2+3)	$ 4,520	4
5	NET INVESTMENT REQUIRED (1−4)	$ 12,185	5

II. NEXT-YEAR ADVANTAGE FROM PROJECT

A. OPERATING ADVANTAGE
(USE FIRST YEAR OF PROJECT OPERATION)*

6	ASSUMED OPERATING RATE OF PROJECT (HOURS PER YEAR)		3,300	6

	EFFECT OF PROJECT ON REVENUE	Increase	Decrease	
7	FROM CHANGE IN QUALITY OF PRODUCTS	$	$	7
8	FROM CHANGE IN VOLUME OF OUTPUT			8
9	TOTAL	$ A	$ B	9

	EFFECT OF PROJECT ON OPERATING COSTS			
10	DIRECT LABOR	$	$ 2,100	10
11	INDIRECT LABOR			11
12	FRINGE BENEFITS		336	12
13	MAINTENANCE		1,055	13
14	TOOLING			14
15	SUPPLIES			15
16	SCRAP AND REWORK		600	16
17	DOWN TIME		525	17
18	POWER			18
19	FLOOR SPACE			19
20	PROPERTY TAXES AND INSURANCE	170		20
21	SUBCONTRACTING			21
22	INVENTORY			22
23	SAFETY			23
24	FLEXIBILITY		400	24
25	OTHER			25
26	TOTAL	$ 170 A	$ 5,016 B	26

27	NET INCREASE IN REVENUE (9A−9B)	$	27
28	NET DECREASE IN OPERATING COST (26B−26A)	$ 4,846	28
29	NEXT-YEAR OPERATING ADVANTAGE (27+28)	$ 4,846	29

B. NON-OPERATING ADVANTAGE
(USE ONLY IF THERE IS AN ENTRY IN LINE 4)

30	NEXT-YEAR CAPITAL CONSUMPTION AVOIDED BY PROJECT:			30
	A DECLINE OF DISPOSAL VALUE DURING THE YEAR		$	A
	B NEXT-YEAR ALLOCATION OF CAPITAL ADDITIONS		$ 422	B
		TOTAL	$ 422	

C. TOTAL ADVANTAGE

31	TOTAL NEXT-YEAR ADVANTAGE FROM PROJECT (29+30)	$ 5.268	31

* For projects with a significant break-in period, use performance after break-in.

Figure 7.3. MAPI analysis of a proposed automatic screw machine.

PROJECT NO.   2   SHEET 2

III. COMPUTATION OF MAPI URGENCY RATING

32   TOTAL NEXT-YEAR ADVANTAGE AFTER INCOME TAX (31 − TAX) $ 2,634

33   MAPI CHART ALLOWANCE FOR PROJECT (TOTAL OF COLUMN F, BELOW) $ 785 *

(ENTER DEPRECIABLE ASSETS ONLY)

Item or Group	Installed Cost of Item or Group A	Estimated Service Life (Years) B	Estimated Terminal Salvage (Percent of Cost) C	MAPI Chart Number D	Chart Percent- age E	Chart Percent- age × Cost (E × A) F
Automatic Screw Machine	$ 16,705	18	5	3	4.7	$ 785
					TOTAL	$ 785

34   AMOUNT AVAILABLE FOR RETURN ON INVESTMENT (32 − 33) $ 1,849

35   **MAPI URGENCY RATING** (34 ÷ 5) · 100   %   15

* Since the chart allowance does not cover future capital additions to project assets, add an annual proration of such additions, if any, to the figure in Line 33.

Figure 7.3. *Continued*

Greater operating speed can be attained on the new equipment, and jobs can be tooled up to take advantage of these new speeds. Based on a check of 11 jobs, the analyst estimates an average gain of 21 per cent. Figured on an 80-hour week, this will result in a direct labor saving of 840 hours a year at $2.50 an hour, or $2,110. Savings in fringe benefits will be $336. In addition there will be a decrease in the cost of scrappage and rework of $600, a decrease in maintenance cost of $1,055, and a decrease in down-time cost of $525. The proposed machine is capable of greater output than the machine it is to replace. At the present time, however, work is not available for the new equipment beyond the 3,300 hours indicated as an operating rate. A value of $400 is assigned to this additional capacity since it will allow greater flexibility. The service life of the new equipment is estimated to be 18 years with a terminal salvage value of 5 per cent. The tax depreciation method is the sum-of-digits and the tax rate is 50 per cent. Property taxes and insurance will increase by $170.

The calculations required by the MAPI procedure are accomplished with the aid of the standard forms of Figure 7.3. Each cost and saving previously outlined is entered in the appropriate place on the form. Item 33 is found by reference to Figure 7.2 since Variant B is applicable. A chart percentage of 4.7 results from a salvage ratio of 5 per cent, a service life of 18 years, and use of the curves for the sum-of-digits depreciation method. The resulting urgency rating is 15 per cent. It is an adjusted, after-tax rate of return which can be used in making the replacement decision.

7.5. REPLACEMENT UNDER INFLATION AND INCREASED PRODUCTIVITY

Inflation and increased productivity are economic realities that have been a part of the decision environment down through history. Although both may have a profound effect upon the procurement and use of producer goods, they are usually disregarded in replacement models because of their unpredictability. Inflation tends to occur in surges and is not felt uniformly throughout the economy. Increased productivity is likely to be even more unpredictable and may occur in discrete and rather significant increments. When it can be assumed that the rate of inflation and increased productivity are consistent rather than erratic over time, their effects can be made part of a decision model. This assumption is not likely to be realistic in the individual case, but its acceptance allows the over-all effect of these two factors upon machine replacement to be illustrated.[4]

---

[4] The illustrations in this section were adapted from P. M. Ghare and P. E. Torgersen, "The Effect of Inflation and Increased Productivity on Machine Replacement," *Journal of Industrial Engineering*, **XV**, No. 4 (July–August, 1964), pp. 201–207.

The replacement criterion. It is assumed that the price increase due to inflation in a given time period is a fixed percentage of the price at the beginning of that time period, and it is the same for all time periods and for all goods and services within the framework of the evaluation. Let

p_o = price of goods or services at some reference time
p_t = price after time t
r = rate of increase as a fraction per time period.

The price after a time period will be equal to the price at the reference time plus the increase during that period. Thus, proceeding in a manner similar to Table 6.2

$$p_1 = p_o + p_o r = p_o(1 + r)$$
$$p_2 = p_1 + p_1 r = p_1(1 + r) = p_o(1 + r)^2$$
$$\cdots \qquad\qquad \cdots \qquad\qquad \cdots$$
$$p_t = p_o(1 + r)^t. \tag{7.3}$$

The effect of rising prices should be considered in evaluating machine replacements, since inflation nullifies the interchangeability of the face value of money and its purchasing power. Thus, the book value of a used machine may not be a reliable indicator of its probable resale value. A method of obtaining a reliable indicator can be developed from the following assumptions:

(1) If the conditions of risk and growth are identical, the market value of two assets with the same life expectancy will be directly proportional to their profit-earning capacity or return. For example, if asset A yields $6 a year and asset B yields $5 a year and if the market value of B is $100, then the market value of A will be $6(100/5) = 120.

(2) The fraction, (profit earned/market value)100, will be called the *rate of return*. With assumption (1) an adequate rate of return is the same for all assets.

(3) If the rate of return is adequate, there will always be a buyer for the asset.

(4) The buyer's decision to buy will be dependent upon the profits earned during the year immediately preceding the decision because this will give him an indication of future profits under similar circumstances, and the information will be current.

The problem of machine replacement involves a choice between an existing machine and a proposed machine. The selection criterion used in this illustration will be the net profits to be obtained from each alternative. In a noninflationary system, such series of profits can be reduced to a common basis, such as an equivalent annual amount. This reduction is no longer valid in an inflationary system. Hence, the comparison must be made on the basis of the merits and demerits of the alternatives as they stand at the time of the decision.

In the dynamic situation, where both the price level and the productivity of the proposed machine may be changing from year to year, the sunk cost resulting from such a change may be tabulated. The *sunk cost* is defined here as the cost of the new machine minus the resale value of the old machine and minus the accumulated depreciation. This definition differs slightly from the traditional definition of sunk cost because the cost of the new machine will vary over time. The sunk cost may be spread over the years for which the existing machine was employed. This can be called the sunk cost per year and would represent the extent to which the losses are accumulated each year in this dynamic situation. If it is desirable to consider the time value of money, this can be done by using an imaginary rate of interest equal to the actual rate of interest plus the rate of inflation.

A general machine replacement model under inflation. A machine has no utility in itself but has utility in the consumer goods it produces. In considering the problem of machine replacement, it is interesting to consider the entire system of producing goods. Such a system can be represented symbolically:

$$\text{Sales} = \text{Materials} + \text{Labor} + \text{Gross Profits}$$

$$S = M + wH + G$$

$$sQ = mQ + wH + G$$

$$\text{Gross Profits} = \text{Net Profits} + \text{Taxes} + \text{Depreciation}$$

$$G = N + T + D$$

$$\text{Taxable Income} = \text{Net Profits} + \text{Taxes}$$

$$I = N + T$$

where S = total sales revenue
  s = unit sale price
  m = unit material price
  M = total material price
  w = wage rate per hour
  H = labor hours
  Q = quantity of processed goods
  G = gross profits
  N = net profits
  T = taxes based on gross profits
  D = depreciation
  I = taxable income.

In an inflationary economy, the following changes may be assumed to take place in the system during the first year.

$$s_1' = s(1 + r)$$
$$m_1' = m(1 + r)$$
$$w_1' = w(1 + r).$$

The primed symbols represent values under inflation. Substituting these in the foregoing basic equation gives

$$G_1' = G(1 + r)$$
$$N_1' + T_1' + D_1' = (N + T + D)(1 + r).$$

Since depreciation is dependent entirely on the original cost of the machine p_o, and its useful life, n, it is independent of the current market value. Thus,

$$D = f(p_o, n).$$

Also, depreciation is a function of expenses incurred in the past only and neither p_o nor n is affected by inflation. Hence,

$$D_1' = D.$$
$$N_1' + T_1' + D = (N + T + D)(1 + r)$$
$$\frac{(N_1' + T_1') - (N + T)}{N + T} = r\left(1 + \frac{D}{N + T}\right) > r. \tag{7.4}$$

The implication of Equation (7.4) is that, all other relations remaining the same, the effect of inflation is to increase the taxable income at a rate faster than the rate of inflation. A corollary of this is that, as the profit-earning capacity of the machine increases faster than the rate of inflation, the resale value of the used machines will not decrease as fast as in a noninflationary system. After t years of such change, the taxable income will be

$$I_t = [(1 + r)^t](N + T) + [(1 + r)^t - 1]D. \tag{7.5}$$

If the capital used is to have the same rate of return as in a noninflationary system, where

$$\frac{N_t + T_t}{\text{justified capital}} = \frac{N + T}{p_o}$$

the justified capital will be

$$p_o(1 + r)^t + \frac{p_o D}{N + T}[(1 + r)^t - 1]. \tag{7.6}$$

Based on the straight-line method of depreciation, the price that a prospective customer would offer for this machine would be $(n - t)/n$ times

Table 7.7. SUNK COST ANALYSIS UNDER INFLATION

Year	Gross Profits	Depreciation	Taxes	Net Profits	Justified Capital	Depreciation Reserve	Market Resale Value	Reserve Resale Value	Cost of New Machine	Sunk Cost	Sunk Cost/Year
1	$61,200	$20,000	$20,600	$20,600	$206,000	$20,000	$185,400	$205,400	$204,000	$ −1,400	$ −1,400
2	62,424	20,000	21,212	21,212	212,120	40,000	169,696	209,696	208,080	−1,616	−808
3	63,672	20,000	21,836	21,836	218,360	60,000	152,852	212,852	212,242	−610	−203
4	64,945	20,000	22,472	22,472	224,720	80,000	134,835	214,835	216,487	+1,652	+413
5	66,244	20,000	23,122	23,122	231,220	100,000	115,610	215,610	220,817	5,207	+1,041
6	67,569	20,000	23,784	23,784	237,840	120,000	95,138	215,138	225,233	10,095	+1,683
7	68,920	20,000	24,460	24,460	244,600	140,000	73,380	213,380	229,738	16,358	+2,337
8	70,298	20,000	25,149	25,149	251,490	160,000	50,298	210,298	234,333	24,035	+3,004
9	71,704	20,000	25,852	25,852	258,520	180,000	25,520	205,520	239,020	33,500	+3,722
10	73,138	20,000	26,569	26,569	265,690	200,000	—	200,000	243,800	43,800	+4,380

the justified capital. Thus, the probable resale value would be

$$p_o\left[(1 + r)^t + \frac{D}{N + T}\{(1 + r)^t - 1\}\right]\left[\frac{n - t}{n}\right]. \tag{7.7}$$

If accrued depreciation is tD, and if interest is neglected, the funds available for replacement would be

$$p_o\left[(1 + r)^t + \frac{D}{N + T}\{(1 + r)^t - 1\}\right]\left[\frac{n - t}{n}\right] + tD. \tag{7.8}$$

This would have to be compared with the probable cost of a new machine which would have inflated through t years to $p_o(1 + r)^t$.

Finally, the excess of available funds over the cost a new machine would be

$$p_o\left[(1 + r)^t + \frac{D}{N + T}\{(1 + r)^t - 1\}\right]\left[\frac{n - t}{n}\right] + tD - p_o(1 + r)^t. \tag{7.9}$$

If this expression is positive there can be a net capital gain by replacement. If it is negative there would be a sunk cost. This means that an appropriate time can be chosen to replace the machine. This will occur when the total sunk cost is a minimum or when there is a capital gain.

Consider the following numerical illustration. Assume that the original cost of a machine is $200,000 and that the expected life is 10 years with no salvage value. Operation of the machine requires 40,000 man-hours per year at $2.00 per hour and raw materials cost $60,000. Sales receipts are expected to be $2.00 per unit for a total of $200,000. An adequate rate of return is 10 per cent and the assumed rate of inflation is 2 per cent. During the first year, the following should occur:

Depreciation (straight-line method)	$ 20,000
Labor charges = 1.02 × $80,000	81,600
Material charges = 1.02 × $60,000	61,200
Sales — 1.02 × $200,000	204,000
Gross profits — $204,000 — 81,600 - 61,200	61,200
Taxable income = $61,200 — 20,000	41,200
Taxes (at 50 per cent)	20,600
Net profits or yield	20,600
Probable resale value from Equation (7.7)	$185,400

In the noninflationary system, the yield and resale value would have been $20,000 and $180,000 respectively.

Calculations for the succeeding ten years are given in Table 7.7 and shown in Figure 7.4. Note that if the machine is sold and replaced by a new machine of the same type within three years, a capital gain would be realized. After three years, there would be a sunk cost. This capital gain, however, does not

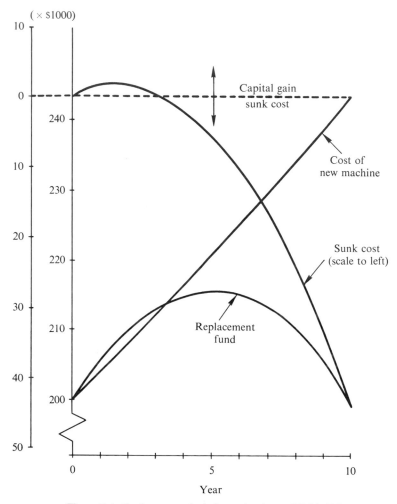

Figure 7.4. Sunk cost analysis from the data of Table 7.7.

include the costs of replacement itself, such as installation costs and loss of production, which might easily exceed the gain indicated.

A replacement model under inflation and increased productivity. Up to this point it has been assumed that the new machine, purchased as a replacement after t years, would be identical to the machine which it replaced. This is a realistic assumption in many cases. In other cases, however, it might be necessary to assume that the newer machine would incorporate some design modifications which would make it more productive. If productivity can be assumed to increase exponentially, then the productivity after t years = original productivity $(1 + r')^t$, where r' = the fractional increase in productivity each year.

Two different meanings may be attributed to the phrase "increase in productivity":

(1) A decrease in the labor and machine time input to obtain a constant desired output;
(2) An increase in output resulting from the same labor and machine time input.

In this development only the first case will be considered.

The cost of the new, more productive machine depends upon the efficiency of the research and development contributing to this increase in productivity. On the other hand, the price that the buyer would be willing to pay for such a machine would be that which would give him an adequate rate of return on his investment. This leads to the following two questions:

(1) The general price level being unchanged, what would be the effect of an increase in productivity on the market price of the new machine?
(2) Under the conditions of inflation, what would be the effect of the availability of a more productive machine on the probable resale value of an existing machine?

If starred symbols are used to denote the use of a more productive machine, with the remainder of the symbols having the same meaning as before, then

$$s^* = s$$
$$m^* = m$$
$$H^* = H\left(\frac{1}{1 + r'}\right)$$

and also

$$G^* = G + wH\left(1 - \frac{1}{1 + r'}\right).$$

If this exponential rise in productivity continues for t years,

$$G_t^* = G + wH\left[1 - \frac{1}{(1 + r')^t}\right]. \tag{7.10}$$

Since the investment that would be justified in a machine would be proportional to the profit-making capacity of that machine

$$\frac{p_o^*}{p_o} = \frac{G^*}{G} = \frac{I^*}{I}.$$

Thus, the prices offered for two alternative machines would be given by

$$p_o^* = p_o\left(\frac{G^*}{G}\right)$$

$$p_t^* = p_o\left\{1 + \frac{wH}{G}\left[1 - \frac{1}{(1 + r')^t}\right]\right\}. \tag{7.11}$$

As an example of the application of Equation (7.11), if the machine considered in the previous illustration were to be replaced after one year by another machine of 3 per cent more productivity, the price that would be offered would be calculated as

$$p_1^* = 200,000 \left\{ 1 + \frac{80,000}{60,000} \left[1 - \frac{1}{1.03} \right] \right\}$$

$$= \$207,770.$$

Extended calculations of this illustration are presented in Table 7.8.

Table 7.8. AN ANALYSIS OF REPLACEMENT PRICE
UNDER INCREASED PRODUCTIVITY

Year	Productivity $100(1 + r')^t$	Justified Price
1	103.0	$207,770
2	106.1	215,330
3	109.3	222,690
4	112.6	229,840
5	115.9	236,580
6	119.4	243,330
7	123.0	249,860
8	126.7	256,200
9	130.5	262,320
10	134.4	268,250

A comparison of the justified prices in Table 7.8 and the prices for the new machines in Table 7.7 indicates that a 3 per cent rise in productivity more than compensates for a 2 per cent rate of inflation. In fact, for the given data, a 3 per cent per annum rise in productivity compensates for a 3.35 per cent per annum inflation rate over a 10-year period. Productivity and inflation in the United States for the last 20 years have been rising at the approximate rate of 3 per cent and 2 per cent per year, respectively. Under these conditions, the prices of capital assets are incurring a relative decrease instead of a relative increase.

As a second example consider the effect of an increase in the productivity of an alternative machine on the probable resale value of a machine already installed and in operation. With a more productive machine available on the market, the extra labor charges involved in working with the existing machine would be avoidable. As a result, the prospective investor could consider the profit-making capacity to be reduced by an amount equal to the extra labor charges. Thus, the reduction in profit is

$$wH \left[1 - \frac{1}{(1 + r')^t} \right].$$

The reduction in the probable resale value would be

$$\frac{\text{reduction in profit}}{\text{adequate rate of return}}\left[\frac{n-t}{n}\right]$$

or

$$\frac{p_0}{N}\,wH\left[1-\frac{1}{(1+r')^t}\right]\left[\frac{n-t}{n}\right]. \tag{7.12}$$

If the machine considered in the preceding illustrations is to be replaced after one year, and if inflation and productivity are rising at 2 per cent and 3

Table 7.9. A SUNK COST ANALYSIS UNDER INFLATION AND INCREASED PRODUCTIVITY

Year	Accumulated Depreciation	Reduction on Resale Value	Resale Value	Replacement Fund	Cost of New Machine	Sunk Cost	Sunk Cost Per Year
1	$20,000	$20,974	$164,426	$184,426	$211,930	$27,504	$27,504
2	40,000	36,794	132,902	172,902	225,940	51,038	25,519
3	60,000	47,650	105,202	165,202	236,270	71,068	23,689
4	80,000	53,712	81,123	161,123	248,690	87,567	21,892
5	100,000	34,076	60,734	160,734	261,180	100,446	20,089
6	120,000	51,994	43,144	163,144	273,990	110,846	18,474
7	140,000	44,878	28,502	168,502	287,090	118,588	16,941
8	160,000	33,718	16,580	176,580	300,220	123,690	15,461
9	180,000	18,698	6,822	186,822	313,470	126,648	14,074
10	200,000	0	0	200,000	327,000	127,000	12,700

per cent, respectively, then the reduction in probable resale value could be calculated from Equation (7.12) as

$$\frac{200,000}{20,000}(80,000)\left[1-\frac{1}{(1.03)^1}\right]\left[\frac{10-1}{10}\right]=\$20,974.$$

This means that the probable resale value after one year would not be $185,400 as given by Table 7.7, but $185,400 − $20,974 = $164,426. Similar calculations can be made for subsequent years, and with replacement costs, the sunk costs can be outlined as in Table 7.9.

The results of this section can be summarized, recognizing that a number of simplifying assumptions have been made. Under inflation, with no increase in productivity, the accumulation of depreciation monies plus the resale value of the existing machine will not keep pace with the rising price of the new machine available for replacement. In effect, a sunk cost will result, and this sunk cost will increase with time. An optimum machine replacement policy appears to require frequent machine replacement, long before the service life is over. With this policy and under favorable conditions, it may be possible to realize a capital gain although installation costs may nullify this gain. Under inflation, increasing productivity reverses the effects of inflation. This compensation of the mal-effects of inflation will result in a sunk cost that appears to decelerate with time. Under these conditions, a machine replacement policy tends to favor using machines until the end of their service life. These trends appear to conform to intuitive reasoning. Without improvements in productivity, a new machine will not be more productive, and it will cost more, owing to inflation. The used machine will then retain a high resale value and replacement will be frequent. With improvements in productivity, the new machine will be more productive than the used machine and the resale value of the latter will be low.

7.6. REPLACEMENTS OF UNITS THAT FAIL

An asset will be replaced when it has failed completely. An asset may be replaced while it is functioning properly if it has achieved a specific probability of failure and if an economic advantage will result. This section is directed to the problem of determining whether to replace on an individual or on a group basis. If the decision is to replace on a group basis, the additional problem of determining the minimum cost replacement interval arises. Since light bulbs exhibit the characteristic of instantaneous and complete failure, they will be used in the examples of this section.

Analysis of failure data. The development of replacement policy for units that fail must be preceded by an analysis of failure data. Suppose that a group of 10,000 light bulbs are installed, and at the end of t time periods the number of bulbs surviving is some function of t. If the population of bulbs is homogeneous, each bulb has the same probability of being in operation at time t as any other bulb.

Although failures would be continuous, it is likely that failure data would be collected and recorded within discrete time intervals. Column B of Table 7.10 gives the number of bulbs functioning properly at the end of each time period. Column C gives the number of bulbs which failed within each time

Table 7.10. ANALYSIS OF LIGHT BULB FAILURE DATA

Period (A)	Survivors (B)	Failures (C)	$P(t)$ (D)	$P_c(t)$ (E)	$P_s(t)$ (F)
0	10,000	—	—	—	1.00
1	9,000	1,000	0.10	0.10	0.90
2	7,000	2,000	0.20	0.22	0.70
3	4,000	3,000	0.30	0.43	0.40
4	2,000	2,000	0.20	0.50	0.20
5	500	1,500	0.15	0.75	0.05
6	0	500	0.05	1.00	0
7	0	0	0	—	—

period. The probability of a bulb failing within each time period is given in Column D. These probabilities are calculated from

$$P(t) = \frac{N_{t-1} - N_t}{N_o} \tag{7.13}$$

where $P(t)$ = probability of failure during the time period t
  N_o = the initial number of units in the group
  N_t = the number of survivors through time t
  N_{t-1} = the number of survivors through time $t - 1$.

The probability that a bulb, having survived to an age $t - 1$, will fail during the interval $t - 1$ to t can be defined as the *conditional probability* of failure. These conditional probabilities are given in Column E. They were calculated from

$$P_c(t) = \frac{N_{t-1} - N_t}{N_{t-1}}. \tag{7.14}$$

Column F gives the probability of survival to an age t. These survival probabilities are calculated from

$$P_s(t) = \frac{N_t}{N_o} \tag{7.15}$$

The probabilities $P(t)$, $P_c(t)$, and $P_s(t)$ in Table 7.10 were calculated from the basic data in Column B. In an actual analysis of failure data, more precision would be obtained by increasing the number of time periods and dividing the survivor data more finely. This example is based on empirical data. If there is good reason to believe that failure data conform to a known theoretical distribution, the entries in Column B could be found by calculation. From these, the respective probabilities could be found.

The number of replacements per period. If the policy of replacing units as they fail is followed, the number of replacements needed in each time period may be found. For simplicity assume that failures occur only at the end of a time period. If failures are replaced, the replacements themselves will eventually fail and must be replaced. These replacements will also fail and require replacement, thus giving rise to the replacement of replacements. If x_t denotes the number of replacements made at the end of the tth period, the number of replacements at the end of each period would be

$$x_o = x_o$$
$$x_1 = x_o[P(1)]$$
$$x_2 = x_o[P(2)] + x_1[P(1)]$$
$$x_3 = x_o[P(3)] + x_1[P(2)] + x_2[P(1)]$$

Table 7.11. CALCULATION OF THE NUMBER OF REPLACEMENTS PER TIME PERIOD

$P(t)$	x_0	x_1	x_2	x_3	x_4	x_5	x_6	x_7	x_8	x_9	x_{10}	x_{11}	x_{12}	x_{13}
$P(6) = 0.05$	500	50	105	170	153	166	152	147	156					
$P(5) = 0.15$	1,500	150	315	512	459	498	456	441	468	465				
$P(4) = 0.20$	2,000	200	420	682	612	664	608	588	624	620	616			
$P(3) = 0.30$	3,000	300	630	1,023	918	996	912	882	936	930	924	921		
$P(2) = 0.20$	2,000	200	420	682	612	664	608	588	624	620	616	614	616	
$P(1) = 0.10$	1,000	100	210	341	306	332	304	294	312	310	308	307	307	308
x_t	10,000	1,000	2,100	3,410	3,061	3,318	3,036	2,933	3,126	3,105	3,075	3,074	3,070	3,080

and so forth. A general expression for x_t would be

$$x_t = N_o\left[P(t) + \sum_{j=1}^{t-1}P(j)P(t-j) + \sum_{b=2}^{t-1}\left\{\sum_{j=1}^{b-1}P(j)P(b-j)\right\}P(t-b) + \cdots\right].$$

(7.16)

As an example, the number of replacements at the end of the third time period would be

$$x_3 = 10,000\left[P(3) + \sum_{j=1}^{2}P(j)P(3-j) + \sum_{b=2}^{2}\left\{\sum_{j=1}^{b-1}P(j)P(b-j)\right\}P(3-b) + \cdots\right]$$

$$= 10,000[0.30 + 0.10(0.20) + 0.20(0.10) + 0.10(0.10)(0.10)] = 3,410.$$

Table 7.11 provides a systematic means for calculating x_t. The calculations could be extended beyond the 13 periods shown. Figure 7.5 illustrates that the number of replacements required per period oscillates until a steady-state condition is achieved. This is called the *maintenance rate*, and it reaches a finite limit as the number of periods increases. The maintenance rate is in its permanent state when it is essentially constant and equal to the reciprocal of the average life.

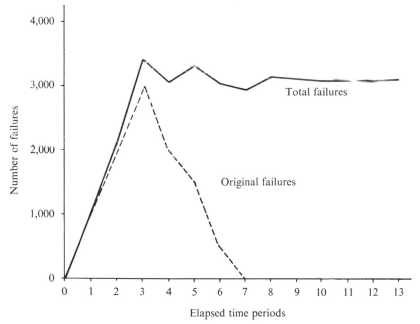

Figure 7.5. Total failures per time period and failures per time period of the original units.

The average life of the units under consideration is given by the expression

$$\sum_{t=0}^{n} t[P(t)].$$

For example, the average life of the light bulbs is $1(0.10) + 2(0.20) + 3(0.30) + 4(0.20) + 5(0.15) + 6(0.05) = 3.25$ periods. Hence, the number of replacements required per time period in the steady-state condition is $10,000/3.25$ or $3,080$. This value agrees with that illustrated by Figure 7.5.

If the cost of replacing one unit is $0.10, the cost per period would be $0.10(3,080)$ or $308. This period cost should be compared with the policy of group replacement. For the comparison to be valid, however, the minimum cost group replacement interval must be found.

The minimum cost group replacement interval. Assume that units are replaced as they fail but, in addition, all units will be replaced at a specified interval. Let

TC = total replacement cost per period through t periods
C_u = cost of unit replacement per unit
C_g = cost of group replacement per unit.

The total cost per period will be the cost of unit replacement per period plus the cost of group replacement per period, or

$$TC = UC + GC.$$

The cost of unit replacement per period may be expressed as

$$UC = \frac{C_u \sum^{t-1} x_t}{t}$$

where the summation of x_t is over $t - 1$ periods, to allow for the replacement of failures in period t as part of the group. The cost of group replacement per period may be expressed as

$$GC = \frac{C_g N_o}{t}.$$

Therefore, the total cost per period with group replacement may be expressed as

$$TC = \frac{C_u \sum^{t-1} x_t}{t} + \frac{C_g N_o}{t}. \tag{7.17}$$

As an example, assume that the population of 10,000 bulbs has a group replacement cost of $0.05 per unit. As before, assume that the cost of unit replacement per unit is $0.10. The total cost per period for various

Table 7.12. TOTAL COST PER PERIOD FOR GROUP REPLACEMENT

Period t	$\sum\limits^{t-1} x_t$	UC	GC	TC
1	0	$ 0	$500	$500
2	1,000	50	250	300
3	3,100	103	167	270
4	6,510	163	125	288

group replacement intervals is calculated from Equation (7.17) and given in Table 7.12. A group replacement interval of three periods will result in a minimum total cost per period. Since this cost is $270, a saving of $308 less $270, or $38 per period, will result if the policy of group replacement is implemented.

QUESTIONS

1. Discuss criteria other than economic that might be included in the replacement decision.

2. Outline the primary considerations leading to replacement.

3. Discuss the treatment of unequal service life in replacement analysis.

4. What is a sunk cost and how should it be treated in replacement analysis?

5. Discuss the minimum cost replacement model in terms of $E = f(x_i, y_j)$.

6. Under what conditions is the minimum cost replacement model applicable?

7. What is the decision criterion of the MAPI algorithm?

8. Discuss the assumptions upon which the analysis for replacement under inflation and increased productivity is based.

9. What replacement policies are available for the case of units that fail?

10. Discuss the cost components in the model for units that fail.

PROBLEMS

1. Plot the equivalent annual cost of capital recovery plus return, the equivalent annual maintenance cost, and the equivalent average annual total cost for the situation described in Table 7.1.

2. A small community secures its water supply from a system of wells. A 6-in., single-stage centrifugal pump in good condition is presently being used. The pump was purchased 4 years ago for $2,200 and has a present book value of $1,200, having been depreciated on the basis of an expected life of 8 years. Design improvements have made the demand for this type of pump small.

The present resale value of the pump is only $500, it probably will be only $200 in 4 years. An improved pump can be purchased for $4,000 which will have an estimated life of 10 years and a $200 trade-in value. The pumping demand is 320 cu ft per minute against an average head of 200 ft. The present pump has an efficiency of 72 per cent when furnishing the foregoing demand. The new pump will have an efficiency of 80 per cent. Power costs $0.025 per horsepower-hour, and either pump must operate 2,400 hours per year. Do the improvements in design justify the purchase of a new pump if the interest rate is 6 per cent?

3. A special-purpose machine was installed 5 years ago at a cost of $9,500. The following table is a record of its annual operating costs, maintenance costs, book value, and salvage value:

Year of Service	Operating Costs for Year	Maintenance Costs for Year	Book Value at End of Year	Salvage Value at End of Year
1	$4,500	$150	$8,000	$500
2	4,550	500	6,500	500
3	4,900	700	5,000	500
4	5,350	900	3,500	500
5	5,750	1,800	2,000	500

If interest is neglected, what is the average annual cost of each year of service? At what service life was this average annual cost minimized?

4. A rancher is considering two bridge designs for a structure to cross a small stream over which he must move livestock. The wooden design would cost $800 and last 10 years. The steel design would cost $1,100 and last 15 years. Each structure has no salvage value and would require the same amount of maintenance. Compare the two alternatives for a life of 30 years at an interest rate of 8 per cent.

5. A special-purpose lathe is being installed at a first cost of $8,000. Maintenance and operating costs are estimated at $5,000 for the first year and increasing by $250 each subsequent year. The book value will decrease at the rate of $500 per year. The resale value is presently $4,000 and will decrease at the rate of $500 per year. Neglecting interest, for what service life would the average annual cost be a minimum?

6. Geopoliticians have long been concerned with theories of who rules the world. One recently developed extension of these theories is concerned with outer space and is referred to as the Milky Way theory. This theory suggests that he who rules the planets, rules the Milky Way. He who rules the Milky Way rules the galaxies, and he who rules the galaxies rules all of outer space. The costs of achieving these objectives are great, however, and a judicious allocation of funds is necessary. Captain Minimax of the United States Space Patrol has provided the following information regarding operations beyond the sunset (three light years or greater): The cost of installing a new astrodome on Space Way Station V-7 is $100 million. These domes are subject to meteorite and

asteroid shower activity (called *dandruff* by the station inhabitants). The showers sometimes result in a rupture of the dome which must be repaired. The probability of incurring a hit by a meteorite or asteroid can be described with a Poisson distribution with a mean of four holes per year. These holes cost $100,000 each to patch. The operating costs of the station are $500,000 per year plus the square of the cumulative number of patches times $10,000. Determine the optimum replacement policy under these conditions.

7. If the cost of money is to be considered (Space bonds pay 4 per cent interest), calculate the optimum replacement policy of Problem 6.

8. A new grinder has been proposed at a cost of $6,500. The salvage value of the existing equipment is $300. It is anticipated that the new equipment will permit labor savings of $2,100 per year. The new grinder has an estimated service life of 15 years and a terminal salvage value of $325. Using the straight-line method of depreciation and Variant B (Figure 7.2) calculate the MAPI urgency rating under a net tax increase of $300 with a tax rate of 50 per cent.

9. Solve the problem developed in Table 7.7 under an assumed rate of inflation of 4 per cent. Sketch the sunk costs and compare to the sunk costs of 2 per cent given in Figure 7.4.

10. Sketch the replacement fund, cost of new machine, and sunk cost values given in Table 7.9.

11. Solve Problem 9 under an assumed rate of inflation of 4 per cent with productivity remaining at 3 per cent. Sketch and compare to the figure developed for Problem 10.

12. Assume the failure pattern of 10,000 light bulbs will follow a Poisson distribution with a mean failure rate of four time units. Assume data is recorded in integer time units, tabulate, and sketch $P(t)$.

13. Calculate and plot the number of replacements needed in Problem 12 until the steady-state condition is achieved.

14. If the unit cost of group replacement in Problem 12 is $0.05 and the unit cost of individual replacement is $0.10, what is the optimal number of time units between group replacement? What is the total cost per period under this optimum time interval?

15. Plot the *TC* function for the data in the Problem 14.

16. Solve Problem 12 for an exponential distribution with a mean failure rate of two time units.

17. Plot the number of replacements needed in Problem 16 until the steady-state condition is achieved.

18. With the same costs of Problem 14, calculate the average total cost per period under the optimum replacement interval.

Part **III**

ECONOMY IN THE CONTROL
OF OPERATIONS

eight

MODELS OF
STATISTICAL CONTROL

*Most operations are performed within an environment composed of
many random variables. Some of these variables may be
treated statistically to facilitate the decision-making process.
Others may require analysis only to ascertain their conformance or lack of
conformance to a stable pattern of variation. This is often the case
when stability of pattern will contribute to the
decision maker's objective.*

*This chapter is directed to developing control models that may
be used to draw conclusions about the stability of random
variable processes. The nature of the process influences the specific
control model to be used. When continuous measurements are under consideration, a pair of control charts called the $\bar{X}$ and R charts may be employed.
If measurement is by attributes, or involves a counting process, either a p
chart or a c chart may be considered. The p chart is used if it
is desirable to convert the count to a fraction or proportion. The c chart
is applicable if the count is left in the form of a whole number. Each of these
control models will be developed and explained
in the following sections.*

8.1. THE CONCEPT OF STATISTICAL CONTROL

Variation is inherent in most aspects of the decision environment. A multitude of chance causes, few of which can be predicted with certainty, may produce a pattern of variation for such diverse characteristics as the dimension of a finished part, the number of defectives per unit quantity of a part, the procurement lead time of an item, and the number of arrivals per time period. Essential in the concept of statistical control is the employment of control limits within which sample values must fall in order that the operation under study be considered "in control." When a sample value falls outside these limits, the decision maker may infer that a stable system of chance causes no longer exists. Action may then be taken to find the cause of the apparent change. If such a cause exists, the operation may be brought back into control, or compensation made for the change in the pattern of variation. This is the concept upon which models of statistical control are based.

Patterns of statistical variation. A stable or probabilistic steady-state pattern of variation exists when the parameters of the statistical distribution describing the system of chance causes remain constant over time. Steady-state variation of this type is normally an exception rather than the rule. Many operations will produce a probabilistic nonsteady-state pattern of variation over time. When this is the case, the mean and/or the variance of

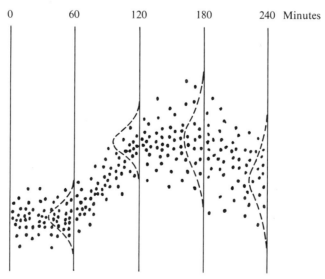

Figure 8.1. A probabilistic nonsteady-state pattern of variation.

the distribution describing the pattern changes with time. Sometimes, the form of the distribution will also undergo change.

A probabilistic nonsteady-state pattern of variation is exhibited in Figure 8.1. Assume that each point shown represented the measured diameter of a small part. A part was produced and measured each minute giving the four-hour pattern of variation shown. The nature of the variation exhibited may be generally described as follows: The mean and the variance of the process remained constant during the first hour. During the second hour, the mean exhibited an increase while the variance remained constant. The variance increased moderately for the third hour while the mean stabilized. During the last hour, the variance maintained its previous value as the mean decreased.

A more specific description of the pattern of variation is possible by developing a histogram of the data for each hour. This requires collecting all data for the hour and treating them as though the process was in a steady-state condition during the hour. Although this leads to an erroneous conclusion about the pattern of variation during the hour, there is no satisfactory alternative. Reducing the time interval from which the data are taken will improve the situation to a degree, but will result in less data from which to construct the histogram. Therefore, the gain from choosing a small interval is partially lost in the description provided by a histogram. The histogram given at the end of each hour in Figure 8.1 is an approximate representation of the distribution of values at the end of that hour, although it cannot be developed from the single point at the end of the hour.

Control limits may be placed about the initial stable pattern of variation to detect subsequent changes from that pattern. In effect, a statistical inference is made when a sample value is considered. If the sample falls within the control limits, the process under study is said to be *in control*. If the sample falls outside the limits, the process is deemed to have changed and is said to be *out of control*.

Figure 8.2 is a representation of control limits placed at a distance $k\sigma$ from the mean of the initial stable pattern of variation of Figure 8.1. If a sample value falls outside the control limits, and the process has not changed, a Type I error of probability α has been made. On the other hand, if a sample value falls within these limits, and the process has changed, a Type II error of probability β has been made. In the first case, the null hypothesis has been rejected in error. In the second, the null hypothesis has not been rejected, with a resulting error. Control limits placed about the histogram of the first hour's data in Figure 8.1 are almost certain to detect a changed pattern of variation for the second hour.

Some economic considerations. If the control limits are set relatively far apart, it is unlikely that a Type I error will be made. The control chart,

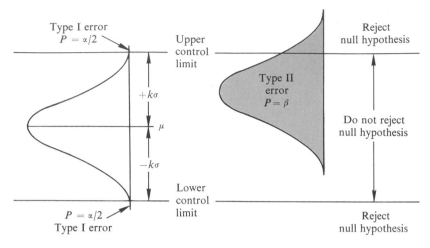

Figure 8.2. A stable and a changed pattern of variation.

however, is then not likely to detect small shifts in the parameter. In effect, the probability, β, of a Type II error is large. If the other approach is taken, and the limits are placed relatively close to the initial stable pattern of variation, the value of α will increase. The advantage gained is greater sensitivity of the chart to the shifts that may occur. The ultimate criterion will be the costs associated with the making of Type I and Type II errors. The limits should be established to minimize the sum of these two costs.

A common misconception in the control of quality is that perfection is the quality standard which should always be defined and attempted as an organizational objective. This reasoning is fallacious because it ignores the costs involved. Rather than strive for perfection, some state less than perfection may be optimum in terms of costs. Consider the concept as illustrated graphically in Figure 8.3. The costs incurred in achieving a level of quality, that is, production and inspection costs, might be described with a decreasing cost function. The costs due to poor quality, that is, producing and selling defectives, might be described by an increasing cost function. The total cost is the sum of these two cost functions. An optimum quality level is defined at that point where total cost is a minimum.

In practice, the two cost functions might not follow the continuous and smooth form indicated in Figure 8.3. Also, it may be difficult to quantify these functions; for example, it is hard to assess the potential loss of sales due to poor quality. This concept is important not for its ability to specify an optimum quality level precisely, but rather for its ability to make one aware that some quality level below perfection may be desirable.

Quality is assessed by inspecting the product at one or more points in the assembly or manufacturing process. Essentially, three choices are available

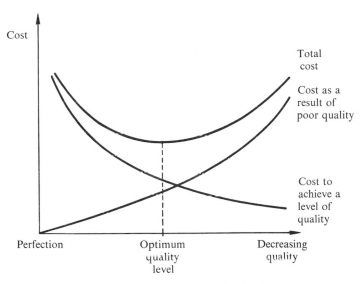

Figure 8.3. The relationship between levels of quality and costs.

at each point in the development of the product: No inspection; sampling inspection where some proportion of the units are measured; or 100 per cent inspection where every unit is assessed. Most decisions will probably result in either no inspection or 100 per cent inspection although the economy of each case should be the deciding factor. Sampling inspection may prove feasible where there are likely to be inconsistencies in the level of quality over time. The primary objective of sampling inspection should then be maintaining control of the process rather than serving as a sorting device for separating good units from defective units.

Applications of the control chart. The *control chart* can be described as a graphical representation of a mathematical model used to monitor a random variable process in order to detect changes in a parameter of that process. Charting statistical data is a test of the null hypothesis that the process from which the sample came has not changed. A control chart is directed to distinguishing between the existence of a stable pattern of variation and the occurrence of an unstable pattern. If an unstable pattern of variation is detected, action may be initiated to discover the cause of the instability. Removal of the assignable cause should permit the process to return to the stable pattern of variation. The control chart finds its most frequent application in this role.

The control chart may also be used for monitoring the solution obtained from a decision model. Most decision models are static in that they do not adapt themselves to the instability of the decision environment. These models are constructed at a point in time for a specific set of values for input parameters. A solution derived from a decision model will be optimal only as long as the input parameters to the model retain the values initially established. An optimum procurement policy will be less than optimum if the actual procurement lead time is out of control with respect to the value initially determined and used in the decision model. An optimum level of service capability in a waiting-line system will cease to be optimum if the statistically described arrival pattern is out of control with respect to the derived model. Models of statistical control provide a means for warning the decision maker that the inputs to his model need revision. In this role, control charts provide a means for converting static to dynamic decision models so that they may be applied in a nonsteady-state environment.

8.2. CONTROL MODELS FOR VARIABLES

When we deal with a continuous operation, control models for variables can be applied. Specifically, two models are available for operations of this type. The $\bar{X}$ chart is a plot over time of sample means taken from a process. It is primarily employed to detect changes in the mean of the process from which the samples came. The R chart is a plot over time of the ranges of these same samples. It is employed to detect changes in the dispersion of the process. These charts are often employed together in control operations.

Constructing the $\bar{X}$ chart. The $\bar{X}$ chart receives its input as the mean of a sample taken from the process under study. Usually, the sample will contain four or five observations, a number sufficient to make the central-limit theorem applicable. Accepting an approximately normal distribution of the sample means allows us to establish control limits with a predetermined knowledge of the probability of making a Type I error. It is not necessary to know the form of the distribution of the process.

The first step in constructing an $\bar{X}$ chart is to estimate the process mean, μ, and the process variance, σ^2. This requires taking m samples each at size n and calculating the mean, $\bar{X}$, and the range, R, for each sample. Table 8.1

Table 8.1. COMPUTATIONAL FORMAT FOR DETERMINING $\bar{X}$ AND R

Sample Number	Sample Values	Mean $\bar{X}$	Range R
1	$x_{11}, x_{12}, \ldots, x_{1n}$	$\bar{X}_1$	R_1
2	$x_{21}, x_{22}, \ldots, x_{2n}$	$\bar{X}_2$	R_2
.	. . .	.	.
m	$x_{m1}, x_{m2}, \ldots, x_{mn}$	$\bar{X}_m$	R_m

illustrates the format that may be used in the calculations. The mean of the sample means, $\bar{\bar{X}}$, is used as an estimate of μ and is calculated as

$$\bar{\bar{X}} = \frac{\sum\limits_{i=1}^{m} \bar{X}}{m}. \tag{8.1}$$

And, the mean of the sample ranges, $\bar{R}$, is calculated as

$$\bar{R} = \frac{\sum\limits_{i=1}^{m} R}{m}. \tag{8.2}$$

The expected ratio between the average range, $\bar{R}$, and the standard deviation of the process has been computed for various sample sizes, n. This ratio is designated d_2 and is expressed as

$$d_2 = \frac{\bar{R}}{\sigma}.$$

Therefore, σ can be estimated from the sample statistic, $\bar{R}$, as

$$\sigma = \frac{\bar{R}}{d_2}. \tag{8.3}$$

Values of d_2 as a function of the sample size may be found in Table 8.2.

The mean of the $\bar{X}$ chart is set at $\bar{\bar{X}}$. The control limits are normally set at $\pm 3\sigma_{\bar{X}}$, which results in the probability of making a Type I error of 0.0027. Since

$$\sigma_{\bar{X}} = \frac{\sigma}{\sqrt{n}}$$

substitution into Equation (8.3) gives

$$\sigma_{\bar{X}} = \frac{\bar{R}}{d_2 \sqrt{n}}$$

and

$$3\sigma_{\bar{X}} = \frac{3\bar{R}}{d_2 \sqrt{n}}. \tag{8.4}$$

The factor $3/d_2\sqrt{n}$ has been tabulated as A_2 in Table 8.2. Therefore, the upper and lower control limits for the $\bar{X}$ chart may be specified as

$$\text{UCL}_{\bar{X}} = \bar{\bar{X}} + A_2\bar{R} \tag{8.5}$$

$$\text{LCL}_{\bar{X}} = \bar{\bar{X}} - A_2\bar{R}. \tag{8.6}$$

Constructing the R chart. The R chart is constructed in a manner similar to the $\bar{X}$ chart. If the $\bar{X}$ chart has already been completed, $\bar{R}$ has been calculated from Equation (8.2). Tabular values of three sigma control limits

Table 8.2. FACTORS FOR THE CONSTRUCTION OF $\bar{X}$ AND R CHARTS*

Sample Size, n	$\bar{X}$ Chart		R Chart	
	d_2	A_2	D_3	D_4
2	1.128	1.880	0	3.267
3	1.693	1.023	0	2.575
4	2.059	0.729	0	2.282
5	2.326	0.577	0	2.115
6	2.534	0.483	0	2.004
7	2.704	0.419	0.076	1.924
8	2.847	0.373	0.136	1.864
9	2.970	0.337	0.184	1.816
10	3.078	0.308	0.223	1.777
11	3.173	0.285	0.256	1.744
12	3.258	0.266	0.284	1.716
13	3.336	0.249	0.308	1.692
14	3.407	0.235	0.329	1.671
15	3.472	0.223	0.348	1.652
16	3.532	0.212	0.364	1.636
17	3.588	0.203	0.379	1.621
18	3.640	0.194	0.392	1.608
19	3.689	0.187	0.404	1.596
20	3.735	0.180	0.414	1.586

* Factors taken from the *A.S.T.M. Manual on Quality Control of Materials* (*with permission*).

for the range have been compiled for varying sample sizes and are included in Table 8.2. The upper and lower control limits for the R chart are then specified as

$$\text{UCL}_R = D_4\bar{R} \tag{8.7}$$

$$\text{LCL}_R = D_3\bar{R}. \tag{8.8}$$

Since $D_3 = 0$ for sample sizes of $n \leq 6$ in Table 8.2, the $\text{LCL}_R = 0$. Actually, three sigma limits yield a negative lower control limit which is recorded as zero. This means that, with samples of six or fewer, it will be impossible for a value on the R chart to fall outside the lower limit. In effect, the R chart will not be capable of detecting reductions in the dispersion of the process output.

Application of the $\bar{X}$ and R charts. Once the control limits have been specified for each chart, the data used in constructing the limits are plotted on these same charts. Should all values fall within both sets of limits, the charts are ready for use. Should one or more values fall outside one set of limits, however, further inquiry is needed. A value outside the limits on the $\bar{X}$ chart indicates that the process may have undergone some change in regard to its central tendency. A value outside the limits on the R chart is evidence that the process variability may have been out of control. In either case, one should search for the source of the change in process behavior. If one or two values fall outside the limits and an assignable cause can be found, then these one or two values may be discarded and revised control limits calculated. If the revised limits contain all the remaining values, the control chart is ready for implementation. If they do not, the procedure may be repeated before using the control chart.

There is an advantage to constructing and testing the R chart first. Since an estimate of the variance of the sample means is obtained from $\bar{R}$, the construction of the $\bar{X}$ chart will depend upon the control of process variability. If the $\bar{X}$ chart is first constructed and all $\bar{X}$ values fall within the limits, the chart may still have to be revised if process variability is not in control after constructing the R chart. In effect, a revised estimate of process variation will have to be included in new limits on both the R and $\bar{X}$ charts.

Assume that control charts are to be established to monitor the weight in ounces of the contents of containers being filled on an assembly line. The containers should hold at least 10 oz. In order to guarantee this weight, the process must be set to deliver slightly more than this amount. Samples of five have been taken every 30 minutes. The sample data, together with the sample means and sample ranges, are given in Table 8.3.

Table 8.3. THE WEIGHT OF THE CONTENTS OF CONTAINERS IN OUNCES

Sample Number	Sample Values					Mean $\bar{X}$	Range R
1	11.3	10.5	12.4	12.2	12.0	11.7	1.9
2	9.6	11.7	13.0	11.4	12.8	11.7	3.4
3	11.4	12.4	11.7	11.4	12.4	11.9	1.0
4	12.0	11.9	13.2	11.9	12.2	12.2	1.3
5	12.4	11.9	11.7	11.6	10.5	11.6	1.9
6	13.8	12.5	13.9	11.9	11.4	12.7	2.5
7	13.3	11.6	13.2	10.7	11.4	12.0	2.6
8	11.1	11.3	13.2	12.8	12.0	12.1	2.1
9	12.5	11.9	13.8	11.6	13.0	12.6	2.2
10	12.1	11.7	12.0	11.7	12.9	12.1	1.2
11	11.7	12.6	12.3	11.2	10.8	11.7	1.8
12	13.8	12.3	12.4	14.1	11.3	12.8	2.8
13	10.6	11.8	13.1	12.8	11.7	12.0	2.5
14	12.0	11.2	12.1	11.7	12.1	11.8	0.9
15	11.5	13.1	13.9	11.9	10.7	12.2	3.2
16	13.4	12.6	12.4	11.9	11.8	12.4	1.6
17	12.1	13.1	14.1	11.4	12.3	12.6	2.7
18	11.5	13.2	12.4	12.6	12.2	12.4	1.7
19	13.8	14.2	13.5	13.2	12.8	13.5	1.4
20	11.5	11.4	13.1	11.6	10.8	11.7	2.3

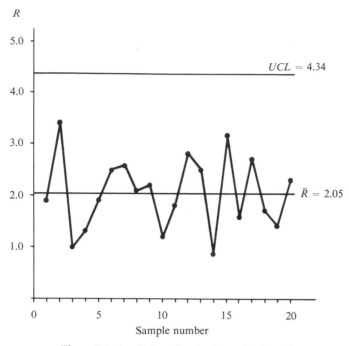

Figure 8.4. An R chart for the data of Table 8.3.

An R chart is first constructed from these data. Using Equation (8.2), $\bar{R}$ is calculated as 2.05. The control limits are then determined from Equations (8.7) and (8.8) as

$$\text{UCL}_R = 2.115(2.05) = 4.34$$

$$\text{LCL}_R = 0(2.05) = 0.$$

These limits are used to construct the R chart of Figure 8.4. Since all values fall within the control limits, the R chart is accepted as a means of assessing subsequent process variation. Had a point fallen outside the calculated limits, that point would have had to be discarded and limits recalculated. Attention should next be directed to the $\bar{X}$ chart. The mean of the sample means, $\bar{\bar{X}}$, is found from Equation (8.1) to be 12.19. The mean of the sample ranges, $\bar{R}$, has already been calculated as 2.05. Preliminary control limits for the $\bar{X}$ chart can now be calculated from Equations (8.5) and (8.6) as

$$\text{UCL}_{\bar{x}} = 12.19 + 0.577(2.05) = 13.37$$

$$\text{LCL}_{\bar{x}} = 12.19 - 0.577(2.05) = 11.01.$$

These limits are used to construct the $\bar{X}$ chart shown in Figure 8.5.

The 20 sample means may now be plotted. It is noted that the mean of sample number 19 exceeds the upper control limit. This would indicate that at this point in time, the universe from which this sample was selected was not exhibiting a stable pattern of variation. Some change occurred between the time of selecting sample number 18 and sample number 19. It is further noted that after sample number 19, the process returned to its original state. One may base action on the assumption that these statements are true; particularly if one thinks that some recognized assignable cause effected the change. Actually, the mean of sample number 19 might have exceeded the control limit by chance, and a Type I error might have been made. Alternatively, the pattern of variation might have shifted some time before sample number 18 and/or not returned after this time. Then a Type II error would have been made at these other points in time.

The data of sample number 19 should now be discarded and the control limits recalculated for the remaining pattern of variation. The mean of the remaining sample means is 12.12. The range is not recalculated because it is assumed that the process variation did not change when sample number 19 was selected. The control limits are now revised to

$$UCL_{\bar{x}} = 12.12 + 0.555(2.05) = 13.26$$
$$LCL_{\bar{x}} = 12.12 - 0.555(2.05) = 10.98.$$

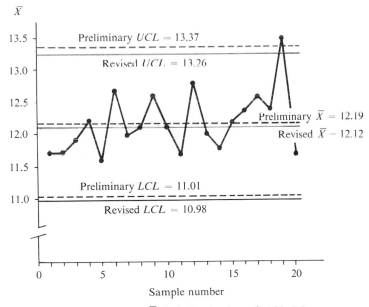

Figure 8.5. An $\bar{X}$ chart for the data of Table 8.3.

These are indicated on the control chart of Figure 8.5 and again checked to determine that no sample means exceed these limits. It is noted that no further changes are necessary and the control chart of Figure 8.5, with the revised limits, and the chart of Figure 8.4 may now be employed to monitor the process. This control model may be implemented to test future process variation to see that it does not change from that used to construct the chart.

8.3. OPERATING CHARACTERISTICS OF $\bar{X}$ CHARTS

The decision to implement a control model should be based upon its anticipated operating effectiveness. This requires consideration of the objective sought and the actual design, implementation, and maintenance of the chart. This section discusses two features of the control chart as an operational model. The first deals with the relationship between specification limits and control limits. The second discusses the power of the control chart to detect changes in the pattern of variation and is directly related to the objective sought by the decision maker. Although the illustrations presented are directed to the control of quality by the $\bar{X}$ chart, note that the concepts are applicable to statistical control and statistical control models in general.

Specification limits and control limits. Two limits may be established for the dimension of a workpiece. The *specification limit* is that limit within which the dimension must fall for the workpiece to be classified as acceptable. This limit is sometimes called a *tolerance* limit and is specified when the part is designed. A *control limit*, on the other hand, is a measure of the inherent capability of the process producing the part. It is a measure of process dispersion when the process is operating in a steady-state or "in control" condition.

As an example of the relationship of the specification limits to the control limits, consider the situation illustrated in Figure 8.6. Note that the process capability of six sigma limits is within the specification limits. If the workpiece dimension can be centered at 5.000, there should be no control problems other than the routine assessment of the stability of the pattern of variation. If samples of $n = 4$ are taken, control limits of $\alpha = 0.0027$ will be established as $\text{UCL}_{\bar{X}} = 5.0075$ and $\text{LCL}_{\bar{X}} = 4.9925$.

Under the conditions of Figure 8.6, it is possible for the mean of the process to shift and for the dimensions of all workpieces still to be within the specification limits. A process being out of control does not mean that defectives are being produced. Should the specification limits be approximately the same as the process capability, a shift detected on the $\bar{X}$ chart is a good indication that a proportion of the produced units are defective. Under these conditions, it is likely that a large sample size will be taken at

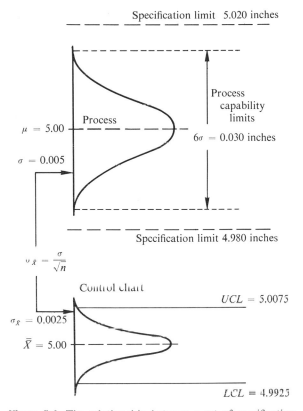

Figure 8.6. The relationship between a set of specification limits and control limits.

frequent intervals to detect shifts in the process as quickly as possible. In a few instances, the process capability limits may exceed the specification limits. Then, even though the process be maintained in control, defectives will be produced.

Three alternatives are available in this latter situation: First, one may accept the production of some defectives. These will either be sorted and removed through 100 per cent inspection or permitted to remain with the acceptable units. Second, one might redesign the product. In particular, the need for the specification limit might be questioned. This limit might be increased without a sacrifice in the performance of the product. Third, one might change the manufacturing process to permit production with a tighter process capability. This alternative would probably be implemented only after the first two had been attempted and rejected.

The power of the control chart. Control charts are employed to detect changes in a pattern of variation. The probability of the chart indicating that a change has occurred when in fact it has not, is the probability of making a Type I error. If three sigma limits are used on the $\overline{X}$ chart, this probability is approximately 0.0027; an unlikely event.

Of at least equal concern to the decision maker, is the probability of making or not making a Type II error. When changes in the pattern of variation do occur, the decision maker is concerned with the model's ability to detect these changes. The probability of making a Type II error can be demonstrated with an Operating Characteristic or OC curve. An OC curve for an $\overline{X}$ chart of three sigma limits is illustrated in Figure 8.7. The ordinate

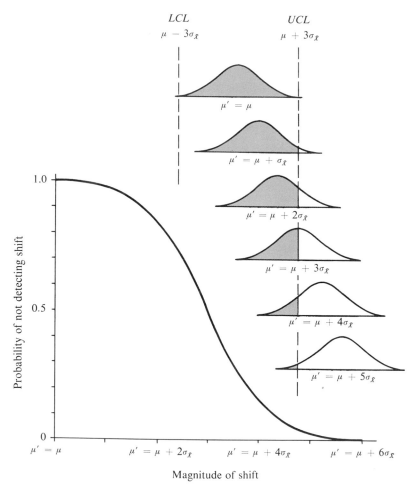

Figure 8.7. An operating characteristic curve for an $\overline{X}$ chart.

is the probability of not detecting a shift in the mean of a pattern of variation, assuming that only the mean and not the dispersion has shifted. The magnitude of the shift in the mean is defined in terms of k as $\mu + k\sigma_{\bar{x}}$. This permits one such OC curve to describe all $\bar{X}$ charts with three sigma limits. Superimposed upon the OC curve of Figure 8.7 are a series of distributions of changes of $\mu + 1\sigma_{\bar{x}}$, $\mu + 2\sigma_{\bar{x}}$, and so forth. The shaded area in each case represents the probability of a point falling within the limits after the shift, and hence, the probability of making a Type II error. Note that the new mean of the process is defined as μ', and that the dispersion is assumed to remain constant.

Consider the following examples. Using the data given in Figure 8.7, the $\text{UCL}_{\bar{x}} = 5.0075$ and $\text{LCL}_{\bar{x}} = 4.9925$, and samples of $n = 4$ are taken. Assume the process variation remains constant at $\sigma = 0.005$, and that the mean of the process has shifted to $\mu = 5.005$. The question raised concerns the probability of detecting this shift in the first sample. This shift can be expressed as

$$\mu' = 5.005$$
$$= \mu + k\sigma_X$$

where $\mu = 5.000$ and $\sigma_X = \dfrac{\sigma}{\sqrt{n}} = \dfrac{0.005}{4} = 0.0025.$

Thus, $\mu' = \mu + 2\sigma_{\bar{x}}$.

From Figure 8.7, the probability of not detecting this shift and of making a Type II error is 0.84, or the area under the normal distribution from $-\infty$ to $+1\sigma$.

In the second case, assume an identical situation except that a sample of $n = 9$ is being used. The shift can now be expressed as

$$\mu' = \mu + k\sigma_{\bar{x}}$$

with

$$\sigma_{\bar{x}} = \frac{0.005}{\sqrt{9}} = 0.0017.$$

Thus, $\mu' = \mu + 3\sigma_{\bar{x}}$.

From Figure 8.7, the probability of not detecting this shift reduces to 0.50, or the area under the normal distribution from $-\infty$ to 0.0σ.

In the last case, again assume a sample of $n = 4$, this time with a shift in the process mean to $\mu' = 5.010$. This shift is expressed as

$$\mu' = 5.010$$
$$= \mu + k\sigma_{\bar{x}}$$

with $\mu = 5.000$

and $\sigma_{\bar{x}} = 0.0025.$

Thus, $\mu' = \mu + 4\sigma_{\bar{x}}$.

The probability of not detecting this shift is only 0.16, or the area under the normal distribution from $-\infty$ to -1σ.

The $\bar{X}$ chart has been described as the control device used primarily in detecting shifts in the mean of the basic pattern of variation. The R chart is designed to detect shifts in the dispersion. It is possible to construct an OC curve for R charts after a table of the distribution of ranges has been compiled. If OC curves are constructed for both $\bar{X}$ and R charts, it would be possible to calculate the probability of detecting a shift in both the mean and dispersion on either the $\bar{X}$ or R chart or both. It is also possible to construct OC curves for control charts by attributes. In each case, the OC curve provides a measure of the relative ability of the control chart to detect changes in the basic pattern of variation.

8.4. CONTROL MODELS FOR ATTRIBUTES

Often an observation yields only a two-valued classification: A simple yes or no, correct or incorrect, acceptable or defective. A milling machine may be either in use or idle. The surface finish of a piece of furniture may be acceptable or may not. The dimension of a part may either fall within or outside a set of specification limits. With such a classification system, the proportion of measurements falling in one class during a specified time period or other sample unit may be monitored over time or over many such samples with a p chart. In other cases, observation may yield a multivalued, but still discrete classification system. A clerical operation may have been performed correctly, or it may contain one, two, or more errors. An employee may suffer none, one, or more lost-time accidents during a given time period. The number of arrivals to a service facility during a specified hour of the day will be a discrete number. In general, the number of objects, states, or events occurring during a period of time, or within a sample unit, may be monitored with a c chart. This section will develop control models that may be used with attribute sampling.

The p chart for constant sample size. When the item sampled is assessed and then placed into one of two defined classes, the proportion of units falling into one class may be controlled over time or from one sample to another with a p chart. The probability distribution describing this situation is the binomial. The mean of this distribution and its standard deviation were expressed in Equation (3.6) as

$$\mu = np$$
$$\sigma = \sqrt{np(1 - p)}.$$

These parameters may be expressed as proportions by dividing by the sample size, n. If $\bar{p}$ is then defined as an estimate of the proportion parameter μ/n, and s_p as an estimate of σ/n, then these statistics can be expressed as

$$\bar{p} = \frac{\text{total number in the class}}{\text{total number of observations}} \qquad (8.9)$$

$$s_p = \sqrt{\frac{\bar{p}(1 - \bar{p})}{n}}. \qquad (8.10)$$

The application of the p chart will be illustrated with an example of a work-sampling study. This work measurement technique is used to obtain

Table 8.4. THE NUMBER OF TIMES A DAY THE DESK CALCULATORS ARE IN USE

Working Day	Times in Use	Proportion	Working Day	Times in Use	Proportion
1	22	0.22	12	46	0.46
2	33	0.33	13	31	0.31
3	24	0.24	14	24	0.24
4	20	0.20	15	22	0.22
5	18	0.18	16	22	0.22
6	24	0.24	17	29	0.29
7	24	0.24	18	31	0.31
8	29	0.29	19	21	0.21
9	18	0.18	20	26	0.26
10	27	0.27	21	24	0.24
11	31	0.31			
			Total	546	

information about the activities of men or machines, usually in less time and at lower cost than by conventional means. Random and instantaneous observations are taken by classifying the activity at a point in time into one and only one category. In the most simple form, the categories "idle" and "at work" are used. The control chart is useful in work-sampling studies in that the observed proportions can be verified as "in control" and following a stable pattern of variation or "out of control" with an unstable pattern. In the latter case, a search can be undertaken for an assignable cause.

Consider the case of a work-sampling study involving desk calculators in an office. The objective was to determine the proportion of time the calculators were in use as opposed to the time they were idle. One hundred observations were taken each day over all working days in a month. The number of times the calculators were in use, and the proportion for each day are given in Table 8.4. From this table and Equation (8.9), $\bar{p}$ is established as

$$\bar{p} = \frac{546}{(21)(100)} = 0.260.$$

The standard deviation of the data is calculated with Equation (8.10) as

$$s_p = \sqrt{\frac{(0.26)(0.74)}{100}} = 0.044.$$

With $\bar{p} = 0.26$ as the best estimate of the population proportion, a control chart may now be constructed. Control limits in work sampling are usually established at $\bar{p} \pm 2s_p$ and these limits will not vary from one day to another in this example, since a constant sample size has been maintained for each day. With these control limits, the probability of making a Type I error may be defined as $\alpha = 0.0456$ if the normal distribution is used as an approximation. Such an approximation is realistic for this example by the requirements of Figure 3.13. The binomial will approximate the normal distribution if $n > 50$ and $0.20 < p < 0.80$. If these requirements were not met or a more accurate estimate were needed, the binomial distribution would have had to be employed. The control limits for the p chart are defined and calculated as

$$\text{UCL}_p = \bar{p} + 2s_p \tag{8.11}$$
$$= 0.260 + 2(0.044) = 0.348$$

$$\text{LCL}_p = \bar{p} - 2s_p \tag{8.12}$$
$$= 0.260 - 2(0.044) = 0.172.$$

The p chart is constructed as shown in Figure 8.8. A plot of the data indicates that day number 12 was not typical of the pattern of use established by the rest of the month. Subsequent investigation reveals that personnel from another department were also using the machines that one day because their equipment had preceded them in a move to another building. As this is an atypical situation, the sample is discarded and a revised mean and standard deviation are calculated as

$$\bar{p} = \frac{500}{(20)(100)} = 0.250$$

$$s_p = \sqrt{\frac{(0.25)(0.75)}{100}} = 0.043.$$

Revised control limits are now calculated and placed on the same control chart as

$$\text{UCL}_p = \bar{p} + 2s_p$$
$$= 0.250 + 2(0.043) = 0.336$$
$$\text{LCL}_p = \bar{p} - 2s_p$$
$$= 0.250 - 2(0.043) = 0.164.$$

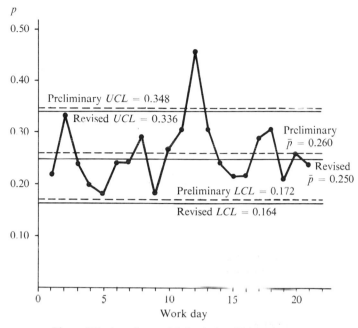

Figure 8.8. A p chart of daily desk calculator usage.

It is noted that no further days fall outside these limits and that the chart and data, without day number 12, can be taken as a stable pattern of variation of calculator usage.

The p chart with variable sample size. Under certain conditions it will be necessary to use a variable sample size in the construction of a p chart. When 100 per cent inspection is occurring and the production output varies, the sample size will also vary. If the variation is not great, however, an average daily production output might be used without any great sacrifice in the validity of the control chart. If the sample size does vary widely, a p chart with varying control limits must be designed.

The data in columns 2 and 3 of Table 8.5 represent the daily inspection record of an aluminum die casting operation. These data are given as an hourly record extending over two sequential shifts. Column 3 is the hourly proportion defective. Column 4 represents a three sigma spread calculated each hour and dependent upon the output for that hour. The final two columns then represent the variable control limits. These are spaced about the average number of defectives which may be calculated as

$$\bar{p} = \frac{36}{720} = 0.050.$$

Table 8.5. THE NUMBER OF OBSERVED DEFECTIVES FROM AN ALUMINUM DIE CASTING OPERATION

Hour	Number Inspected	Number Defective	p Fraction Defective	$3s_p =$ $3\sqrt{\dfrac{(0.05)(0.95)}{n}}$	$UCL =$ $\bar{p} + 3s_p$	$LCL =$ $\bar{p} - 3s_p$
1	48	5	0.104	0.094	0.144	0
2	36	5	0.139	0.109	0.159	0
3	50	0	0.000	0.093	0.143	0
4	47	5	0.064	0.095	0.145	0
5	48	0	0.042	0.094	0.144	0
6	54	3	0.056	0.089	0.139	0
7	50	0	0.000	0.093	0.143	0
8	42	1	0.024	0.101	0.151	0
9	32	5	0.156	0.116	0.166	0
10	40	2	0.050	0.103	0.153	0
11	47	2	0.043	0.095	0.145	0
12	47	4	0.085	0.095	0.145	0
13	46	1	0.022	0.096	0.146	0
14	46	0	0.000	0.096	0.146	0
15	48	3	0.063	0.094	0.144	0
16	39	0	0.000	0.105	0.155	0

It can be noted that all hourly fraction defectives fall within the variable control limits. This is enough to assume that the process is in control. The control chart itself is given in Figure 8.9. Had any of these hourly values exceeded the control limits, that hour would have had to be discarded, a revised $\bar{p}$ again calculated, and control limits recalculated for all the remaining hours with this new $\bar{p}$. This could then be used to assess the stability of hourly proportion defectives for subsequent shifts.

These same data could have been plotted instead upon a stabilized p chart. Such a chart includes a record of the sample deviations from $\bar{p}$ expressed in terms of s_p, thus eliminating the sample size from the calculation of the control limit. Thus, the sample value recorded on the chart is

$$\frac{p - \bar{p}}{s_p} = \frac{p - \bar{p}}{\sqrt{\dfrac{\bar{p}(1 - \bar{p})}{n}}} \tag{8.13}$$

The necessary calculations for the data given in the first three columns of Table 8.5 have been undertaken and expressed in Table 8.6. The stabilized p chart is shown in Figure 8.10. The limits are a constant $\pm 3s_p$. The use of either a p chart with varying control limits or a stabilized p chart is a matter of preference. In the first case, the more recognizable fraction defective is

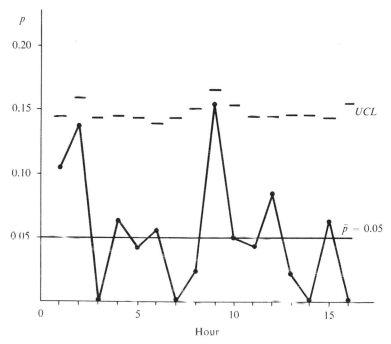

Figure 8.9. A p chart of fraction defective with varying
control limits.

Table 8.6. CALCULATIONS FOR A STABILIZED p CHART USING DATA FROM TABLE 8.5

Hour	p Fraction Defective	$\sqrt{\dfrac{(0.05)(0.95)}{n}}$	$p - \bar{p}$	$\dfrac{p - \bar{p}}{s_p}$
1	0.104	0.031	+0.054	+1.74
2	0.139	0.036	+0.089	+2.47
3	0.000	0.031	−0.050	−1.61
4	0.064	0.032	+0.014	+0.44
5	0.042	0.031	−0.008	−0.26
6	0.056	0.030	+0.006	+0.20
7	0.000	0.031	−0.050	−1.61
8	0.024	0.034	−0.026	−0.76
9	0.156	0.039	+0.106	+2.72
10	0.050	0.034	0.000	0.00
11	0.043	0.032	−0.007	−0.22
12	0.085	0.032	+0.035	+1.09
13	0.022	0.032	−0.028	−0.88
14	0.000	0.032	−0.050	−1.61
15	0.063	0.031	+0.013	+0.42
16	0.000	0.035	−0.050	−1.61

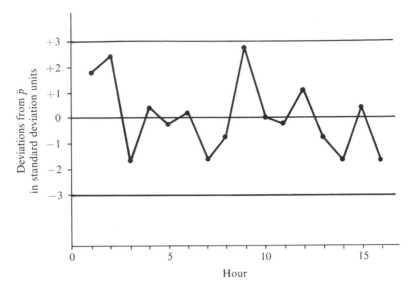

Figure 8.10. A stabilized p chart.

used as the ordinate. In the second case, the use of constant control limits may be deemed more advantageous. Both charts, however, require more computation than is necessary with the p chart of constant sample size.

The c chart with constant sample size. Some random variable processes may provide numerical data that are recorded as a number rather than a proportion. For example, the number of arrivals per hour demanding service at a toll booth is of interest when deciding upon the level of service capability to provide. If the number of arrivals per hour deviates from the stable pattern of variation, it may be necessary to compensate by either opening or closing certain toll booths. Since the arrival process described is not under the control of the decision maker, this is his only possible course of action if he is to maintain a minimum cost service policy.

The Poisson distribution is usually used to describe the number of arrivals per time period. Here, the opportunity for the occurrence of an event, n, is large but the probability of each occurrence, p, is quite small. The mean and the variance of the Poisson distribution are equal and were given in Equation (3.7) as $\mu = \sigma^2 = np$. These parameters can be estimated from the statistics with $\bar{c}$ and s_c^2 defined as these estimates. In many applications, values for n and p cannot be determined but their product np can be established. Then the mean and variance can be estimated as

$$\bar{c} = s_c^2 = \frac{\sum (np)}{m} \tag{8.14}$$

Table 8.7. NUMBER OF ARRIVALS PER HOUR DEMANDING SERVICE AT A TOLL BOOTH

Hour Number	np Number of Arrivals	Hour Number	np Number of Arrivals
1	6	11	6
2	4	12	4
3	3	13	2
4	5	14	2
5	4	15	4
6	6	16	8
7	5	17	2
8	4	18	3
9	2	19	5
10	5	20	4
		Total $= 84$	

Consider the application of a c chart to the arrival process previously described. Data for the past 20 hours have been collected and are presented in Table 8.7. The mean of the arrival population may be estimated from $\bar{c}$ with Equation (8.14) as

$$\bar{c} = \frac{84}{20} = 4.20.$$

And, the standard deviation may be estimated as

$$s_c = \sqrt{\bar{c}}$$
$$= \sqrt{4.20} = 2.05.$$

With these estimates, the control chart may now be constructed. Control limits may be established as $\bar{c} \pm 3s_c$. The probability of making a Type I error can be determined either from the Thorndike chart of Figure 3.7 or the cumulative values of Appendix A, Table A.1. For the example under consideration

$$\text{UCL}_c = \bar{c} + 3s_c$$
$$= 4.2 + 3(2.05) = 10.35 \qquad (8.15)$$

$$\text{LCL}_c = \bar{c} - 3s_c$$
$$= 4.2 - 3(2.05) < 0. \qquad (8.16)$$

There is no lower control limit. The probability of making a Type I error is the probability of eleven or more arrivals in a given hour from a population with $\bar{c} = 4.2$. This is $1 - P(10 \text{ or less})$ or $1 - 0.994 = 0.006$. Alternatively the control limit could have been defined as a probability limit. If it were thought desirable to define $\alpha \leq 0.01$, the control limit would have been specified as 9.5. Under this control policy the probability of detecting 10 or more arrivals would satisfy $\alpha \leq 0.01$.

In the c chart of Figure 8.11 all values fell within the control limits and the chart can be installed as originally formulated. Had a value exceeded a limit, this value would have to be discarded and revisions made. This will

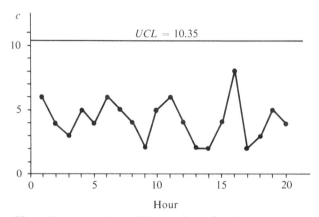

Figure 8.11. A c chart of the number of arrivals per hour demanding service at a toll booth.

be the case when, in using the chart, a value appears outside of the limit. Action would be initiated to alter the service capability to meet the new demand pattern. At the same time, a new chart based upon the recent data will be constructed and implemented. In this way the decision maker is informed of conditions in the system that require modification of operating policy.

The c chart with variable sample size. Under some conditions, the sample size, n, may vary from one unit to another. In quality control, a unit may consist of a day's production and this may vary from one day to the next. A c chart may be constructed to monitor the number of lost-time accidents per month in a plant where the work force fluctuates in size from one month to the next. In these and other similar cases, either varying control limits must be used or the data be converted into variations in standard deviation units and plotted on a stabilized c chart. In either case, the approach is similar to that used for the p chart with variable sample size.

Consider the following situation: It is desired to establish a control chart on the number of defects produced in a certain assembly line operation. The amount of time an inspector can spend checking the output varies from

Table 8.8. THE NUMBER OF OBSERVED DEFECTS FROM AN ASSEMBLY LINE OPERATION

Shift (8 hr)	Hours of Inspection	Proportion of Shift, y	Defects Found, x	$\dfrac{c}{\dfrac{x}{y}}$	$3s_c = 3\sqrt{\dfrac{(\bar{c})}{y}}$	$UCL = \bar{c} + 3s_c$	$LCL = \bar{c} - 3s_c$
1	6.0	0.750	5	6.66	7.49	12.15	0
2	4.0	0.500	4	8.00	9.16	13.82	0
3	3.0	0.375	2	5.33	10.59	15.25	0
4	5.5	0.670	1	1.49	7.91	12.57	0
5	4.0	0.500	3	6.00	9.16	13.82	0
6	6.2	0.775	2	2.58	7.36	12.02	0
7	5.5	0.670	1	1.49	7.91	12.57	0
8	4.8	0.600	1	1.61	8.35	13.01	0
9	2.5	0.312	1	3.21	11.61	16.27	0
10	5.0	0.625	2	3.20	8.18	12.82	0
11	6.4	0.800	3	3.75	7.25	11.91	0
12	4.0	0.500	5	10.00	9.16	13.82	0
13	2.0	0.250	1	4.00	12.95	17.61	0
14	2.1	0.262	3	11.45	12.71	17.37	0
15	4.4	0.550	3	5.45	8.74	13.40	0
16	8.4	1.051	7	6.65	6.31	10.97	0
17	3.2	0.400	1	2.50	10.25	14.91	0

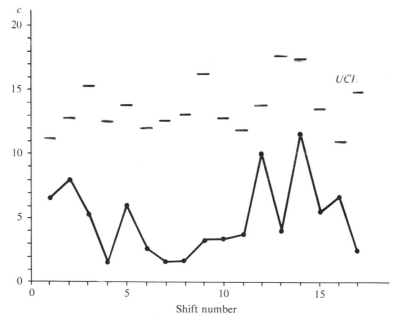

Figure 8.12. A c chart of defects per unit with varying control limits.

day to day because of other assigned duties. If the output of the assembly line is constant, the fraction of the day spent in inspection is proportional to the amount of product inspected. Table 8.8 gives data pertaining to the inspection operation. The amount of inspection time spent during the 17 shifts was equivalent to 77/8 or 9.63 shifts. Therefore, the average number of defects found per shift was 45/9.63 = 4.66. This is used as an estimate of the population parameter $\bar{c}$ in computing control limits. The computations establishing the varying limits are given in the last four columns of Table 8.8. These are used to construct the control chart of Figure 8.12. All data points fall within the limits. Therefore, the chart may be used as a means of testing the variability in defects for future output of the assembly line operation.

QUESTIONS

1. What is the difference between a stable and an unstable pattern of variation?

2. What is the relationship between a stable pattern of variation, control limits, and a Type I error?

3. What is the relationship between an unstable pattern of variation, control limits, and a Type II error?

4. Cite an example of some consumer goods produced and sold at a quality level of less than perfection.

5. What are the two cost components of total quality cost? Give examples of the cost in each component.

6. What are the two general classes of applications of the control chart? Give an example of each.

7. What is meant by *measurement by variables*?

8. Why is it advantageous to work with the mean of samples rather than individual sample values in constructing and using a control chart?

9. What is the primary function of the $\bar{X}$ chart in relation to detecting unstable patterns of variations; the R chart?

10. Under what conditions is it necessary to construct "revised" control limits?

11. What are process capability limits and how are they important in product design?

12. If the process capability limits exceed the specification limits, what alternatives might be considered?

13. What is meant by the *power* of a control chart? What factors influence this value?

14. Under what conditions might a process or parameter vary through a continuum and still be controlled by a control chart for attributes?

15. What are the two types of control charts for attributes? Give an example of a process that might be controlled by each.

PROBLEMS

1. Samples of $n = 5$ were taken from a process for a period of time. The process average was estimated to be $\bar{\bar{X}} = 0.0200$ in. and the process range was estimated as $\bar{R} = 0.0020$ in. Specify the control limits for an $\bar{X}$ chart; an R chart.

2. Control charts by variables are to be established on the tensile strength in pounds of a yarn. Samples of five have been taken each hour for the past 20 hours. These were recorded as follows:

Hour																				
1	2	3	4	5	6	7	8	9	10	11	12	13	14	15	16	17	18	19	20
50	44	44	48	45	47	42	52	44	43	47	49	47	43	44	45	45	50	46	45
50	46	44	52	46	44	46	46	46	44	45	42	51	46	43	47	45	49	47	44
48	50	44	48	46	43	46	45	46	49	44	41	50	46	40	51	47	45	48	49
42	47	47	48	48	40	48	42	46	47	42	46	48	48	40	48	47	47	46	43
43	45	48	46	50	45	46	51	43	45	50	46	42	46	46	46	46	44	45	46

(a) Construct an $\bar{X}$ chart based on these data.
(b) Construct an R chart based on these data.

3. A lower specification limit of 40 lb is required for the condition of Problem 2. Sketch the relationship between the specification limit and the control limits. What proportion, if any, of the yarn will be defective?

4. Control limits are established on a process with a mean of 20,000 psi and a standard deviation of 1,000 psi. Samples of 4 units are taken and tested every 30 minutes. A lower or minimum specification of 15,000 psi has been established. Should the process mean shift to 18,000 psi, what proportion of produced units will be defective?

5. In Problem 4, should the process mean shift to 18,000 psi and the dispersion double, what proportion of produced units will be defective?

6. In Problem 4, after how many samples would it be 99 per cent certain that a shift on the $\bar{X}$ chart would be detected?

7. The total number of students enrolled in a course and the number that failed that course are given as follows for an 11-year period.

Semester	Number Enrolled	Failures	Semester	Number Enrolled	Failures
1	70	4	12	65	4
2	52	3	13	70	7
3	60	4	14	49	2
4	43	2	15	55	1
5	53	1	16	58	1
6	57	1	17	63	2
7	61	3	18	63	3
8	59	4	19	65	3
9	48	3	20	55	4
10	59	2	21	58	1
11	63	3	22	60	2

Assume the educational process is in control with regard to the proportion of students failing the course. Construct a p chart and record the data of the last five semesters.

8. Develop a stabilized p chart for the situation of Problem 7 and plot the data for the last five semesters.

9. Recently, geese have come to be used to weed cotton fields in southern Texas, sometimes replacing migratory farm workers or chemical weed killers. *Cotton-goosing*, the term used to describe this process, can be accomplished with approximately two geese per acre. One farmer is reported to have tested the weeding habits of a sample of 100 geese to determine the proportion of time the geese were idle or not weeding. His work-sampling data represent the number idle of the 100 geese observed each day for a period of one month. Were the work

June Date	Number Idle	Date	Number Idle	Date	Number Idle
1	12	11	6	21	6
2	10	12	4	22	8
3	5	13	11	23	7
4	8	14	7	24	7
5	14	15	9	25	13
6	5	16	8	26	7
7	6	17	11	27	6
8	5	18	5	28	7
9	4	19	8	29	11
10	4	20	4	30	10

habits of the cotton-goosing geese in control for this month?

10. A p chart has indicated that the process average is 0.05. Assume this now changes to 0.10, what is the probability of detecting this shift if an inspection unit consists of 100 units? Use the Poisson approximation.

11. The number of detected defects per day, per sample size of 300 cotton trousers, are given below for a 4-week production period.

Day	Number of Defects	Day	Number of Defects
1	7	11	6
2	8	12	8
3	5	13	5
4	9	14	2
5	3	15	4
6	8	16	2
7	5	17	6
8	5	18	5
9	15	19	3
10	8	20	7

Construct a c chart for these data. Does it appear as though there existed an assignable cause of variation during any of this time?

nine

METHODS OF
ACCEPTANCE SAMPLING

*The control models of the previous chapter dealt with the
statistical stability of a pattern of variation. These statistical
control models were applied as a direct monitor on the process
through verifying the output of the process. The acceptance sampling methods
derived in this chapter are concerned with the output of a process
beyond the point of immediate process control. Their objective is
to determine whether a discrete quantity of the output of a process is
acceptable against some criterion of quality. Consequently, a sample from
the lot must be assessed and the lot must be either accepted or rejected
in accordance with the findings of the sample.*

*Methods of acceptance sampling lend themselves to inspection
requirements, for acceptance purposes, in product quality control.
Inspection can be applied to incoming materials, to materials and
components in the manufacturing process, or to the finished product.
Inspection may also be applied to verifying accounting records and
to determining the accuracy of clerical work. In each case, the quality
of the submitted lot is judged on the basis of a sample
taken from the lot.*

9.1. THE CONCEPT OF ACCEPTANCE SAMPLING

The quality of a group of items may be verified in one of three ways. Every item in the lot may be inspected, a sample of items may be taken from the lot and inspected, or no inspection may be used. In the third case it is assumed that the quality of the lot certainly exceeds some minimum acceptable standard. In the former cases, the lot may be accepted or rejected, depending upon the outcome of the inspection process.

The level of verification chosen should consider the cost of inspection measured against the cost of accepting and perhaps using defective items. In general, acceptance sampling will be more economical than 100 per cent inspection when the occurrence of a defective in an accepted lot is not prohibitively expensive or when an inspection process requires the destruction of the item. Acceptance sampling will be more economical than no inspection when some expense is incurred in accepting defectives and the number of defectives differ from one lot to the next. The concept of acceptance sampling is presented in this section.

Acceptance sampling plans. The most elementary acceptance sampling plan calls for the random selection of a sample of size n, from a lot containing N items. The entire lot is then accepted if the number of defectives found in the sample is equal to or less than c, the acceptance number. For example, a sampling inspection plan might be defined as $N = 1,000$, $n = 50$, and $c = 1$. This designation means that a sample of 50 items is to be taken from the lot of 1,000. If zero or one defective is found in the sample, the whole lot is accepted. If more than one defective is found, the lot is rejected. A rejected lot can either be returned to the producer or it can be retained and subjected to a 100 per cent screening process. The former action is called a *nonrectifying inspection program*; the latter, a *rectifying* inspection program.

The type of inspection sampling described by N, n, and c, uses inspection by attributes and a single sample of size n. Other attribute inspection plans might use two samples before requiring the acceptance or rejection of a lot. A third procedure might use multiple samples or a sequential sampling process in evaluating a lot. Each of these methods—single, double, and multiple sampling—rests upon a system of inspection by attributes of items logically grouped into lots. When it is not feasible to divide a continuous production process into discrete lots, a special class of attribute sampling methods must be used. These continuous sampling models verify the quality of the process output through inspection of a proportion of the items produced.

Inspection may also be by variables. Here a measurement is obtained and recorded as a continuous dimension, subject only to the limitations of the measuring instrument or the convenience of measurement. rather than as a simple classification of acceptable versus defective units. Acceptance sampling by variables represents a whole class of acceptance sampling models, each member of which still retains the element of a sample selected from a discrete lot, but with quality verified through the measuring of a continuous dimension.

The operating characteristics curve. Acceptance sampling plans attempt to discriminate between lots of acceptable and lots of unacceptable items.

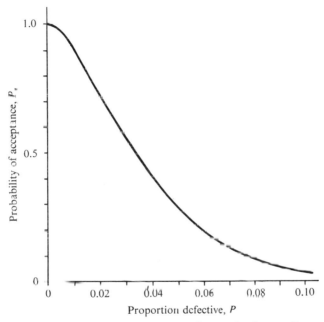

Figure 9.1. An operating characteristic curve for the sampling plan $n = 50$, $c = 1$.

The relative ability of a sampling plan to meet this objective can be demonstrated with an operating characteristic curve. An OC curve defines the probability of a lot being accepted (or finding c fewer defectives in a sample) for different levels of proportion defective.

An operating characteristic curve for the sampling plan $N = 1,000$, $n = 50$, $c = 1$ is illustrated in Figure 9.1. The abscissa refers to the proportion defective in the lot. The ordinate refers to the probability of accepting a lot at a specified level of proportion defective. Note that if N contains no defectives, if $p = 0$, then the lot is certain to be accepted. If the lot contains 10 defectives, and if $p = 0.01$, then the probability of accepting the lot is

0.91. The probability distribution appropriate to these calculations is the hypergeometric. For ease of calculation, however, the Poisson distribution is used as an approximation, as was illustrated in Figure 3.13. Thus, the Thorndike chart of Figure 3.7 may be used to develop an OC curve quickly. As an example, at $p = 0.03$ in Figure 9.1, $np = (50)(0.03) = 1.50$ and the

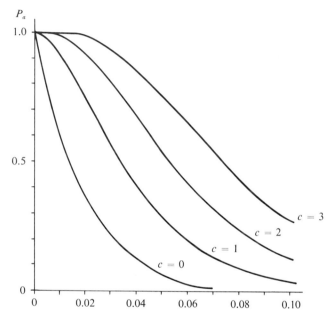

Figure 9.2. *OC* curves for different acceptance numbers with a constant sample size, $n = 50$.

probability of the occurrence of one or fewer defects would be 0.56. Note that because the Poisson distribution is used as an approximation, the OC curve is independent of the lot size.

A good sampling plan will have a high probability of accepting those lots which contain few defectives and a low probability of accepting lots having an excessive number of defectives. The OC curve illustrates how well a given sampling plan discriminates between good and bad lots. *Good* and *bad* are relative terms and a lot containing 1 per cent defective might be considered quite good in one instance and very poor in another. Consider Figure 9.2 which illustrates a number of OC curves with only the acceptance number, *c*, differing in each case. The relative shapes of these curves are quite similar in that they are nearly parallel through their middle sections. In effect, increasing the acceptance number slides the OC curve to the right.

This is indicative of a definition of good lots which contain more defectives. As an example, the sampling plan $c = 3$, $n = 50$ might be used to accept lots where material up to 5 per cent defective is considered to represent a good lot. If no more than 2 per cent defective is considered acceptable, then the sampling plan $c = 1$, $n = 50$ might be employed. This is true only in

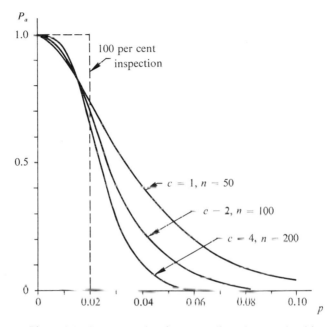

Figure 9.3. *OC* curves for three sampling plans, each with the same ratio of acceptance number to sample size.

approximate terms because the shape of the OC curve is not solely dependent upon the sample size. Actually, both sample size and acceptance number are parameters upon which the form of the OC curve depends.

Once an acceptable proportion defective is defined, the relative ability of a sampling model to discriminate between lots containing more or fewer defectives will, in large measure, be dependent upon the sample size. As an example, consider the OC curves of Figure 9.3, each of which contains the same ratio of acceptance number to sample size. Note that as the sample size increases, the OC curve becomes steeper. In general, this is desirable in a sampling plan, although the expense involved in this greater discriminating ability is the cost of a larger sample size. The ideal discrimination of a vertical line is indicated in Figure 9.3 with a dashed line. This, however, can be achieved only with 100 per cent inspection.

Consumer and producer risks. Two parties are involved in an inspection sampling procedure, the party submitting the lot and the party to whom the lot is consigned if accepted. These two parties are referred to as the *producer* and the *consumer*, respectively. The parties may represent a seller and a buyer of a product, or they may represent two departments within the same organization. As an example, castings from a foundry department may be

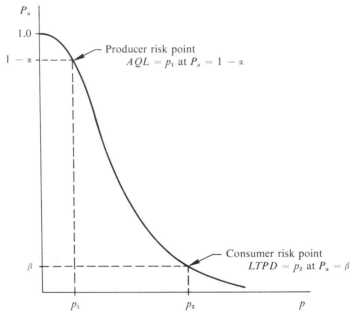

Figure 9.4. An *OC* curve passing through a Consumer Risk Point and a Producer Risk Point and possessing a unique value of n and c.

delivered for acceptance to the machining department. In another situation, the producer may be an accounting department and the consumer may be represented by an auditor who either accepts or rejects a number of accounting records against some criterion of accounting quality. In each case, the producer usually desires that material relatively free from defectives have a high probability of being accepted. The consumer desires that it will be unlikely for the lot to be accepted if it contains a high proportion of defectives.

The concept of producer and consumer risks can be defined in terms of two points on an operating characteristic curve. The producer risk point occurs at a fraction defective, p_1; the consumer risk point occurs at, p_2. Four values are used to specify these two points which, in turn, may be used to construct the OC curve for a specific acceptance sampling plan.

(1) The Acceptable Quality Level, AQL: This indicates a good level of quality and low proportion of fraction defective, referred to as p_1, for which it is desired to have a high probability of acceptance.

(2) The Producer's Risk, α: The probability that lots of the quality level given as the AQL will not be accepted where $\alpha = 1 - P_a$. In effect this is the probability of making a Type I error; that is, of rejecting a lot when it should be accepted.

(3) The Lot Tolerance Per Cent Defective, LTPD: This level of quality, given as p_2, is deemed to be quite poor and it is desired to reject lots of this quality or at least have a low probability of acceptance.

(4) The Consumer's Risk, β: The probability, P_a, that lots of a quality level at the LTPD will be accepted. A value of $P_a = 0.10$ at p_2 is often used in acceptance sampling. This probability represents the likelihood of making a Type II or β error; that is, of accepting a lot when it should be rejected.

Each of these values is illustrated on the OC curve of Figure 9.4. The development of a sampling plan from the producer risk point and the consumer risk point is presented in the next section.

9.2. ACCEPTANCE SAMPLING BY ATTRIBUTES

Most acceptance sampling plans involve inspection by attributes. Often a unit can be assessed only in the two-valued classification of acceptable or defective. In other situations, it may be advantageous to take a continuous dimension and reduce it to a dichotomous assessment of within specifications and acceptable, or defective and outside specification limits. In either case, the function of the acceptance sampling model is to accept those lots containing few defectives and reject those lots containing many defectives. This objective is often defined in terms of a producer and a consumer risk.

Developing a single sampling plan. When two required points, such as a consumer and a producer risk point, are given as the basis for a sampling plan, the effect is to require the solution to two equations for two unknowns. An iterative, trial-and-error solution, using the Poisson distribution as an approximation, can be easily effected with the Thorndike chart of Figure 3.7, or the cumulative Poisson tables in Appendix A, Table A.1.

As an example, assume that a single sampling plan is desired which will yield an OC curve passing through a producer risk of $\alpha = 0.05$ at an AQL $= 0.01$, and a consumer risk of $\beta = 0.10$ at an LTPD of 0.04. The solution is facilitated if a table is constructed as illustrated in Table 9.1. This table permits the solution for n and c in the following equations:

$$(1 - 0.05) = \sum_{0}^{c} \frac{e^{-0.01n}(0.01n)^c}{c!}$$

$$0.10 = \sum_{0}^{c} \frac{e^{-0.04n}(0.04n)^c}{c!}.$$

These equations represent the producer and consumer risk points respectively.

Table 9.1. A TABLE USED TO DETERMINE A SINGLE SAMPLING PLAN APPROXIMATING $\alpha = 0.05$ AT AN AQL $= 0.01$ AND $\beta = 0.10$ AT LTPD $= 0.04$

c	p_1n $(P_a = 0.95)$	p_2n $(P_a = 0.10)$	p_2/p_1	
0	0.05	2.31	46.2	
1	0.35	3.89	11.1	
2	0.82	5.33	6.50	
3	1.36	6.68	4.91	
4	1.97	8.00	4.06	LTPD
5	2.61	9.30	3.56	AQL

In Table 9.1, if an acceptance number of $c = 0$ is required, and if $P_a = 0.95$, then p_1n must be 0.05. This value was obtained by interpolation in the cumulative Poisson tables. Less precise values may be obtained more quickly from the Thorndike chart, although this specific value lies outside the limits of the chart. The second value, for $c = 1$ at $P_a = 0.95$, yields $p_1n = 0.35$. If $c = 2$ and $P_a = 0.95$, then $p_1n = 0.82$, and so forth. This process is repeated for $P_a = 0.10$ to find the values given in the third column. The fourth column in Table 9.1 is completed by recording the ratio of p_2/p_1. In this example, the ratio of fraction defective of consumer to producer risk points was given as $0.04/0.01 = 4.0$. Therefore, this process is continued until the desired ratio of $p_2/p_1 = 4.0$ is bracketed.

The desired sampling plan calls for an acceptance number somewhere between $c = 4$ and $c = 5$. Because both the acceptance number and the sample size must be integers, it is not possible to achieve the precise requirement that was given. One of the four plans listed in Table 9.2 must be selected with the associated degree of protection. The data from Table 9.2 are developed directly from Table 9.1 as follows: With $c = 4$ and $P_a = 0.95$, p_1n was taken to be 1.97, and if $p = .01$ at the producer risk point, then $n = 197$. This sampling plan of $c = 4$, $n = 197$ will yield an $\alpha = 0.05$ as required but will yield a $\beta = 0.107$ which is slightly higher than desired. If $c = 4$ and it

Table 9.2. FOUR SAMPLING PLANS WHICH BRACKET $\alpha = 0.05$ AT AN AQL $= 0.01$ AND $\beta = 0.10$ AT LTPD $= 0.04$

Plan	α at p_1	β at p_2
$c = 4, n = 197$	0.050	0.107
$c = 4, n = 200$	0.053	0.100
$c = 5, n = 261$	0.050	0.052
$c = 5, n = 233$	0.032	0.100

is desired that the OC curve go through the consumer risk point, then $n = p_2 n/p_2 = 8.00/0.04 = 200$. With $c = 4$ and $n = 200$, β is established at 0.10 and α will be $1 - P_a$ or $1 - 0.947 = 0.053$. Similarly α and β can be found for $c = 5$.

The four plans of Table 9.2 were obtained by alternating in holding α as required and solving for β and then maintaining β while solving for α. These four plans are sketched in Figure 9.5 with the risk point bracketing effect magnified so that it will be more evident. Once these four plans have been defined, it is likely that a plan will be selected and used which results in a

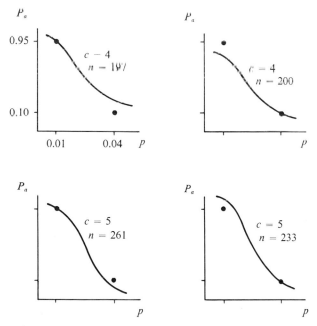

Figure 9.5. The four sampling plans of Table 9.2 (not to scale).

compromise in regard to α and β. In this example $c = 4$ yields two plans fairly close to the consumer and producer risk points. One or the other might be selected. The plan $c = 4$, $n = 200$, would have the advantage of a convenient sample size which would facilitate subsequent computations. In other cases, the average sample size for one or the other acceptance number could be used.

Average outgoing quality. When rejected lots are returned to the supplier, the acceptance sampling plan does not significantly improve the quality level of lots submitted to the plan. A few defectives may be detected and discarded from samples of accepted lots, but no profound improvements can be realized here without resulting in the rejection of the lot. The sampling plan can and should function as a screening process and permit the acceptance of good lots and the rejection and return of poor quality lots. This will result in some improvement if there is a large variation in the level of quality, from one lot to another.

When a rectifying inspection program is employed and rejected lots are subjected to a 100 per cent inspection, significant and predictable quality improvements can be realized. Under a rectifying inspection program, an average outgoing level, AOQ, and an average inspection load, I, can be predicted for varying levels of incoming fraction defective. In addition, an average outgoing quality limit, AOQL, the worst possible average outgoing quality level, can be forecast and related to a specific incoming level of fraction defective. This latter value gives assurance regarding the poorest average quality level that might leave the inspection station.

If it is assumed that all lots arriving at an inspection station contain the same proportion of defectives, p, and if rejected lots are subjected to 100 per cent inspection, the

$$\text{AOQ} = \frac{P_a(p)(N - n)}{N - pn - (1 - P_a)p(N - n)} . \tag{9.1}$$

The numerator in Equation (9.1) represents the average number of defectives in each lot beyond the point of inspection. Defectives will be found only in the proportion of lots which have been accepted, P_a, and will constitute $p(N - n)$ in number. The denominator represents the average lot size, where N is the original lot size, pn is the reduction in size due to defectives found and discarded in the sample, and $(1 - P_a)p(N - n)$ is the reduction in lot size due to defectives found and discarded during the 100 per cent screening process. By similar reasoning, the average inspection can be shown to be

$$I = n + (1 - P_a)(N - n). \tag{9.2}$$

As an example, if a lot size of $N = 10,000$ is assumed and each lot contains 200 defectives, then for the sampling plan previously developed of $n = 200$

and $c = 5$, P_a can be found to be 0.785, and from Equation (9.1),

$$AOQ = \frac{(0.785)(0.02)(9,800)}{10,000 - (0.02)(200) - (0.215)(0.02)(9,800)}$$

$$= \frac{153.86}{10,000 - 4 - 42.14} = 0.01546.$$

The average inspection can be found from Equation (9.2) to be

$$I = 200 + (0.215)(9,800) = 2,307.00.$$

It should be recognized that these values of AOQ and of I are expected or average values that will be approached in the long run over many lots. In regard to the proportion defective, one specific lot will either contain somewhere between 195 to 200 defectives if the lot is accepted and it is assumed to contain no defectives if the lot is rejected. By the same token, either 200 items will be inspected if the lot is accepted or the total of 10,000 units will be verified if it is rejected. In the long run, however, the foregoing results for AOQ and I will represent the average for all lots submitted at a value of $p = 0.02$.

Under some conditions, it might be desired to retain a constant lot size whether a lot is accepted or rejected and regardless of the number of defectives discarded during the sampling and/or screening process. A constant lot size can be maintained if defectives are replaced by units which are assumed to be selected, inspected, and inserted in the place of the defectives if they are acceptable. Under these conditions of replacement, the

$$AOQ = \frac{P_a(p)(N - n)}{N}. \tag{9.3}$$

The average inspection increases slightly to

$$I = \frac{n + (1 - P_a)(N - n)}{1 - p}. \tag{9.4}$$

The average outgoing quality and the average inspection will vary as a function of the level of incoming proportion defective. With the sampling plan $n = 200$, $c = 5$, under the condition of nonreplacement of defectives, the AOQ and I are given in Table 9.3 and sketched in Figure 9.6 and Figure 9.7. Note that the average outgoing quality increases as the proportion defective in incoming lots increases until it reaches a maximum value. This value is referred to as the *average outgoing quality limit*, AOQL. From this point on, a pronounced number of lots are being rejected and screened under 100 per cent inspection. This latter effect is resulting in a continuing reduction in the average outgoing quality, as can be seen in Figure 9.7. The concept of an average outgoing quality limit is often employed in specifying a sampling plan.

Table 9.3. AVERAGE OUTGOING QUALITY AND AVERAGE INSPECTION FOR THE SINGLE SAMPLING PLAN OF $N = 10,000$, $n = 200$, $c = 5$ UNDER RECTIFYING INSPECTION WITHOUT REPLACEMENT

Proportion Defective in Submitted Lots p	Probability of Acceptance P_a	Average Outgoing Quality AOQ	Average Inspection I
0	1.000	0	200.0
0.005	0.999	0.00490	209.8
0.010	0.983	0.00964	366.6
0.015	0.916	0.01349	1,023.2
0.020	0.785	0.01546	2,307.0
0.025	0.616	0.01524	3,924.0
0.030	0.446	0.01334	5,629.2
0.035	0.301	0.01059	7,050.2
0.040	0.191	0.00774	8,128.2
0.045	0.116	0.00533	8,863.2
0.050	0.067	0.00344	9,343.4

Sampling plans have been devised for varying values of AOQL and presented in tabular form. With this limit as the worst average quality level that can be expected to occur, a plan with a known AOQL can be selected along with other desired criteria.

The concept of a level of average outgoing quality and a level of average inspection rests upon the assumption of the detection and removal of all defectives from screened lots. Further, the values obtained for AOQ and I are expected values that will occur in the long run. Over a short time period

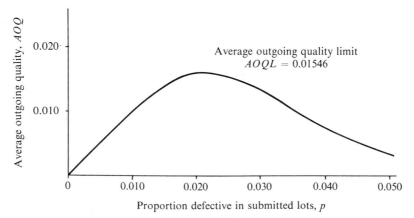

Figure 9.6. Average outgoing quality for the data of Table 9.3.

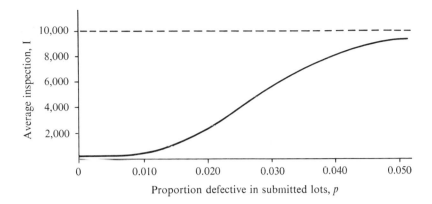

Figure 9.7. Average inspection for the data of Table 9.3.

some variation from these values can be expected. The concept of an average outgoing quality level and average inspection has found wide application in the field of product acceptance. In recent years it has also been found applicable in auditing accounting records and verifying clerical activities.

Double sampling plans. A single sampling plan requires a decision to accept or reject a lot on the basis of the evidence offered from a single sample. A double sampling plan permits the acceptance or rejection of a lot after a single sample, but also permits the alternative of taking a second sample before making the decision. A double sampling plan is defined with a lot size and two sample sizes and two acceptance numbers, designated respectively as N, n_1, n_2, c_1, and c_2, with c_2 always larger than c_1.

Under a double sampling program, a sample n_1 is taken from the lot N. If c_1 or fewer defectives are detected, the lot is accepted. If more than c_2 defectives are found, the lot is rejected. If c_2 or less, but more than c_1 defectives are found, then a second sample n_2 is taken. The lot is finally accepted if c_2 or fewer defectives are found in the combined sample of $n_1 + n_2$. The lot is rejected if more than c_2 defectives are found in $n_1 + n_2$.

The operation of a double sampling plan and the OC curve which defines this plan can be illustrated with an example. Assume that $N = 10,000$, $n_1 = 50$, $n_2 = 80$, $c_1 = 0$, and $c_2 = 3$. This plan states that if no defectives, $c_1 = 0$, are found in the first sample of $n_1 = 50$, the lot is immediately accepted. If more than $c_2 = 3$ defectives are found, the lot is immediately rejected. If 1, 2, or 3 defectives are found, then a second sample, $n_2 = 80$, is taken. If $c_2 = 3$ or fewer total defectives are found in the combined sample of $n_1 + n_2 = 130$, the lot is accepted. If more than $c_2 = 3$ are found, it is rejected.

The probabilities associated with each of these alternatives can be calculated for any value of proportion defective. In the preceding example, assume

Table 9.4. A COMPUTATIONAL SCHEME FOR FINDING P_{a2} AT $p = 0.02$ IF $N = 10,000$, $n_1 = 50$, $n_2 = 80$, $c_1 = 0$, AND $c_2 = 3$

Defects in n_1	Probability	Defects in n_2 to Accept	Probability
1	0.368	2 or less	0.783
2	0.184	1 or less	0.525
3	0.061	0	0.202

that the lot of 10,000 units contains 200 defectives, $p = 0.02$. The probability of accepting this lot on the first sample, P_{a1}, is the probability of finding no defectives in a sample of 50 taken from a lot with $p = 0.02$. Using the Poisson approximation, for $c = 0$ at $np = 1.00$, gives $P_{a1} = 0.368$. The probability of rejecting on the first sample is the probability of finding more than three defectives in the sample. This is $1 - P(3 \text{ or fewer})$ and $P_{r1} = 0.019$.

The probability of accepting the lot after inspecting the second sample requires the use of conditional probabilities as demonstrated in Table 9.4. This probability is

$$P_{a2} = (0.368)(0.783) + (0.184)(0.525) + (0.061)(0.202) = 0.397.$$

The probability of rejection on the second sample must therefore be

$$P_{r2} = 1 - P_{a1} - P_{r1} - P_{a2}$$
$$= 1 - 0.368 - 0.019 - 0.397 = 0.216.$$

The total probability of acceptance is

$$P_{a1} + P_{a2} = 0.368 + 0.397 = 0.765.$$

And the total probability of rejection is

$$P_{r1} + P_{r2} = 0.019 + 0.216 = 0.235.$$

Also, the probability of making a decision to accept or reject the lot after the first sample is

$$P_{a1} + P_{r1} = 0.368 + 0.019 = 0.387.$$

And, the probability of requiring a second sample is

$$P_{a2} + P_{r2} = 0.397 + 0.216 = 0.613.$$

Similar probabilities can be calculated for varying levels of fraction defective. These may be used to develop the OC curves illustrated in Figure 9.8.

The average number of units inspected as a sample of each lot, ASN, will vary with the proportion defective, and thus, with the probability of making

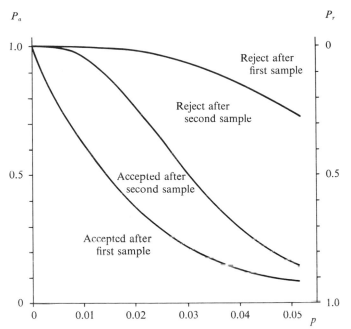

Figure 9.8. *OC* curves for the double sampling plan $n_1 = 50$, $n_2 = 80$, $c_1 = 0$, $c_2 = 3$.

a decision on the first sample. This probability is

$$\text{ASN} = n_1 + n_2(1 - P_{a1} - P_{r1}). \tag{9.5}$$

Under a rectifying inspection program, the average inspection and average outgoing quality can be developed both for the case of nonreplacement and for the case of replacement of defectives. The average number of items inspected with the nonreplacement of defectives will be

$$I = n_1 + n_2(1 - P_{a1}) + (N - n_1 - n_2)(1 - P_{a1} - P_{a2}). \tag{9.6}$$

As with single sampling, the AOQ is the ratio of the number of accepted defectives to the lot size. Defectives will be retained when they are not detected after a lot is accepted on the first or the second sample. If defectives which are found are not replaced to maintain a constant lot size, this lot size will be reduced by the elimination of defectives during the sampling and screening process. Thus, this proportion can be expressed as

$$\text{AOQ} = \frac{P_{a1}p(N - n_1) + P_{a2}p(N - n_1 - n_2)}{N - pI}. \tag{9.7}$$

The equations for average inspection and average outgoing quality can be developed in a similar manner for the case of replacement of defectives.

Double sampling plans have the advantage of permitting the acceptance of good lots and the rejection of very poor lots with less inspection than a single sampling plan with a comparable OC curve. The double sampling plan also has the psychological advantage of giving a marginal lot a second chance, by permitting the taking of a second sample. The obvious disadvantage is the fluctuation in inspection workload that occurs as the quality level of incoming material varies.

Multiple and sequential sampling plans. A double sampling plan may defer a decision to accept or reject a lot until a second sample has been taken. A further extension of this is possible under multiple and sequential sampling. A multiple sampling plan is a simple extension of double sampling and may call for three or more samples before a decision is made. Sequential sampling is different only in that it does not call for specific sample sizes of n_1, n_2, n_3, etc., but calls for a continuous sequential sampling of units until the decision is made to accept or reject the lot. Sequential sampling is the limiting case of multiple sampling where $n_1 = n_2 = n_3 = \cdots = n_n = 1$.

The number if items inspected in sequential sampling is determined by the cumulative results of the inspection process. The sampling plan is defined by h_1, h_2, and s. This results in two parallel limit lines

$$c = h_2 + sn \tag{9.8}$$

$$c = -h_1 + sn. \tag{9.9}$$

These limit lines are illustrated in Figure 9.9. They divide the area into regions of rejection, continued sampling, and acceptance. As soon as one of these two limit lines is reached or crossed, the lot is accepted or rejected.

A sequential sampling plan can be developed that will meet specified producer and consumer risk points. With α, β, p_1, and p_2 as illustrated in Figure 9.4, it can be shown[1] that

$$h_1 = \frac{\log\left[(1 - \alpha)/\beta\right]}{\log\left\{[p_2(1 - p_1)]/[p_1(1 - p_2)]\right\}} \tag{9.10}$$

$$h_2 = \frac{\log\left[(1 - \beta)/\alpha\right]}{\log\left\{[p_2(1 - p_1)]/[p_1(1 - p_2)]\right\}} \tag{9.11}$$

$$s = \frac{\log\left[(1 - p_1)/(1 - p_2)\right]}{\log\left\{[p_2(1 - p_1)]/[p_1(1 - p_2)]\right\}} \tag{9.12}$$

For example, consider a sequential sampling plan defined as $h_1 = 1.00$,

---

[1] A. Wald, *Sequential Analysis* (New York: John Wiley & Sons, Inc., 1947).

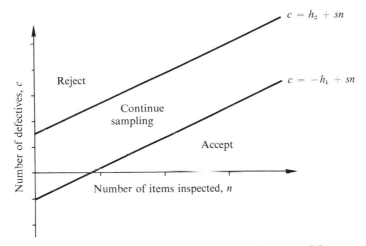

Figure 9.9. A graphical representation of a sequential sampling plan.

$h_2 = 1.50$, and $s = 0.12$. Assume a lot containing no defectives is submitted to this plan. How large a sample will be necessary to accept the lot? Acceptance will be possible when the line of $c = -1.00 + 0.120n$ is reached or crossed at $c = 0$ into the region of acceptance. With a sample of $n = 9$, this will be possible. As a second example, assume a lot is rejected after the twentieth unit was found to be a defective. How many total defectives would have to be found in the sample of 20? If rejection occurred on the twentieth unit then at $n = 20$, the total number of defectives found must have just reached or exceeded $1.500 + 0.120 (20)$ or, $c = 4$.

Multiple and sequential sampling plans may be expressed as OC curves, or may be developed from consumer and producer risk points on an OC curve. The advantages in their use are extensions of the advantages of double sampling plans over single sampling plans of comparable protection. Very good lots and rather poor lots can be accepted or rejected with even smaller sample sizes, but the inspection workload problem becomes still more pronounced and dependent upon the quality level of the incoming material.

Sampling plans for continuous production. Under some conditions, the formation of inspection lots may be artificial. Where production is continuous, or flows on a conveyor line, the use of inspection lots may be impractical and expensive. To meet the need for a sampling plan to verify the quality of a continuous production process, Dodge developed his CSP-1 plan[2] which can be described as follows: Inspect every unit until "i" consecutive units have

---

[2] H. F. Dodge, "A Sampling Plan for Continuous Production," *Annals of Mathematical Statistics*, **XIV**, 264–79.

been found without detecting a defective. At this point, continue inspection by only verifying the fraction "f" of the units in such a fashion as to insure an unbiased sample. As soon as a defective is found, return to 100 per cent inspection. A continuous sampling plan under this type of a rectifying inspection program is defined by i and f. The relationship between i and f and AOQL is illustrated in Figure 9.10. Note that with $i = 50$ and $f = 0.20$, an AOQL of approximately 0.015 can be expected.

The functioning of a sampling plan for continuous production will depend upon the level of fraction defective encountered in the production flow. The average number of pieces that will be inspected under the 100 per cent inspection portion of the cycle will be

$$u = \frac{1 - (1 - p)^i}{(p)(1 - p)^i}.$$ (9.13)

And the average number of units passed under the sampling portion will be

$$v = \frac{1}{fp}.$$ (9.14)

Thus, the average cycle will consist of $u + v$ total units. The average proportion of the produced units which must be inspected will then be

$$F = \frac{u + fv}{u + v}.$$ (9.15)

And the average proportion of produced units which will be accepted without inspection will be

$$P_a = 1 - F = \frac{v(1 - f)}{u + v}.$$ (9.16)

The last equation is the equivalent of the probability of acceptance under lot-by-lot inspection and can be used to construct an OC curve for a given sampling plan.

As an example, with $p = 0.05$, and a sampling plan of $f = 0.20$, $i = 50$, the average number of pieces inspected following the finding of a defective is

$$u = \frac{1 - (0.95)^{50}}{(0.05)(0.95)^{50}} = \frac{1 - 0.077}{(0.05)(0.077)} = 240.$$

The average number of pieces passed under the sampling procedure is

$$v = \frac{1}{(0.20)(0.05)} = 100.$$

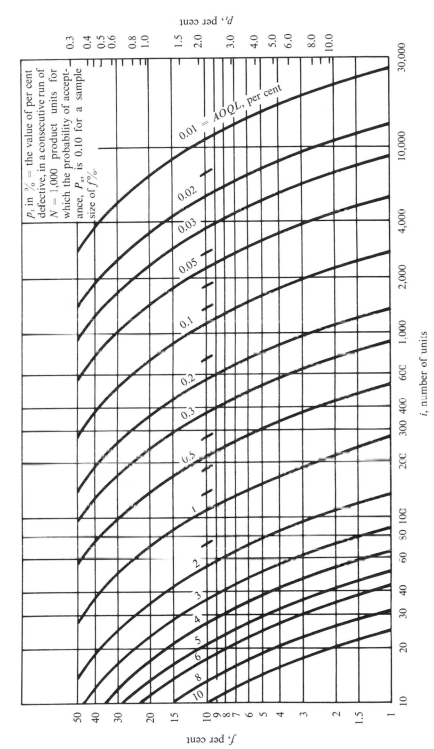

Figure 9.10. Curves for determining values of f and i for a given value of AOQL in Dodge's plan for continuous production. (*Reproduced by permission from "A Sampling Inspection Plan for Continuous Production" by H. F. Dodge.*)

Within the figure:

p_t in % = the value of per cent defective, in a consecutive run of $N = 1,000$ product units for which the probability of acceptance, P_a, is 0.10 for a sample size of f%.

$0.01 = AOQL$, per cent

i, number of units

f, per cent

p_t, per cent

241

The average proportion of total units inspected is

$$F = \frac{240 + 20}{340} = 0.765.$$

And, the probability of acceptance at $p = 0.05$ is

$$P_a = 1 - 0.765 = 0.235.$$

Because this is a rectifying inspection program, it is possible to develop the AOQ at varying levels of fraction defective. The AOQ expresses the proportion of defectives which are accepted. If it is assumed that detected defectives are replaced to maintain a constant rate of production flow, then the

$$AOQ = P_a(p) = \frac{v(1 - f)(p)}{u + v}. \tag{9.17}$$

This equation can be used to develop an average outgoing quality function similar to the one in Figure 9.6. It will then verify the AOQL expressed in Figure 9.10.

9.3. ACCEPTANCE SAMPLING BY VARIABLES

If a quality characteristic can be measured, it is possible to devise an acceptance sampling plan that will verify the quality of a lot under inspection by variables. In some cases, however, the quality characteristic is observable only as an attribute. In other cases, the cost of attribute assessment under a go, no-go, arrangement is much more economical than variable inspection. And finally, in still other situations, acceptance criteria may have to be applied to many quality characteristics. Although this is feasible with one plan under attribute verification, the use of variables inspection will require as many inspection plans as there are significant quality characteristics.

If these limitations are not serious, some advantages can be gained by employing an acceptance sampling plan using variables inspection. Superior protection in the form of a steeper OC curve can be achieved under variables inspection with the same sample size. As a corollary of this advantage, comparable protection can be obtained with a smaller sample size. This might be a very desirable advantage when a unit must be destroyed to be tested. The second major advantage of variables inspection lies within the records of the data which are collected. Variables data will be more useful when marginal product performance must be assessed and will provide a better basis for a quality improvement program. In addition, errors of measurement will be more noticeable under variables inspection.

Two classes of acceptance sampling by variables are considered in this section. The first assumes that the population variance is known and constant. An example problem will be presented for this assumption. The second case will deal with the situation where the variance is unknown or assumed to vary from lot to lot.

Known and constant sigma plans. A variables sampling plan can be defined with a sample size of n, and an acceptance average of the sample referred to as $\bar{X}_a$. As an illustration, a variables sampling plan used to test the breaking strength of concrete might be defined as $n = 10$, $\bar{X}_a = 4,900$ psi. This plan calls for testing 10 specimens and accepting the lot if the mean breaking strength of the 10 specimens equals or exceeds 4,900 psi. If it can be assumed that the population is normally distributed with a variance that is known and constant, a variables sampling plan can be developed that will yield an OC curve meeting specified producer and consumer risk points.

As an example, assume that steel castings are produced in a batch process and records indicate that the distribution of yield points can be assumed to be normal with $\sigma = 3,000$ psi. Castings with a yield strength of 62,000 psi are considered good and should be accepted 95 per cent of the time. A yield strength of only 59,000 psi is not considered good, and castings from this batch should be rejected 90 per cent of the time. The consumer and producer risk points are thus specified as $\alpha = 0.05$ at 62,000 psi, and $\beta = 0.10$ at 59,000 psi.

If lots at the producer risk point are to be accepted as indicated, the following relationship is applicable

$$\frac{\bar{X}_a - 62,000}{3,000/\sqrt{n}} = -1.645$$

where -1.645 refers to the standard normal deviate which defines the area, and thus the probability of acceptance of 0.95. Similarly, at the consumer risk point, the relationship is

$$\frac{\bar{X}_a - 59,000}{3,000/\sqrt{n}} = +1.282$$

where $+1.282$ defines the probability of 0.10. These two equations are solved for the two unknowns, $\bar{X}_a$ and n. This solution yields the variables sampling plan, $n = 9$, $\bar{X}_a = 60,318$. The sampling plan does not yield an OC curve that passes precisely through the two desired points since n must be an integer. The indicated value of $\bar{X}_a$ is a compromise between the two values which would yield OC curves passing exactly through the one or the other point.

One can construct a complete OC curve for the preceding variables sampling plan by calculating the probability of acceptance at varying levels of

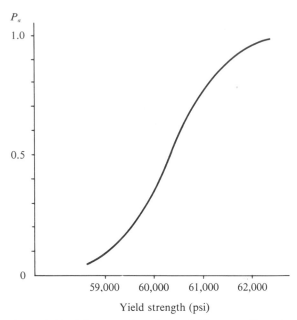

Figure 9.11. OC curve for the variables sampling plan
$n = 9$, $\bar{X} = 60$, 318 psi with $\sigma = 3{,}000$ psi.

batch yield strength. For example, with the yield strength assumed to be
60,000 psi, this represents a standard normal deviate of

$$\frac{60{,}318 - 60{,}000}{3{,}000/\sqrt{9}} = +0.318.$$

This deviation corresponds to $P_a = 0.375$. The complete OC curve for the
example problem is shown in Figure 9.11.

The example solution considered only one tolerance; a lower limit of
59,000 psi at which it was desired to accept no more than 1 lot in 10. If an
upper tolerance limit also exists, then an upper and a lower acceptance limit,
designated $\bar{X}_{Ua}$ and $\bar{X}_{La}$ respectively, must be specified along with the sample
size. Under these conditions, the acceptance criteria can be developed as if
two separate single limit plans were to be used. Two equations would be
developed for each limit and a solution obtained for $\bar{X}_{Ua}$, $\bar{X}_{La}$, and n. A
modified value of OC would have to be considered in order to provide for the
possibility of making a Type I error by rejecting a lot at either acceptance
limit. If the quality level corresponding to α lies midway between the tolerance
limits, then $\alpha/2$ can be used in obtaining the standard normal deviates.

When a specification rather than a tolerance is provided, another approach might be used in developing variables sampling plans. In this case the proportion defective can be calculated as the area within the distribution which lies outside the specification limit. Values of α and β will correspond to proportion defectives and an acceptance limit can be obtained from the same parameters used to obtain attribute plans.

Unknown and variable sigma plans. When the variance of the population being sampled is unknown, or is assumed to vary from one lot to the next, it must be estimated from the sample. The student's "t" distribution (a distribution not described or tabulated herein) should be used as the test statistic. In effect, a sample of size n is drawn from the lot and the population mean and standard deviation estimated from this sample where

$$s = \sigma \sqrt{\frac{n}{n-1}}.$$

The decision statistic is

$$\frac{\bar{X} - \bar{X}_a}{s/\sqrt{n}}$$

where $\bar{X}_a$ is the AQL. If the decision statistic is numerically equal to or less than the "t" deviate at a probability α, the lot would be accepted.

The difficulty in working with unknown sigma plans is that the OC curve is dependent upon the population variance. If this variance changes from one lot to another, no meaningful OC curve can be developed.

9.4. SYSTEMS OF ACCEPTANCE SAMPLING PLANS

Recently, there have been developed a number of systems of acceptance sampling plans which have facilitated the widespread use of acceptance sampling in industry. These systems generally serve to bridge the gap between academic interest in developing such plans and the industrial need for acceptance sampling. Although many systems of sampling plans are available, only three of the more widely used will be introduced in this section. The first two were developed for the Department of Defense and consist of sets of acceptance sampling plans. The first is for inspection by attributes (MIL-STD-105D),[3] and the second for inspection by variables (MIL-STD-414).[4] Both are applicable under nonrectifying inspection. The third system is referred to as the

---

[3] *Military Standard 105D, Sampling Procedures and Tables for Inspection by Attributes* (Washington, D.C.: Government Printing Office, 1963.)

[4] *Military Standard 414, Sampling Procedures and Tables for Inspection by Variables for Percent Defective.* (Washington, D.C.: Government Printing Office, 1957.)

Dodge-Romig tables[5] and consists of four sets of tables for inspection by attributes under a rectifying inspection procedure.

Department of Defense sampling plans. MIL-STD-105D has evolved from its inception in 1942 through four revisions to its present form. The latest revision was an international undertaking by a committee made up of personnel from military agencies of Great Britain, Canada, and the United States. It is not only the military use in accepting products under government procurement contracts which has made the system so widely known. Industry has also been quick to adopt this standard to meet its own acceptance sampling needs.

This system rests upon, and first introduced the concept of an Acceptable Quality Level, AQL, which was defined and illustrated in Figure 9.4. The acceptance criteria are selected to protect the producer against the rejection and the return of submitted lots of this quality level or better. In conjunction with the concept of an AQL, the system includes the use of "tightened inspection" and "reduced inspection" as alternatives which are available to protect the consumer if it is necessary and justified in light of the previous quality history of the producer. A plan under tightened inspection will yield a steeper OC curve and one under reduced inspection will yield a flatter OC curve. One or the other may be called upon in lieu of "normal inspection" if certain criteria are met.

Another interesting aspect of MIL-STD-105D is the provision for classifying defects on the basis of their severity. Definitions are given for varying levels of the seriousness of defects and the acceptable quantity of each level is built into the acceptance sampling plan. Thus, more minor defects would be permitted and only one or a few critical defects may be grounds for the rejection of a lot. This standard includes sets of single, double, and multiple sampling plans and specifies a sample size that is dependent upon and increases with lot size in an absolute sense but decreases in a relative sense.

MIL-STD-414 is quite similar to MIL-STD-105D in that it is based on the concept of an AQL; uses lot-by-lot acceptance; provides for normal, tightened, or reduced inspection depending on the previous quality history of the supplier; and relates sample size to the size of the lot. MIL-STD-414 uses variables rather than attributes inspection. It can be used with either single or double specification limits and provides two sets of tables: One for the case of "variability known" and the other for "variability unknown." With the latter set, the variability of the lot may be estimated through a "standard deviation method" as previously described or a "range method."

In the simple case of a single specification limit with known lot variability, a sampling plan of $n = 8$ and $k = 1.68$ would be obtained under Inspection

---

[5] H. F. Dodge and H. G. Romig. *Sampling Inspection Tables—Single and Double Sampling*, 2nd ed. (New York: John Wiley & Sons, Inc., 1959.)

Level II, with a lot size of 1,500, at normal inspection and an AQL = 0.015 (1.50 per cent). If it were further assumed that the process had a variability of $\sigma = 0.010$ in. and only a lower specification limit of 1.000 in., then the acceptance criteria would be met if

$$\frac{\bar{X} - 1.000}{0.010} \geq 1.68,$$

where $\bar{X}$ is the mean of the sample of eight units.

The Dodge Romig-sampling plans. The Dodge-Romig volume is based on a rectifying inspection program and contains the following four sets of tables:

(1) Single sampling lot tolerance tables
(2) Double sampling lot tolerance tables
(3) Single sampling AOQL tables
(4) Double sampling AOQL tables.

The first two sets of tables contain sampling plans assuming $\beta = 0.10$ for lot tolerance per cent defectives, LTPD, of 0.5 per cent, 1.0 per cent, 2.0 per cent, 3.0 per cent, 4.0 per cent, 5.0 per cent, 7.0 per cent, and 10.0 per cent. Table 9.5 is a Single Sampling Lot Tolerance Table with the LTPD = 0.05 or 5 per cent. In effect, all the plans on this one table have OC curves which pass through the consumer risk point of LTPD = 0.05 at $\beta = 0.10$. The six columns in this table are for different values of process average per cent defective. The plan selected at a given column of process average and row of lot size will minimize total inspection under a rectifying inspection program while providing the desired consumer protection. Although these tables are designed to minimize total inspection under a rectifying inspection program and yield the indicated value of AOQL, they can be used under nonrectifying inspection and still yield the indicated consumer risk point protection.

The second two sets of tables contain sampling plans with AOQL values of 0.10 per cent, 0.25 per cent, 0.50 per cent, 0.75 per cent, 1.0 per cent, 1.5 per cent, 2.0 per cent, 2.5 per cent, 3.0 per cent, 4.0 per cent, 5.0 per cent, 7.0 per cent, and 10.0 per cent. Table 9.6 is a Double Sampling AOQL Table with the AOQL = 0.02 or 2 per cent. All the plans listed on this table will yield this value of AOQL. The selection criterion is again one of minimizing total inspection if rejected lots are subject to 100 per cent screening.

9.5. THE ECONOMY OF ACCEPTANCE SAMPLING

An acceptance sampling plan may be described as a formalized procedure designed to assess the quality of a product group with some predetermined probability of error. This assessment is an operation that should be performed with economy. Economy requires that one develop an effectiveness function

Table 9.5. EXAMPLE OF DODGE-ROMIG SINGLE SAMPLING LOT TOLERANCE TABLES

(Lot Tolerance per cent Defective = 5.0; Consumer's Risk = 0.10)

Process Average %	0–.05			.06–.50			.51–1.00			1.01–1.50			1.51–2.00			2.01–2.50		
Lot Size	n	c	AOQL %	n	c	AOQL %	n	c	AOQL %	n	c	AOQL %	n	c	AOQL %	n	c	AOQL %
1–30	All	0	0	All	0	0	All	0	0	All	0	0	All	0	0	All	0	0
31–50	30	0	.49	30	0	.49	30	0	.49	30	0	.49	30	0	.49	30	0	.49
51–100	37	0	.63	37	0	.63	37	0	.63	37	0	.63	37	0	.63	37	0	.63
101–200	40	0	.74	40	0	.74	40	0	.74	40	0	.74	40	0	.74	40	0	.74
201–300	43	0	.74	43	0	.74	70	1	.92	70	1	.92	95	2	.99	95	2	.99
301–400	44	0	.74	44	0	.74	70	1	.99	100	2	1.0	120	3	1.1	145	4	1.1
401–500	45	0	.75	75	1	.95	100	2	1.1	100	2	1.1	125	3	1.2	150	4	1.2
501–600	45	0	.76	75	1	.98	100	2	1.1	125	3	1.2	150	4	1.3	175	5	1.3
601–800	45	0	.77	75	1	1.0	100	2	1.2	130	3	1.2	175	5	1.4	200	6	1.4
801–1,000	45	0	.78	75	1	1.0	105	2	1.2	155	4	1.4	180	5	1.4	225	7	1.5
1,001–2,000	45	0	.80	75	1	1.0	130	3	1.4	180	5	1.6	230	7	1.7	280	9	1.8
2,001–3,000	75	1	1.1	105	2	1.3	135	3	1.4	210	6	1.7	280	9	1.9	370	13	2.1
3,001–4,000	75	1	1.1	105	2	1.3	160	4	1.5	210	6	1.7	305	10	2.0	420	15	2.2
4,001–5,000	75	1	1.1	105	2	1.3	160	4	1.5	235	7	1.8	330	11	2.0	440	16	2.2
5,001–7,000	75	1	1.1	105	2	1.3	185	5	1.7	260	8	1.9	350	12	2.2	490	18	2.4
7,001–10,000	75	1	1.1	105	2	1.3	185	5	1.7	260	8	1.9	380	13	2.2	535	20	2.5
10,001–20,000	75	1	1.1	135	3	1.4	210	6	1.8	285	9	2.0	425	15	2.3	610	23	2.6
20,001–50,000	75	1	1.1	135	3	1.4	235	7	1.9	305	10	2.1	470	17	2.4	700	27	2.7
50,001–100,000	75	1	1.1	160	4	1.6	235	7	1.9	355	12	2.2	515	19	2.5	770	30	2.8

From H. F. Dodge and H. G. Romig, *Sampling Inspection Tables* (New York:) John Wiley & Sons, Inc., 1959. *Reprinted by permission.*

Table 9.6. EXAMPLE OF DODGE-ROMIG DOUBLE SAMPLING AOQL TABLES

(Average Outgoing Quality Limit = 2.0%)

Process Average %, range 0-.04:

Lot Size	Trial 1 n_1	c_1	Trial 2 n_2	n_1+n_2	c_2	p_t %
1-15	All	0	—			
16-50	14	0	—	—		13.6
51-100	21	0	12	33	1	11.7
101-200	24	0	13	37	1	11.0
201-300	26	0	15	41	1	10.4
301-400	26	0	16	42	1	10.3
401-500	27	0	16	43	1	10.3
501-600	27	0	16	43	1	10.3
601-800	27	0	17	44	1	10.2
801-1,000	27	0	17	44	1	10.2
1,001-2,000	33	0	37	70	2	8.4
2,001-3,000	34	0	41	75	2	8.2
3,001-4,000	34	0	41	75	2	8.2
4,001-5,000	34	0	41	75	2	8.2
5,001-7,000	35	0	40	75	2	8.1
7,001-10,000	35	0	40	75	2	8.1
10,001-20,000	35	0	40	75	2	8.1
20,001-50,000	35	0	40	75	2	8.1
50,001-100,000	35	0	45	80	2	8.0

Process Average %, range .05-.40:

Lot Size	Trial 1 n_1	c_1	Trial 2 n_2	n_1+n_2	c_2	p_t %
1-15	All	0	—			
16-50	14	0	—	—		13.6
51-100	21	0	12	33	1	11.7
101-200	24	0	13	37	1	11.0
201-300	26	0	15	41	1	10.4
301-400	26	0	16	42	1	10.3
401-500	30	0	35	65	2	9.0
501-600	31	0	34	65	2	8.9
601-800	31	0	39	70	2	8.8
801-1,000	32	0	38	70	2	8.8
1,001-2,000	33	0	37	70	2	8.5
2,001-3,000	34	0	41	75	2	8.2
3,001-4,000	38	0	62	100	3	7.3
4,001-5,000	38	0	62	100	3	7.3
5,001-7,000	38	0	62	100	3	7.3
7,001-10,000	38	0	62	100	3	7.3
10,001-20,000	39	0	66	105	3	7.2
20,001-50,000	43	0	92	135	4	6.6
50,001-100,000	43	0	92	135	4	6.6

Process Average %, range .41-.80:

Lot Size	Trial 1 n_1	c_1	Trial 2 n_2	n_1+n_2	c_2	p_t %
1-15	All	0	—			
16-50	14	0	—	—		13.6
51-100	21	0	12	33	1	11.7
101-200	24	0	13	37	1	11.0
201-300	29	0	31	60	2	9.1
301-400	30	0	35	65	2	9.0
401-500	30	0	35	65	2	9.0
501-600	35	0	55	90	3	7.9
601-800	35	0	60	95	3	7.7
801-1,000	36	0	59	95	3	7.6
1,001-2,000	37	0	63	100	3	7.5
2,001-3,000	41	0	84	125	4	7.0
3,001-4,000	41	0	89	130	4	6.9
4,001-5,000	42	0	88	130	4	6.9
5,001-7,000	44	0	116	160	5	6.4
7,001-10,000	45	0	115	160	5	6.3
10,001-20,000	45	0	115	160	5	6.3
20,001-50,000	47	0	148	195	6	6.0
50,001-100,000	85	1	185	270	8	5.2

Process Average %, range .81-1.20:

Lot Size	Trial 1 n_1	c_1	Trial 2 n_2	n_1+n_2	c_2	p_t %
1-15	All	0	—			
16-50	14	0	—	—		13.6
51-100	21	0	12	33	1	11.7
101-200	27	0	28	55	2	9.6
201-300	29	0	31	60	2	9.1
301-400	33	0	52	85	3	8.2
401-500	34	0	58	90	3	7.9
501-600	35	0	55	90	3	7.9
601-800	38	0	82	120	4	7.3
801-1,000	38	0	87	125	4	7.2
1,001-2,000	43	0	112	155	5	6.5
2,001-3,000	75	1	115	190	6	6.1
3,001-4,000	80	1	140	220	7	5.8
4,001-5,000	80	1	175	255	8	5.5
5,001-7,000	85	1	205	290	9	5.3
7,001-10,000	85	1	210	295	9	5.2
10,001-20,000	90	1	260	350	11	5.1
20,001-50,000	130	2	300	430	13	4.7
50,001-100,000	135	2	345	480	14	4.5

Process Average %, range 1.21-1.60:

Lot Size	Trial 1 n_1	c_1	Trial 2 n_2	n_1+n_2	c_2	p_t %
1-15	All	0	—			
16-50	14	0	—	—		13.6
51-100	21	0	12	33	1	11.7
101-200	27	0	28	55	2	9.6
201-300	32	0	48	80	3	8.4
301-400	33	0	52	85	3	8.2
401-500	36	0	74	110	4	7.5
501-600	37	0	78	115	4	7.4
601-800	38	0	82	120	4	7.3
801-1,000	70	1	100	170	6	6.5
1,001-2,000	80	1	160	240	8	5.8
2,001-3,000	115	2	195	310	10	5.3
3,001-4,000	120	2	255	375	12	5.0
4,001-5,000	125	2	285	410	13	4.9
5,001-7,000	125	2	320	445	14	4.8
7,001-10,000	165	3	335	500	15	4.5
10,001-20,000	170	3	425	595	18	4.4
20,001-50,000	205	4	515	720	22	4.3
50,001-100,000	250	5	615	865	26	4.1

Process Average %, range 1.61-2.00:

Lot Size	Trial 1 n_1	c_1	Trial 2 n_2	n_1+n_2	c_2	p_t %
1-15	All	0	—			
16-50	14	0	—	—		13.6
51-100	23	0	23	46	2	10.9
101-200	27	0	28	55	2	9.6
201-300	32	0	48	80	3	8.4
301-400	36	0	69	105	4	7.6
401-500	60	1	90	150	6	7.0
501-600	65	1	95	160	6	6.8
601-800	70	1	120	190	7	6.4
801-1,000	70	1	145	215	8	6.2
1,001-2,000	110	2	205	315	11	5.5
2,001-3,000	160	3	310	470	15	4.7
3,001-4,000	235	5	415	650	20	4.3
4,001-5,000	275	6	475	750	23	4.2
5,001-7,000	280	6	575	855	26	4.1
7,001-10,000	320	7	645	965	29	4.0
10,001-20,000	395	9	835	1,230	37	3.9
20,001-50,000	480	11	1,090	1,570	46	3.7
50,001-100,000	580	13	1,460	2,040	58	3.5

From H. F. Dodge and H. G. Romig, *Sampling Inspection Tables* (New York: John Wiley & Sons, Inc., 1959). *Reprinted by permission.*

that relates the variables under direct control of the decision maker with those not under his direct control. In acceptance sampling, the decision maker can specify the sampling plan to be used. The quality characteristics of the product group, the costs of assessment, and the costs of accepting defectives are not directly under his control. Therefore, in selecting a sampling plan that will result in a minimum total system cost, he must consider these parameters.

In practice, it is difficult to ascertain the precise costs of inspection and costs of accepting defectives. Often, these costs are assumed to be linear with little empirical justification. The quality characteristics of a product group may also be difficult to estimate although the quality history of a producer could serve as a guide. In spite of these difficulties, an economic evaluation is useful in the selection of an acceptance sampling plan.

Total system cost under rectifying inspection. If it is assumed that defectives are replaced to maintain a constant lot size, the expected total cost per lot would be

$$TC = (AOQ)(N)(C_d) + (I)(C_i).\qquad(9.18)$$

The cost of accepting a defective is designated C_d and the cost of inspecting one item is C_i. Substituting Equation (9.3) for AOQ and Equation (9.4) for I reduces Equation (9.18) to

$$TC = (P_a)(p)(N - n)C_d + \left[\frac{n + (1 - P_a)(N - n)}{(1 - p)}\right]C_i.\qquad(9.19)$$

If the expected level of defectives varies from one lot to another it will be necessary to apply Equation (9.19) to each group. The total system cost would then be a weighted average based on the fraction of lots having each level of defectives.

As an example of the application of the foregoing model, consider the data of Table 9.3. The sampling plan was $N = 10,000$, $n = 200$, and $c = 5$. Suppose that the cost of accepting a defective is \$5.00 and the cost of inspecting one item is \$0.10. It is estimated that half of the lots submitted will contain no defectives, one-fourth of the lots will contain 2 per cent defectives, and the remaining one-fourth of the lots will contain 4 per cent defective. Under these conditions, the total cost for each level of defectives will be

$$TC_{p=0} = (1)(0)(9,800)(\$5.00) + \left[\frac{200 + (1 - 1)(10,000 - 200)}{(1 - 0)}\right]\$0.10$$
$$= \$20.00$$

$$TC_{p=0.02} = (0.785)(9,800)(0.02)(\$5.00)$$
$$+ \left[\frac{200 + (1 - 0.785)(10,000 - 200)}{(1 - 0.02)}\right]\$0.10$$
$$= \$1,003.70$$

$$TC_{p=0.04} = 0.04 = (0.191)(9,800)(0.04)(\$5.00)$$
$$+ \left[\frac{200 + (1 - 0.191)(10,000 - 200)}{(1 - 0.04)} \right] \$0.10$$
$$= \$1,201.52$$

The weighted total cost would be

$$TC = \tfrac{1}{2}TC_{p=0} + \tfrac{1}{4}TC_{p=0.02} + \tfrac{1}{4}TC_{p=0.04}$$
$$= \tfrac{1}{2}(\$20.00) + \tfrac{1}{4}(\$1,003.70) + \tfrac{1}{4}(\$1,201.52) = \$561.31.$$

The total system cost under this sampling plan may now be compared with no inspection and with 100 per cent inspection. With no inspection, the only cost would be that of accepting defectives. This is computed as

$$TC = [\tfrac{1}{2}(0) + \tfrac{1}{4}(0.02)(10,000) + \tfrac{1}{4}(0.04)(10,000)]\$5.00 = \$750.00.$$

Under 100 per cent screening, the cost is that of inspection. This is computed as

$$TC = (10,000)\$0.10 = \$1,000.00.$$

In this example, the sampling plan is more economical than either no inspection or the complete 100 per cent screening of every item. This does not mean, however, that this is the most economical sampling plan available. The minimum cost sampling plan would have to be found by trial-and-error methods.

Total system cost under nonrectifying inspection. Under a nonrectifying inspection program, only accepted lots are retained, and the total cost must be adjusted to reflect the inspection costs of lots which are returned. The solution to the problem of the previous example under nonrectifying inspection can be obtained from

$$TC = (ALQ)(N)(C_d) + \frac{(n)(C_i)}{p_{AL}}. \tag{9.20}$$

The proportion defective in accepted lots is designated ALQ and the proportion of accepted lots is p_{AL}. Table 9.7 gives the computations necessary for the application of Equation (9.20). The total cost is

$$TC = (0.00784)(10,000)(\$5.00) + \frac{(200)(\$0.10)}{0.7440} = \$418.88.$$

The foregoing solution is fairly simple although it is only an approximation in that a few defectives can be expected to be found and discarded in the sample of accepted lots. A correction for this omission should not, however, appreciably alter the preceding answer.

The economy of acceptance sampling reduces to selecting a sampling plan which minimizes the costs of inspection and the costs of accepting defectives. The decision maker is often faced with making this decision on the basis of incomplete and sometimes erroneous data. He must make his decision with the available data and rely upon intuition and some subjective judgment to carry the evaluation through to a final sampling procedure. In a practical

Table 9.7. A COMPUTATIONAL SCHEME FOR FINDING THE PROPORTION OF ACCEPTED LOTS AND THE PROPORTION DEFECTIVE IN ACCEPTED LOTS UNDER NONRECTIFYING INSPECTION

Proportion Defective (A)	Proportion of Lots (B)	Probability of Acceptance (C)	Proportion of Accepted Lots $P_{AL} = \Sigma\, BC$	Proportion Defective in Accepted Lots $ALQ = \dfrac{\Sigma\, ABC}{\Sigma\, BC}$
0	0.50	1.000	0.5000	0
0.02	0.25	0.785	0.1962	0.00393
0.04	0.25	0.191	0.0478	0.00191
			0.7440	$\dfrac{0.00584}{0.7440} =$ 0.00584 0.00784

case, a sampling plan would probably be selected from an established system or table of acceptance sampling plans. These plans might specify error criteria, and an intuitive reconciliation would have to be made between these criteria and some estimate of sampling and other costs. Attempts would be made to facilitate the identification of defectives by removing as much of the subjective human element as possible. Nevertheless, it might well be noted that the identification of defectives might be superior under a sampling plan than under 100 per cent inspection.

QUESTIONS

1. How does the objective of an inspection sampling plan differ from that of a control model?

2. What is the difference between a rectifying and nonrectifying inspection program?

3. What does an operating characteristic curve illustrate?

4. Discuss the general relationship between the sample size and the form of an OC curve.

5. Define and illustrate the consumer risk point on an OC curve; the producer risk point.

6. Why is it usually necessary to bracket the two desired points on an OC curve?

7. Discuss the relationship between the average outgoing quality limit and the average outgoing quality.

8. List the relative advantages and disadvantages of single, double, and multiple or sequential sampling.

9. Under what conditions is it desirable to use a sampling plan for continuous production rather than a lot-by-lot plan?

10. What are the limitations in the use of acceptance sampling by variables; the advantages?

11. What are the unique features of MIL-STD-105D and MIL-STD-414?

12. What sets of tables are included in the Dodge-Romig system?

13. What costs are associated with the operation of an acceptance sampling plan?

14. Discuss acceptance sampling in terms of variables directly under control of a decision maker and variables not directly under his control.

PROBLEMS

1. Sketch the OC curves for the sampling plans $c = 0, n = 100; c = 1, n = 100; c = 2, n = 100.$

2. Sketch the OC curves for the sampling plans $c = 1, n = 100; c = 2, n = 200; c = 5, n = 500.$

3. Develop the four single sampling plans which bracket the producer and consumer risk points of $\alpha = 0.05$ at $AQL = 0.01$ and $\beta = 0.10$ at $LTPD = 0.06.$

4. Develop the plans which bracket $\alpha = 0.05$ at $AQL = 0.01$ and $\beta = 0.10$ at $LTPD = 0.08.$

5. Sketch I and the AOQ and specify the AOQL for the plan $c = 1, n = 100, N = 1,000,$ under rectifying inspection with nonreplacement of defectives. Do the same for $c = 0, n = 50, N = 1,000.$

6. Sketch the OC curves for the double sampling plan $N = 1,000, n_1 = 50, n_2 = 80, c_1 = 0,$ and $c_2 = 3.$ Do the same for the double sampling plan $N = 1,000, n_1 = 85, n_2 = 120, c_1 = 1, c_2 = 6.$

7. At a $p = 0.02,$ what is the probability of making a decision on the first sample for each of the plans in the previous problem at $p = 0.01$; at $p = 0.04$?

8. At a $p = 0.02,$ what is the ASN, I, and the AOQ under rectifying inspection with replacement of defectives for the two plans in Problem 6?

9. Define the sequential sampling that meets the producer and consumer risk points of $\alpha = 0.05$ at $AQL = 0.005$ and $\beta = 0.10$ at $LTPD = 0.020.$

10. With the plan of Problem 9, what are the minimum number of units which would have to be inspected to accept a lot?

11. With the continuous sampling plan $i = 200$ and $f = 0.10$, develop an OC curve and calculate the AOQL and compare this latter value with that obtained from Figure 9.10.

12. Specify the variables sampling plan with a known and constant $\sigma = 1.00$ in. and a consumer and producer risk point of $\alpha = 0.05$ at 1.00 in. and $\beta = 0.10$ at 3.00 in.

13. In 1215, the Chinese city of Yen-King, the modern Peking, was besieged by the Mongols under Genghis Khan. When all the metal inside the city had been used up for cannon balls, the defenders began melting down silver and eventually gold, and their ancient muzzleloaders finally poured golden shot into the Mongols' camp. In the end, however, the city was taken and destroyed, later to be rebuilt by Kublai Khan. The resistance to the siege was reported to have been influenced by the quality control procedures used in conjunction with the casting of the cannon balls.

   Two hundred and fifty lots of 50 silver cannon balls each were cast within the city and delivered to the guns on the walls. There they were subjected to the nonrectifying inspection program by attributes of $N = 50$, $n = 10$, $c = 0$. Rejected lots were returned where they were melted down into coins to be used as bribe money. After the silver balls in accepted lots were exhausted, gold balls were cast, verified under a Dodge CSP-1 plan obtained from the still undiscovered Western Hemisphere, and fired. The specific plan called for $i = 50$, $f = 0.10$.

   Archaeologists have since discovered that half of the lots of silver balls contained no defectives whereas the other half were probably 10 per cent defective. The gold balls were probably all 5 per cent defective. They also discovered that when a cannon had fired 10 defective balls it became inoperative; that the city began its resistance with 150 cannon and it fell when all the cannon became inoperative. How many gold cannon balls were fired?

14. Assume the following distribution of defectives in incoming lots with a rectifying inspection program and the plan $N = 1,000$, $n = 100$, $c = 1$:

Proportion Defective	Proportion of Lots
0.00	0.10
0.01	0.20
0.02	0.40
0.03	0.20
0.04	0.10

   If the cost of accepting defectives is \$1.00 per defective and the inspection cost is \$0.05 per piece, what would be the cost per lot of this sampling program? Compare this to the costs of 100 per cent inspection and no inspection.

15. Solve Problem 14 under a nonrectifying inspection program.

Part IV

ECONOMY OF PROCUREMENT
AND INVENTORY OPERATIONS

ten

DETERMINISTIC PROCUREMENT

AND INVENTORY MODELS

*The procurement and inventory process under consideration
in this chapter may be described as follows. A stock of a certain
item is maintained to meet a demand. When the number of these items
on hand and on order falls to a predetermined level, action
is initiated to procure a replenishment quantity from one of several possible
sources. The objective is to determine the procurement level,
the procurement quantity, and the procurement source in the light of the relevant
costs and the properties of demand and procurement lead time,
so that the sum of all costs associated with the procurement and inventory system
will be minimized.*

*Systems having the foregoing characteristics are found in many
operational settings. A procurement and inventory process may exist
to meet the demand for raw materials and component parts in manufacturing,
to meet the demand for consumer goods at the factory, wholesale,
or retail level, to meet the demand for spare parts caused by a wing of
military aircraft, and so forth. The first portion of this chapter
describes the procurement and inventory system in general terms.
The deterministic models which follow are based on the supposition that any
item is available from more than one source. By considering the item
in this multisource context, these models can be used to make source decisions.
This will be illustrated by applying each model to situations
requiring determination of the procurement level, the procurement quantity,
and the procurement source.*

10.1. THE PROCUREMENT AND INVENTORY SYSTEM

A multisource procurement and inventory system is illustrated schematically in Figure 10.1. It exists as a result of the demand stimulus, D. The inventory holding portion of the system (stock) is of primary importance. It serves as a means for making procurement action independent of demand upon the system. Maintaining the stock on hand at an appropriate level contributes to the economy of the procurement and inventory process. Therefore,

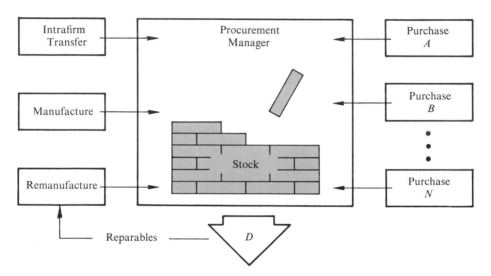

Figure 10.1. The multisource procurement and inventory system.

in satisfying demand, the procurement manager must decide *when* to procure, *how much* to procure, and *from what source* to procure. The following paragraphs describe the source alternatives available to the decision maker and indicate the source dependent parameters associated with each.

The purchase alternative. Purchasing may be one of the inventory replenishment sources that exist. Actually, several vendors, represented by $A, B, \ldots, N$ in Figure 10.1, may come under consideration.

Associated with each vendor will be a certain procurement lead time capability. The simplest lead time pattern may be described as deterministic. In this special case, the future lead time for a given procurement order can be predicted with certainty. Procurement lead time considered in this restricted sense is only an approximation of reality. In the general case, *lead time* may be described as a random variable which takes on values in accordance with a specific probability distribution. Since lead time is a component of the inventory process and since alternate vendors are unlikely to exhibit identical lead time characteristics, this source dependent parameter indicates that the inventory process and the procurement process are related.

The replenishment rate for purchasing will be essentially instantaneous since replenishment stock is usually received in one shipment. Under this condition, the stock on hand will increase by an amount equal to the procurement quantity in an instant of time.

The cost per unit of the item procured will depend upon the vendor chosen. Each vendor resides in a unique supply-demand environment and may be expected to price the item accordingly. In addition to differing unit price, it is unlikely that each vendor will quote an identical quantity discount schedule. Therefore, item cost should be considered as an important difference in alternate vendors.

Procurement cost is the summation of the cost elements arising from the series of acts beginning with the initiation of procurement action and ending with the receipt of replenishment stock. Certain of these costs will depend on the vendor chosen as, for instance, the cost of follow-up action required to insure timely delivery. Since procurement cost is a component of the inventory process, as well as a function of the vendor chosen, this is further indication of the relationship between the inventory process and the procurement process.

The intrafirm transfer alternative.

An important variation of the purchase alternative is the transfer of stock between procurement managers who are members of the same organization. As an example, assume that a factory distributor in need of replenishment stock places an order with another factory distributor in an adjacent territory. Such action is justified if it results in an economic advantage to the organization as a whole.

Procurement lead time for the intrafirm transfer of stock is usually shorter than that for the purchase alternative. It has the same characteristics, however, and is usually made up of many of the same time elements. A reduced lead time is often the primary incentive for considering the intrafirm transfer alternative.

The replenishment rate for intrafirm transfer would normally be instantaneous. If the requested item is in stock, it will usually be shipped to the requesting organizational unit in one batch and in the amount requested.

Item cost to the receiving organization unit should simply be equal to the cost of the item to the shipping organizational unit plus handling and inventory expenses involved. The addition of a profit for intrafirm transfer is not usually justified, since the interests of the organization as a whole are of prime importance.

Procurement cost for the intrafirm transfer alternative will be made up of cost components similar to those for the purchase alternative. Because of the nature of each source, however, it is not likely that the two will be the same.

The manufacture alternative. It may be economically advantageous to procure replenishment stock from a manufacturing facility within the organization, if such a facility exists. When this is the case, the procurement manager is faced with a manufacture or purchase decision.

Associated with the manufacturing source will be a certain procurement lead time capability. Although manufacturing lead time will be a random variable, its variance may be more easily controlled than the variance in purchase lead time.

The replenishment rate for remanufacturing is normally finite. Items being manufactured accumulate as they are made, whereas purchased items are received at one time. This is an important difference between the manufacture and purchase alternatives.

Item cost for the manufacture alternative involves a summation of the costs of direct labor, direct material, and factory burden. In addition, manufacturing progress or learning will occur, which may result in a significant reduction in the number of direct labor hours per unit as the number of units produced increases. This brings about a corresponding reduction in item cost analogous to the price discount schedule for the purchase alternative.

Procurement cost for manufacturing will be composed of the cost elements incurred in production planning, set-up and tear down, scheduling, and other costs arising from the set of acts required in the initiation of manufacturing action. Evidently this cost will differ significantly from procurement cost for the purchase alternative.

The remanufacture alternative. The possibility of remanufacturing should be considered in those cases where a remanufactured item may be used to satisfy demand. This is often the case with automotive and aircraft components.

Remanufacturing lead time may be considerably shorter than the procurement lead time from any other source. This occurs, in part, because the process normally requires only a few manufacturing operations.

The replenishment rate for remanufacturing will be finite because remanufactured items accumulate as they are made in the same manner as manufactured items.

As for manufacturing, item cost will involve the cost elements of direct labor, direct material, and factory burden. The direct material item must include the cost of reparables; a necessary input for this source alternative. In addition, manufacturing progress will be experienced during remanufacturing with its resulting effects.

Procurement cost for the remanufacturing alternative will be analogous to that for the manufacturing alternative. It will be composed of those cost elements arising from the set of acts required in preparation of remanufacturing.

10.2. THE DECISION ENVIRONMENT

The procurement and inventory system described in Section 10.1 includes parameters dependent on the source and some which are independent of it. Four of these—procurement lead time, the replenishment rate, item cost, and procurement cost—were discussed in Section 10.1. Each was classified as source dependent since its specific value depends upon the source chosen. Three others—demand, holding cost, and shortage cost—are source independent. These discussed in the following paragraphs. Finally, the general structure of decision models for procurement and inventory operations will be presented.

Demand. Demand is the primary stimulus on the procurement and inventory system and the justification for its existence. Specifically, the system may exist to meet the demand of customers, the spare parts demand of an operational weapons system, the demand of the next step in a manufacturing process, and so forth. The characteristics of demand, although independent of the source chosen to replenish inventories, will depend upon the nature of the environment giving rise to demand.

The simplest demand pattern may be classified as deterministic. In this special case, the future demand for an item may be predicted with certainty. Demand considered in this restricted sense is only an approximation of reality. In the general case, demand may be described as a random variable which takes on values in accordance with a specific probability distribution.

Holding cost. Inventory holding costs are incurred as a function of the quantity on hand and the time duration involved. Included in these costs are the real out-of-pocket costs, such as insurance, taxes, obsolescence, warehouse rental or other space charges, and operating costs, such as light, heat, maintenance, and security. In addition, capital invested in inventories is unavailable for investment elsewhere. The rate of return foregone represents a cost of carrying inventory.

The inventory holding cost per unit of time may be thought of as the sum of several cost components. Some of these may depend upon the maximum inventory level incurred. Others may depend upon the average inventory level. Still others, like the cost of capital invested, will depend upon the value of the inventory during the time period. The determination of holding cost per unit for a specified time period depends upon a detailed analysis of each cost component.

Shortage cost. Shortage cost is the penalty incurred for being unable to meet a demand when it occurs. This cost does not depend upon the source chosen to replenish stock but is a function of the number of units short and the time duration involved.

The specific dollar penalty incurred when a shortage exists depends upon the nature of the demand. For instance, if the demand is that of customers upon a retail establishment the shortage cost would include the loss of good will. In this case, shortage cost would be small relative to the cost of the item. If, however, the demand is that of the next step in a manufacturing process, the cost of a shortage may be high relative to the cost of the item. Being unable to meet the requirement for raw material or a component part may result in lost production or even closing of the plant. Therefore, in establishing shortage cost, the seriousness of the shortage condition and its time duration must be considered.

The decision model. The inventory process resulting from procurement action and demand will exhibit a sawtooth function which depends upon the

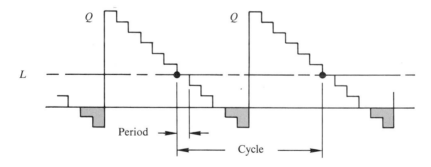

Figure 10.2. Deterministic inventory process with instantaneous replenishment.

procurement level, the procurement quantity, the demand rate, the procurement lead time, and the replenishment rate. The total system cost will depend upon the exhibited geometry and the item cost, the procurement cost, the holding cost, and the shortage cost. Since procurement lead time, the replenishment rate, item cost, and procurement cost are source dependent, evidently both the geometry of the inventory process and the total system cost will be source dependent. If both demand and procurement lead time are deterministic, as is assumed in this chapter, the resulting inventory process will be deterministic, as is shown in Figure 10.2.

The inventory function is illustrated as it would appear to the bookkeeping system. Two basic time elements are involved which may be defined as follows:

(1) Period—the element of elapsed time between review of the stock position. This is usually a day but it may be any other time unit.
(2) Cycle—the number of periods occurring between successive procurement actions.

Stock level review and adjustment occur at the end of each period resulting in the step function shown. The stock level at the end of one period is equal to the stock level at the beginning of the next. In this context, the inventory level is periodically reviewed as opposed to a theoretical continuous review system.

The primary objective of the procurement and inventory system is to meet demand at minimum cost. This involves the assignment of appropriate values to the decision variables of when to procure, how much to procure, and from what source to procure by constructing and manipulating a mathematical model of the form

$$E = f(x_i, y_j)$$

where E — measure of effectiveness sought (minimize total system cost)
x_i = policy variables of when to procure and how much to procure
y_j = source-dependent and source-independent parameters of procurement lead time, the replenishment rate, item cost, procurement cost, demand, holding cost, and shortage cost.

The following sections deal with the development of deterministic decision models having these general characteristics. The following symbolism will be adopted:

TC = total system cost per period
L = procurement level
Q = procurement quantity
D = demand rate in units per period
T = lead time in periods
P = number of periods per cycle
R = replenishment rate in units per period
C_i = item cost per unit
C_p = procurement cost per procurement
C_h = holding cost per unit per period
C_s = shortage cost per unit short per period.

Additional notation will be adopted and defined as required in the derivation of specific decision models.

10.3. THE PURCHASE ALTERNATIVE

If demand for the item is to be met by purchasing (or intrafirm transfer) once per year, the cost incident to purchasing will occur once per year, but the large quantity received will result in a relatively high inventory holding cost for the year. Conversely, if purchasing action is initiated several times per year, the cost incident to purchasing will be incurred several times per year, but since small quantities will be received, the cost of holding inventory will be relatively small. If the decision is to be based on economy of the total operation, the procurement level and procurement quantity resulting in a minimum cost for each vendor must be determined.

A purchase decision model. If it is assumed that the demand for the item is deterministic, that the procurement lead time is deterministic, that the

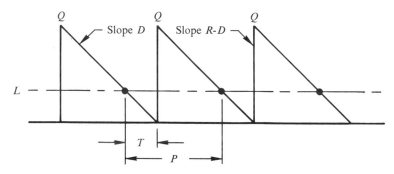

Figure 10.3. Infinite replacement rate with infinite shortage cost.

replenishment rate is infinite, and that shortage cost is infinite, the resulting inventory process may be represented graphically as in Figure 10.3.

The total system cost per period will be the sum of the item cost for the period, the procurement cost for the period, and the holding cost for the period; that is,

$$TC = IC + PC + HC.$$

The item cost for the period will be the item cost per unit times the demand rate in units per period, or

$$IC = C_i D.$$

The procurement cost for the period will be the purchase cost per purchase divided by the number of periods per cycle, or

$$PC = \frac{C_p}{P}.$$

But, since P is the procurement quantity divided by the demand rate,

$$PC = \frac{C_p D}{Q}.$$

Since the maximum number of units in stock is Q, the average inventory during the period will be $Q/2$. Therefore, the holding cost for the period will be the holding cost per unit times the average number of units on hand for the period, or

$$HC = \frac{C_h Q}{2}.$$

The total system cost per period will be the sum of the item cost per period, the procurement cost per period, and the holding cost per period, or

$$TC = C_i D + \frac{C_p D}{Q} + \frac{C_h Q}{2}. \tag{10.1}$$

The procurement quantity resulting in a minimum total system cost may be found by differentiating with respect to Q, setting the result equal to zero, and solving for Q as follows:

$$\frac{dTC}{dQ} = - \frac{C_p D}{Q^2} + \frac{C_h}{2} = 0$$

$$Q^2 = \frac{2 C_p D}{C_h}$$

$$Q = \sqrt{\frac{2 C_p D}{C_h}}. \tag{10.2}$$

In this simple model, no shortages were allowed since shortage cost was assumed to be infinite. Since this is the case, the procurement level would be

$$L = DT. \tag{10.3}$$

The minimum total system cost may be found by substituting the minimum cost procurement quantity into Equation (10.1) as follows:

$$TC_{\min} = C_i D + \frac{C_p D}{\sqrt{2 C_p D / C_h}} + \frac{C_h \sqrt{2 C_p D / C_h}}{2}$$

$$= C_i D + \sqrt{2 C_p C_h D}. \tag{10.4}$$

A purchase decision. For simplicity, assume that only one vendor is under consideration as a possible source of replenishment stock. In this case, it is necessary to determine only the procurement level and the procurement quantity resulting in a minimum cost; the source being fixed by restriction. Suppose that the item has a demand of three units per period, the procurement lead time is 16 periods, the item cost is \$6.10 per unit, the procurement cost is \$8.00 per procurement, and the holding cost per unit per period is \$0.004.

Item cost per period, procurement cost per period, holding cost per period, and total cost per period may be tabulated as a function of Q to illustrate the nature of the cost components. The results shown in Table 10.1 were developed from Equation (10.1). It is evident from the table that item cost per period is constant, procurement cost per period decreases, and holding cost per period increases with increasing values of Q. It is not possible to pick the minimum cost procurement quantity from the table because of the number of decimal places exhibited. The curve generated by these points is flat in the region of its minimum.

Table 10.1. COST COMPONENTS FOR PURCHASE DECISION

Q	IC	PC	HC	TC
0	$18.30	$ ∞	$0.00	$ ∞
10	18.30	2.40	0.02	20.72
20	18.30	1.20	0.04	19.54
30	18.30	0.80	0.06	19.16
40	18.30	0.60	0.08	18.98
50	18.30	0.48	0.10	18.88
60	18.30	0.40	0.12	18.82
70	18.30	0.34	0.14	18.78
80	18.30	0.30	0.16	18.76
90	18.30	0.27	0.18	18.75
100	18.30	0.24	0.20	18.74
110	18.30	0.22	0.22	18.74
120	18.30	0.20	0.24	18.74
130	18.30	0.18	0.26	18.74
140	18.30	0.17	0.28	18.75

The minimum cost procurement quantity and procurement level may be found directly by substituting into Equation (10.2) and Equation (10.3) as follows:

$$Q = \sqrt{\frac{2(\$8)(3)}{\$0.004}} = 110 \text{ units,}$$

$$L = 3(16) = 48 \text{ units.}$$

Under the conditions assumed, the procurement manager would initiate purchasing action when his stock falls to 48 units for a purchase quantity 110 units from the vendor specified.

10.4. THE MANUFACTURE ALTERNATIVE

If demand for the item is to be met by manufacturing (or remanufacturing) once per year, the cost of initiating manufacturing action will occur only once per year, but the large quantity produced will result in a relatively high inventory holding cost for the year. Conversely, if manufacturing action is initiated several times per year, this cost will be incurred several times per year, but since small quantities will be produced, the cost of holding inventory will be relatively small. If the decision is to be based on economy of the total operation, the procurement level and procurement quantity resulting in a minimum cost must be determined.

A manufacture decision model. Minimum-cost manufacturing quantities are determined in a manner similar to that employed in determining minimum-cost purchase quantities. The difference in analysis occurs because a purchased lot is received at one time, whereas a production lot accumulates as it is made. If it is assumed that demand for the item is deterministic, that

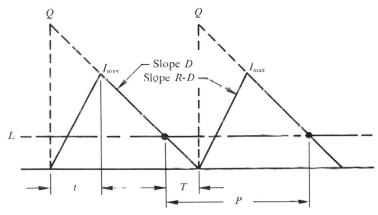

Figure 10.4. Finite replenishment rate with infinite shortage cost.

procurement lead time is deterministic, that the replenishment rate is finite $(R > D)$, and that shortage cost is infinite, the resulting inventory process may be represented graphically as in Figure 10.4.

The total system cost per period will be the sum of the item cost for the period, the procurement cost for the period, and the holding cost for the period; that is,

$$TC = IC + PC + HC.$$

The item cost for the period will be the item cost per unit times the demand in units per period, or

$$IC = C_i D.$$

The procurement cost for the period will be set-up cost per setup divided by the number of periods in the cycle, or

$$PC = \frac{C_p}{P}.$$

But, since P is the procurement quantity divided by the demand rate,

$$PC = \frac{C_p D}{Q}.$$

The average number of units on hand during the period, I_{av}, will be the maximum number of units in stock, I_{max}, divided by 2, or

$$I_{max} = t(R - D) = \frac{Q}{R}(R - D).$$

$$I_{av} = \frac{Q}{2R}(R - D).$$

The holding cost for the period will be the holding cost per unit period times the average number of units on hand for the period, or

$$HC = \frac{C_h Q}{2R}(R - D).$$

The total system cost per period will be the sum of the item cost per period, the procurement cost per period, and the holding cost per period, or

$$TC = C_i D + \frac{C_p D}{Q} + \frac{C_h Q}{2R}(R - D). \qquad (10.5)$$

The procurement quantity resulting in a minimum total system cost may be found by differentiating with respect to Q, setting the result equal to zero, and solving for Q as follows:

$$\frac{dTC}{dQ} = -\frac{C_p D}{Q^2} + \frac{C_h}{2R}(R - D) = 0$$

$$Q^2 = \frac{2C_p D}{C_h[1 - (D/R)]}$$

$$Q = \sqrt{\frac{2C_p D}{C_h[1 - (D/R)]}}. \qquad (10.6)$$

As for the purchase decision model, no shortages were allowed since shortage cost was assumed to be infinite. Since this is the case, the procurement level would be

$$L = DT. \qquad (10.7)$$

The minimum total system cost may be found by substituting the minimum cost procurement quantity into Equation (10.5) as follows:

$$TC_{min} = C_i D + \frac{C_p D}{\sqrt{2C_p D/C_h[1 - (D/R)]}}$$

$$+ \frac{C_h \sqrt{2C_p D/C_h[1 - (D/R)]}}{2R}(R - D)$$

$$= C_i D + \sqrt{2C_p[1 - (D/R)]C_h D}. \qquad (10.8)$$

Equation (10.6) reduces to Equation (10.2) and Equation (10.8) reduces to Equation (10.4) as $R \to \infty$. Thus, the purchase decision model is a special case of the manufacture decision model.

A manufacture decision. Suppose that the item under consideration is to be manufactured and that the item cost due to manufacturing is $6.00 per unit. Also suppose that the demand is 3 units per period, the procurement lead time is 12 periods, the procurement (setup) cost is $50, the holding cost per unit per period is $0.004, and the production rate is 18 units per period.

Table 10.2. COST COMPONENTS FOR MANUFACTURE DECISION

Q	IC	PC	HC	TC
0	$18.00	$ ∞	$0.00	$ ∞
30	18.00	5.00	0.05	23.05
60	18.00	2.50	0.10	20.60
90	18.00	1.67	0.15	19.82
120	18.00	1.25	0.20	19.45
150	18.00	1.00	0.25	19.25
180	18.00	0.83	0.30	19.13
210	18.00	0.71	0.35	19.06
240	18.00	0.63	0.40	19.03
270	18.00	0.56	0.45	19.01
300	18.00	0.50	0.50	19.00
330	18.00	0.45	0.55	19.00
360	18.00	0.42	0.60	19.02

Item cost per period, procurement cost per period, holding cost per period, and total cost per period may be tabulated as a function of Q to illustrate the nature of the cost components. From Equation (10.5) the results of Table 10.2 may be developed. It is evident from the table that item cost per period is constant, procurement cost per period decreases, and holding cost per period increases with increasing values of Q. As before, it is not possible to pick the minimum cost procurement quantity because of the number of decimal places given. Again, the curve generated by these points is flat in the region of its minimum.

The minimum cost procurement level and procurement quantity may be found directly by substituting into Equation (10.6) and Equation (10.7) as follows:

$$Q = \sqrt{\frac{2(\$50)(3)}{\$0.004[1 - (3/18)]}} = 300 \text{ units,}$$

$$L = 3(12) = 36 \text{ units.}$$

Under the conditions assumed, the procurement manager would initiate manufacturing action when his stock falls to 36 units for a manufacturing quantity of 300 units from the manufacturing source specified.

10.5. MAKING THE SOURCE DECISION

The examples of the previous sections assumed that the source was fixed by restriction. Suppose now that no such restriction exists and that the procurement level, procurement quantity, and procurement source are to be determined. The computational procedure required involves the determination of the minimum total system cost for each source. The source giving rise to the minimum of the minimum costs is the source chosen. The procurement level and procurement quantity at which the absolute minimum occurred is also specified. The end result is the operation of the procurement and inventory system at minimum cost. The following paragraphs are presented in order to illustrate the computational procedure.

Purchase or manufacture. Suppose that the demand for a given item may be met by either purchasing or manufacturing. Also, assume that the item in question is the item used in the examples of the previous sections. The demand rate assumed was three units per period and the holding cost per unit per period was $0.004. Source-dependent parameters assumed were as follows:

	Purchase	*Manufacture*
Procurement lead time	16	12
Item cost	$6.10	$ 6.00
Procurement cost	$8.00	$50.00
Replenishment rate	∞	18

The minimum total system cost for the purchase alternative may be found from Equation (10.4) as

$$TC_{min} = \$6.10(3) + \sqrt{2(\$8)(\$0.004)(3)} = \$18.74.$$

And the minimum total system cost for the manufacture alternative may be computed from Equation (10.8) as

$$TC_{min} = \$6.00(3) + \sqrt{2(\$50)[1 - (3/18)](\$0.004)(3)} = \$19.00.$$

Therefore, the minimum cost procurement source is the purchase alternative even though the item cost for purchasing is higher than the item cost for manufacturing. (Comparison of the values given in Table 10.1 and Table 10.2 verifies this conclusion.)

The minimum cost purchase quantity was shown previously to be 110 units and the minimum cost procurement level was 48 units. Therefore, the minimum cost procurement and inventory policy for this example is that policy requiring procurement action to be initiated when the stock falls to 48 units, for a procurement quantity of 110 units, from the purchase source.

Evaluating alternate vendors. Suppose that the demand for an item may be met by purchasing from one of two vendors. Also, assume that the demand rate is three units per period and that the holding cost per unit per period is $0.003. The source-dependent parameters are as follows:

	Vendor A	*Vendor B*
Procurement lead time	14	10
Item cost	$4.20	$4.35
Procurement cost	$9.00	$7.00

The minimum total system cost for Vendor A may be found from Equation (10.4) as

$$TC_{min} = \$4.20(3) + \sqrt{2(\$9)(\$0.003)(3)} = \$13.00.$$

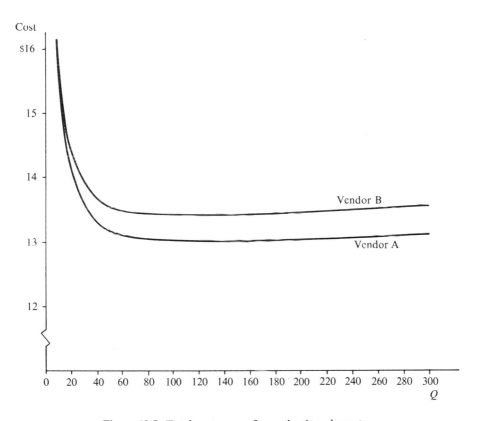

Figure 10.5. Total cost curves for evaluating alternate vendors.

And for Vendor B, the same equation may be used, giving

$$TC_{\min} = \$4.35(3) + \sqrt{2(\$7)(\$0.003)(3)} = \$13.40.$$

Therefore, the minimum cost procurement source is Vendor A. The minimum cost procurement quantity may be computed from Equation (10.2) as

$$Q = \sqrt{\frac{2(\$9)(3)}{\$0.003}} = 134 \text{ units.}$$

The minimum cost procurement level may be found from Equation (10.3) as

$$L = 3(14) = 42 \text{ units.}$$

For the conditions of this example, the minimum cost procurement and inventory policy is that policy requiring procurement action to be initiated when the stock level falls to 42 units, for a procurement quantity of 134 units, from Vendor A. The situation is illustrated graphically in Figure 10.5. The total cost curves for each vendor were developed from Equation (10.1). As is usually the case, the curves are flat in the region of their minimums.

10.6. MODELS FOR VARIABLE ITEM COST

Item cost is a source-dependent parameter in that its value depends upon the procurement source chosen. This fact was illustrated in the examples presented in the previous section. In those examples, however, item cost was not taken to be a function of the procurement quantity. This is an exception rather than the rule. Most vendors will quote a price discount schedule which allows for a reduction in the price per unit as the number of units purchased increases. Similarly, the reduction in the number of direct labor hours per unit as the number of units produced increases will result in a reduction in item cost. In each case, item cost will be a function of the procurement quantity chosen. The following paragraphs present, for the previously developed models, modifications that take variable item cost into consideration.

The price discount schedule. In the purchase alternative, item cost may depend upon the procurement quantity, owing to discounts allowed by the vendor for large orders. The price per unit is usually quoted for various purchase quantities as follows:

Purchase Quantity	Price per Unit
$1 \leq Q \leq Q_1$	C_{i_1}
$Q_1 < Q \leq Q_2$	C_{i_2}
$Q_2 < Q \leq Q_3$	C_{i_3}

Total system cost for the purchase alternative was given by Equation (10.1). Since the first term involves C_i, this equation will result in a different total cost function for each price in the schedule. Each price will have an applicable range, as previously indicated. Consequently, each total cost function will be valid for only a segment of its range and is, therefore, discontinuous. Hence, the least cost procurement quantity cannot be found by direct differentiation. It will be necessary to use the following procedure to find the minimum cost procurement quantity:

(1) Calculate the minimum cost Q by use of Equation (10.2).

(2) Find the total system cost by use of Equation (10.4) using the C_i value applicable to the Q value found in step 1.

(3) Calculate the total system cost for the smallest Q in the next higher Q range using Equation (10.1).

(4) If the TC value found in step 3 is greater than the TC value found in step 2, the result in step 2 is a minimum total system cost. If the TC value found in step 3 is less than the TC value found in step 2 proceed to step 5.

(5) Calculate the total system cost for the smallest Q in the next higher Q range using Equation (10.1).

(6) If the TC value found in step 5 is greater than the TC value found in step 4, the Q value of step 4 will result in a minimum total system cost. If the TC value found in step 5 is less than the TC value found in step 4, proceed to the next Q range and repeat steps 5 and 6 until the TC value starts increasing.

(7) If the highest Q range is reached without the total cost increasing, then the smallest Q in the highest Q range will give the minimum total system cost.

A purchase decision with variable item cost. As an example of the application of the price discount procedure just outlined, consider the following situation: A specified vendor is supplying replenishment stock to meet a demand of 10 units per period. Procurement cost is $16.00 per procurement, holding cost is $0.20 per unit per period, procurement lead time is 12 periods, and item cost is quoted in accordance with the following schedule:

Purchase Quantity	Price per Unit
1–49	$5.20
50–99	$4.90
100 and above	$4.60

Application of Equation (10.2) gives the minimum cost procurement quantity of

$$Q = \sqrt{\frac{2(\$16)10}{\$0.20}} = 40 \text{ units.}$$

Since this procurement quantity falls in the first price break, $5.20 is used as the item cost in Equation (10.4), resulting in

$$TC = \$5.20(10) + \sqrt{2(\$16)(\$0.20)(10)} = \$60.00.$$

Next, the total system cost resulting from the smallest Q in the next higher price range is found from Equation (10.1) as

$$TC = \$4.90(10) + \frac{\$16(10)}{50} + \frac{\$0.20(50)}{2} = \$57.20.$$

Since this value is less than the total system cost of the previous step, the total system cost for the smallest Q in the next higher price range is calculated from Equation (10.1) as

$$TC = \$4.60(10) + \frac{\$16(10)}{100} + \frac{\$0.20(100)}{2} = \$57.60.$$

This value is now greater than the total system cost of the previous step. Therefore, the minimum cost procurement quantity is 50 units. The minimum cost procurement level is found from Equation (10.3) to be 10(12) = 120 units.

In this example, the procurement level is greater than the procurement quantity. Therefore, the stock on hand will always be lower than the procurement level. This requires that procurement action be initiated when the stock on hand plus the stock on order falls to the procurement level. The number of periods per cycle will be 50/10 or five. Thus, procurement action would be initiated every five periods for a procurement quantity of 50 units.

The manufacturing progress function. It was shown in Chapter 5 that item cost is a function of the number of items produced, the manufacturing progress factor, the number of direct labor hours required for the first unit, the direct labor rate, the factory burden rate, and the direct material cost. Item cost was given by Equation (5.11).

Total system cost for manufacturing or remanufacturing was given by Equation (10.5). Since item cost occurs in only the first term, the minimum cost procurement quantity given by Equation (10.6) and the minimum cost procurement level given by Equation (10.7) will still hold. The effect of manufacturing progress, however, is lowering of the total system cost. This reduction in total system cost will affect the source decision only.

Equation (10.8) expresses the minimum total system cost for the manufacturing alternative when item cost is not modified because of manufacturing progress. If it is assumed that the discontinuous nature of manufacturing operations does not affect the item cost given by Equation (5.11), Equation (10.8) becomes

$$TC_{min} = \left[\frac{KN^n}{n+1}(lr)(1 + fb) + dm\right]D + \sqrt{2C_p\left(1 - \frac{D}{R}\right)C_h D} \qquad (10.9)$$

where

$$n = \frac{\log \phi}{\log 2}.$$

This equation may be used to find the minimum total system cost for manufacturing where item cost is subject to manufacturing progress.

A manufacturing alternative with variable item cost. As an illustration of the analysis required for the manufacturing model with variable item cost, consider the following situation. Suppose that a manufacturing source is being considered as an alternative to the purchase source of the previous example. Data relating to the manufacturing source under consideration are as follows:

$\phi = 0.80$
$K = 4$ hour
$lr = \$3.00$ per hour
$dm = \$2.40$ per unit
$fb = 0.80$ of direct labor cost
$C_p = \$100$ per procurement
$R = 20$ units per period
$N = 3,000$ units
$T = 8$ periods.

The minimum total system cost for this alternative may be found from Equation (10.9) as

$$TC_{min} = \left[\frac{4(3,000)^{\log 0.80/\log 2}}{(\log 0.80/\log 2) + 1}(\$3.00)(1 + 0.80) + \$2.40\right]10$$

$$+ \sqrt{2(\$100)\left(1 - \frac{10}{20}\right)(\$0.20)(10)}$$

$$= \left[\frac{4(3,000)^{-0.3219}}{0.6781}(\$5.40) + \$2.40\right]10 + \sqrt{\$200}$$

$$= \$48.20 + \$14.14 = \$62.34.$$

Since this value is greater than the minimum total system cost for the purchase alternative, this source of replenishment stock would not be chosen.

10.7. MODELS FOR FINITE SHORTAGE COST

All derivations up to this point were based upon the assumption that shortage cost was infinite. As a result, the decision models presented involved a trade-off between procurement cost and holding cost. When shortage cost is finite, an economic advantage may be gained by allowing some shortages to occur. One seeks the trade-off between procurement cost, holding cost, and shortage cost that will result in a minimum total system cost. Normally, the increase in total system cost due to the shortage condition is more than compensated by the reduction in holding cost. The following paragraphs develop models for the case where shortage cost is finite.

A purchase decision model. If it is assumed that demand for the item is deterministic, that procurement lead time is deterministic, that the replenishment rate is infinite, that shortage cost is finite, and that unsatisfied demand

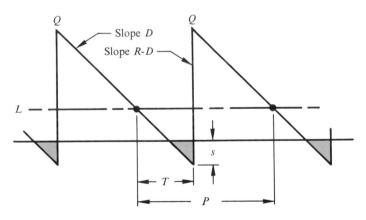

Figure 10.6. Infinite replenishment rate with finite shortage cost.

is not lost, the resulting inventory process may be represented graphically as in Figure 10.6. The number of periods per cycle may be expressed as

$$P = T + \frac{Q - DT}{D} = \frac{Q}{D}.$$

The total number of unit periods of stock on hand during the cycle is

$$I = \frac{(Q + L - DT)}{2}\left[\frac{Q + L - DT}{D}\right]$$

$$= \frac{(Q + L - DT)^2}{2D}.$$

And the total number of unit periods of shortage during the cycle is

$$S = \frac{S}{2}\left(\frac{S}{D}\right)$$
$$= \frac{(DT - L)}{2}\left[\frac{DT - L}{D}\right]$$
$$= \frac{(DT - L)^2}{2D}.$$

The total system cost per period will be the sum of the item cost for the period, the procurement cost for the period, the holding cost for the period, and the shortage cost for the period; that is,

$$TC = IC + PC + HC + SC.$$

Item cost for the period will be the item cost per unit times the demand in units per period, or

$$IC = C_i D.$$

The procurement cost for the period will be the purchase cost per purchase divided by the number of periods per cycle, or

$$PC = \frac{C_p}{P}$$
$$= \frac{C_p D}{Q}.$$

Holding cost for the period will be the holding cost per unit per period multiplied by the average number of units in stock for the period, or

$$HC = \frac{C_h I}{P}$$
$$= \frac{C_h (Q + L - DT)^2}{2Q}.$$

Shortage cost for the period will be the shortage cost per unit per period multiplied by the average number of units short for the period, or

$$SC = \frac{C_s S}{P}$$
$$= \frac{C_s (DT - L)^2}{2Q}.$$

The total system cost per period for the purchase model will be a summation of the four cost components previously developed and may be expressed as

$$TC = C_i D + \frac{C_p D}{Q} + \frac{C_h}{2Q}(Q + L - DT)^2 + \frac{C_s}{2Q}(DT - L)^2. \quad (10.10)$$

Equation (10.10) may be modified as follows:

$$TC = C_i D + \frac{C_p D}{Q} + \frac{C_h Q}{2} - C_h(DT - L) + \frac{C_h(DT - L)^2}{2Q} + \frac{C_s(DT - L)^2}{2Q}$$

Total system cost is a function of two independent variables, L and Q. Taking the partial derivatives of TC with respect to Q and $DT - L$, and setting these equal to zero gives

$$\frac{\partial TC}{\partial Q} = -\frac{C_p D}{Q^2} + \frac{C_h}{2} - \frac{C_h(DT - L)^2}{2Q^2} - \frac{C_s(DT - L)^2}{2Q^2} = 0 \quad (10.11)$$

$$\frac{\partial TC}{\partial(DT - L)} = -C_h + \frac{C_h(DT - L)}{Q} + \frac{C_s(DT - L)}{Q} = 0. \quad (10.12)$$

From Equation (10.12)

$$\frac{DT - L}{Q} = \frac{C_h}{C_h + C_s}. \quad (10.13)$$

Substituting Equation (10.13) into Equation (10.11) gives

$$-\frac{C_p D}{Q^2} + \frac{C_h}{2} - \frac{C_h + C_s}{2}\left(\frac{C_h}{C_h + C_s}\right)^2 = 0$$

$$\frac{C_p D}{Q^2} = \frac{C_h}{2} - \frac{C_h^2}{2(C_h + C_s)}$$

$$\frac{C_p D}{Q^2} = \frac{C_h(C_h + C_s) - C_h^2}{2(C_h + C_s)}$$

$$\frac{C_p D}{Q^2} = \frac{C_h C_s}{2(C_h + C_s)}$$

$$Q^2 = \frac{2C_p D(C_h + C_s)}{C_h C_s}$$

$$Q = \sqrt{\frac{2C_p D(C_h + C_s)}{C_h C_s}}$$

$$Q = \sqrt{\frac{2C_p D}{C_h} + \frac{2C_p D}{C_s}}. \quad (10.14)$$

Equation (10.14) gives the minimum cost procurement quantity as a function of demand, procurement cost, holding cost, and shortage cost.

The minimum cost procurement level may be derived from Equation (10.13) as

$$L = DT - \frac{C_h}{C_h + C_s}(Q).$$

Substituting Equation (10.14) for Q gives

$$L = DT - \frac{C_h}{C_h + C_s}\sqrt{\frac{2C_p D}{C_h} + \frac{2C_p D}{C_s}}$$

$$= DT - \sqrt{\frac{2C_h C_p D}{C_s(C_h + C_s)}}$$

$$= DT - \sqrt{\frac{2C_p D}{C_s[1 + (C_s/C_h)]}}. \tag{10.15}$$

Equation (10.14) and Equation (10.15) may now be substituted back into the total cost equation to yield an expression for minimum total system cost. Rewriting Equation (10.10) gives

$$TC = C_i D + \frac{C_p D}{Q} + \frac{C_h Q}{2}\left(1 - \frac{DT - L}{Q}\right)^2 + \frac{C_s Q}{2}\left(\frac{DT}{Q} - \frac{L}{Q}\right)^2.$$

Substituting Equation (10.13) gives

$$TC_{\min} = C_i D + \frac{C_p D}{Q} + \frac{C_h Q}{2}\left[\frac{C_s^2}{(C_h + C_s)^2}\right] + \frac{C_s Q}{2}\left[\frac{C_h^2}{(C_h + C_s)^2}\right]$$

$$= C_i D + \frac{C_p D}{Q} + \frac{C_h C_s Q}{2}\left[\frac{1}{C_h + C_s}\right]$$

$$= C_i D + C_p D\sqrt{\frac{C_h C_s}{2(C_h + C_s)C_p D}} + \frac{C_h C_s}{2(C_h + C_s)}\left(\sqrt{\frac{2(C_h + C_s)C_p D}{(C_h)(C_s)}}\right)$$

$$= C_i D + \sqrt{\frac{C_p C_h C_s D}{2(C_h + C_s)}} + \sqrt{\frac{C_p C_h C_s D}{2(C_h + C_s)}}$$

$$= C_i D + \sqrt{\frac{2C_p C_h C_s D}{C_h + C_s}}. \tag{10.16}$$

Equation (10.14) reduces to Equation (10.2), Equation (10.15) reduces to Equation (10.3), and Equation (10.16) reduces to Equation (10.4) as $C_s \to \infty$. Thus, the purchase model with infinite shortage cost is a special case of the purchase model with finite shortage cost.

A purchase decision for finite shortage cost. As an example of the computations required in the application of the purchase model for finite shortage cost consider the following situation: A specified vendor is supplying replenishment stock to meet a demand of 10 units per period. Purchasing lead time is 16 periods, item cost is $5.00 per unit, procurement cost is $16.00 per procurement, holding cost is $0.20 per unit per period, and shortage cost is $0.10 per unit short per period.

Total system cost per period may be tabulated as a function of L and Q by the use of Equation (10.10). The resulting values in the region of the minimum cost point are given in Table 10.3. The minimum cost Q and L may be

Table 10.3. TOTAL SYSTEM COST AS A FUNCTION OF L AND Q (dollars)

L \ Q	66	67	68	69	70	71	72
109	54.735	54.711	54.690	54.673	54.659	54.648	54.640
110	54.706	54.685	54.667	54.653	54.642	54.635	54.630
111	54.681	54.663	54.649	54.638	54.630	54.626	54.624
112	54.660	54.646	54.635	54.627	54.622	54.621	54.622
113	54.644	54.633	54.625	54.621	54.619	54.620	54.624
114	54.633	54.625	54.620	54.618	54.619	54.623	54.630
115	54.626	54.621	54.619	54.621	54.624	54.631	54.640
116	54.624	54.622	54.623	54.627	54.634	54.643	54.655
117	54.626	54.627	54.631	54.638	54.647	54.659	54.674
118	54.633	54.637	54.644	54.653	54.665	54.680	54.697
119	54.644	54.651	54.661	54.673	54.687	54.704	54.724

found by inspection. As was expected, the surface generated by the values exhibited is seen to be rather flat.

The minimum cost procurement quantity and procurement level may be found directly by substituting into Equation (10.14) and Equation (10.15) as follows:

$$Q = \sqrt{\frac{2(\$16)(10)}{\$0.20} + \frac{2(\$16)(10)}{\$0.10}} = 69 \text{ units,}$$

$$L = 10(16) - \sqrt{\frac{2(\$16)(10)}{\$0.10[1 + (\$0.10/\$0.20)]}} = 114 \text{ units.}$$

The resulting total system cost at the minimum cost procurement quantity and procurement level may be found from Equation (10.16) as

$$TC_{min} = \$5.00(10) + \sqrt{\frac{2(\$16)(\$0.20)(\$0.10)(10)}{\$0.20 + \$0.10}} = \$54.618.$$

Actually, however, a slightly modified policy must be adopted because the procurement quantity is less than the procurement level and because it is not a multiple of the demand. In this case, the number of periods per cycle is 69/10 or 6.9 periods. Thus, procurement action would be initiated every 7 periods for a procurement quantity of 70 units. This would result in a slightly higher total system cost.

A manufacture decision model. If it is assumed that demand for the item is deterministic, that procurement lead time is deterministic, that the replenishment rate is finite $(R > D)$, that shortage cost is finite, and that

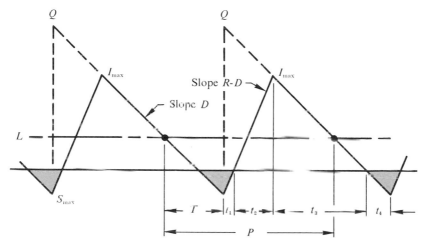

Figure 10.7. Finite replenishment rate with finite shortage cost.

unsatisfied demand is not lost, the resulting inventory process may be repre sented graphically as in Figure 10.7. As before, the number of periods per cycle may be expressed as

$$P = \frac{Q}{D}.$$

The net rate of accumulation during time $t_1 + t_2$ is $R - D$. The maximum accumulation is designated I_{max} in Figure 10.7. The following algebraic relationships are evident:

$$(t_1 + t_2)(R - D) = (t_3 + t_4)D \qquad (10.17)$$

$$t_1 + t_2 = \frac{Q}{R} \qquad (10.18)$$

$$t_3 + t_4 = \frac{I_{max} + DT - L}{D}. \qquad (10.19)$$

From Equations (10.17), (10.18), and (10.19)

$$I_{max} + DT - L = \frac{Q}{R}(R - D)$$

$$I_{max} = \frac{Q}{R}(R - D) + L - DT$$

$$= Q\left(1 - \frac{D}{R}\right) + L - DT. \tag{10.20}$$

The total number of unit periods of stock on hand during the inventory cycle is

$$I = \frac{I_{max}}{2}(t_2 + t_3)$$

$$= \frac{I_{max}^2}{2(R - D)} + \frac{I_{max}^2}{2D}$$

$$= \frac{I_{max}^2}{2}\left(\frac{1}{R - D} + \frac{1}{D}\right).$$

Substituting Equation (10.20) for I_{max} gives

$$I = \frac{[Q(1 - D/R) + L - DT]^2}{2}\left(\frac{1}{R - D} + \frac{1}{D}\right). \tag{10.21}$$

The total number of unit periods of shortage during the cycle is

$$S = \frac{S_{max}}{2}(t_1 + t_4)$$

$$= \frac{S_{max}^2}{2(R - D)} + \frac{S_{max}^2}{2D}.$$

But, since $S_{max} = DT - L$,

$$S = \frac{(DT - L)^2}{2}\left(\frac{1}{R - D} + \frac{1}{D}\right). \tag{10.22}$$

As for the purchase model, the total system cost per period will be the item cost for the period, the procurement cost for the period, the holding cost for the period, and the shortage cost for the period; that is,

$$TC = IC + PC + HC + SC.$$

Item cost for the period will be the item cost per unit times the demand in units per period, or

$$IC = C_i D.$$

The procurement cost for the period will be cost per procurement divided by the number of periods per cycle, or

$$PC = \frac{C_p}{P}$$

$$= \frac{C_p D}{Q} .$$

Holding cost for the period will be the holding cost per unit per period multiplied by the average number of units in stock for the period, or

$$HC = \frac{C_h I}{P}$$

$$HC = \frac{C_h D}{Q} \left\{ \frac{[Q(1 - D/R) + L - DT]^2}{2} \left(\frac{1}{R - D} + \frac{1}{D} \right) \right\}.$$

But, since

$$\frac{D}{Q} \left(\frac{1}{R - D} + \frac{1}{D} \right) = \frac{1}{Q(1 - D/R)}$$

$$HC = \frac{C_h}{2Q(1 - D/R)} [Q(1 - D/R) + L - DT]^2. \qquad (10.23)$$

Shortage cost for the period will be shortage cost per unit per period multiplied by the average number of units short for the period, or

$$SC = \frac{C_s S}{P}$$

$$SC = \frac{C_s D}{Q} \left[\frac{(DT - L)^2}{2} \left(\frac{1}{R - D} + \frac{1}{D} \right) \right].$$

Substituting Equation (10.23) gives

$$SC = \frac{C_s (DT - L)^2}{2Q(1 - D/R)} .$$

The total system cost per period for the manufacturing model will be a summation of the four cost components just developed and may be expressed as

$$TC = C_i D + \frac{C_p D}{Q} + \frac{C_h}{2Q(1 - D/R)} [Q(1 - D/R) + L - DT]^2$$

$$+ \frac{C_s (DT - L)^2}{2Q(1 - D/R)} . \qquad (10.24)$$

Equation (10.24) may be modified as follows:

$$TC = C_i D + \frac{C_p D}{Q} + \frac{C_h Q(1 - D/R)}{2} - C_h(DT - L)$$
$$+ \frac{C_h(DT - L)^2}{2Q(1 - D/R)} + \frac{C_s(DT - L)^2}{2Q(1 - D/R)}.$$

As for the purchase model, total system cost is a function of two independent variables, L and Q. Taking the partial derivative of TC with respect to Q and $DT - L$, and setting these equal to zero gives

$$\frac{\partial TC}{\partial Q} = -\frac{C_p D}{Q} + \frac{C_h(1 - D/R)}{2} - \frac{C_h(DT - L)^2}{2Q^2(1 - D/R)} - \frac{C_s(DT - L)^2}{2Q^2(1 - D/R)} = 0$$
$$(10.25)$$

$$\frac{\partial TC}{\partial(DT - L)} = -C_h + \frac{C_h(DT - L)}{Q(1 - D/R)} + \frac{C_s(DT - L)}{Q(1 - D/R)} = 0. \quad (10.26)$$

From Equation (10.26)

$$\frac{DT - L}{Q} = \frac{C_h(1 - D/R)}{C_h + C_s}. \quad (10.27)$$

Substituting Equation (10.27) into Equation (10.25) gives

$$-\frac{C_p D}{Q^2} + \frac{C_h(1 - D/R)}{2} - \frac{C_h^3(1 - D/R)}{2(C_h + C_s)^2} - \frac{C_s C_h^2(1 - D/R)}{2(C_h + C_s)^2} = 0$$

$$\frac{C_p D}{Q^2} = \frac{C_h C_s(1 - D/R)}{2(C_h + C_s)}$$

$$Q = \sqrt{\frac{2C_p D(C_h + C_s)}{C_h C_s(1 - D/R)}}$$

$$Q = \sqrt{\frac{1}{1 - D/R}} \sqrt{\frac{2C_p D}{C_h} + \frac{2C_p D}{C_s}}. \quad (10.28)$$

Equation (10.28) gives the minimum cost procurement quantity as a function of demand, the replenishment rate, procurement cost, holding cost, and shortage cost.

The minimum cost procurement level may be derived from Equation (10.27) as

$$L = DT - \frac{C_h(1 - D/R)}{C_h + C_s} \sqrt{\frac{1}{1 - D/R}} \sqrt{\frac{2C_p D}{C_h} + \frac{2C_p D}{C_s}}$$

$$= DT - \sqrt{1 - D/R} \sqrt{\frac{2C_p D}{C_s(1 + C_s/C_h)}}. \quad (10.29)$$

Equation (10.28) and Equation (10.29) may now be substituted back into the total cost equation to yield an expression for minimum total system cost.

The result is

$$TC_{min} = C_i D + \sqrt{1 - \frac{D}{R}} \sqrt{\frac{2C_p C_h C_s D}{C_h + C_s}}. \tag{10.30}$$

Equation (10.28) reduces to Equation (10.14), Equation (10.29) reduces to Equation (10.15), and Equation (10.30) reduces to Equation (10.16) as $R \to \infty$. Thus, the purchase model with finite shortage cost is a special case of the manufacture model with finite shortage cost. In fact, it can be shown that all previously derived models are special cases of the manufacture model with finite shortage cost.

A manufacture decision for finite shortage cost. To illustrate the analysis required for the manufacturing model with finite shortage cost, assume that a manufacturing source is being considered as an alternative to the purchase source of the previous example. For simplicity, item cost will not be a function of the procurement quantity; that is, manufacturing progress does not occur. Data relating to the manufacturing source indicates that item cost will be $4.50 per unit, procurement cost will be $100, the production rate is to be 20 units per period, and the lead time is 12 periods.

The minimum total system cost may be calculated from Equation (10.30) as follows:

$$TC_{min} = \$4.50(10) + \sqrt{1 - \frac{10}{20}} \sqrt{\frac{2(\$100)(\$0.20)(\$0.10)(10)}{\$0.20 + \$0.10}} = \$53.17.$$

Since this minimum total system cost is lower than the minimum total system cost for the purchase alternative, manufacturing is to be preferred. The minimum cost procurement quantity and procurement level may be found from Equation (10.28) and Equation (10.29) as follows.

$$Q = \sqrt{\frac{1}{1 - (10/20)}} \sqrt{\frac{2(\$100)(10)}{\$0.20} + \frac{2(\$100)(10)}{\$0.10}} = 245 \text{ units,}$$

$$L - 10(12) \quad \sqrt{1 - (10/20)} \sqrt{\frac{2(\$100)(10)}{\$0.10[1 + (\$0.10/\$0.20)]}} = 38 \text{ units.}$$

Therefore, the demand for the item will be met by manufacturing in lots of 245 units when the stock on hand falls to 38 units.

QUESTIONS

1. What is the justification for procuring and holding inventory?

2. Describe the source alternatives available to the inventory manager.

3. Give several reasons why procurement lead time will depend upon the source chosen.

4. Give several reasons why item cost will depend upon the source chosen.

5. Give several reasons why procurement cost will depend upon the source chosen.

6. What factors should be considered in arriving at a specific value for holding cost?

7. What factors should be considered in arriving at a specific value for shortage cost?

8. Classify all parameters of the procurement and inventory system in terms of $E = f(x_i, y_j)$.

9. Describe the trade-off relationships in the models for infinite shortage cost; finite shortage cost.

10. Item cost may be a function of both the source and the procurement quantity. Explain.

PROBLEMS

1. A contractor has a requirement for cement that amounts to 300 bags per day. No shortages are to be allowed. Cement costs $1.20 per bag, holding cost is $0.01 per bag per day, and it costs $15 to process a purchase order.
   (a) Find the minimum cost purchase quantity.
   (b) Find the minimum cost procurement level if purchase lead time is 2 days.
   (c) Calculate the total system cost per day.

2. A power plant manufacturer requires 64 pistons per day in his assembly operations. No shortages are to be allowed. The machine shop can produce 400 pistons per day. The cost associated with initiating manufacturing action is $400 and the holding cost is $0.30 per piston per day. The manufacturing cost is $92 per piston.
   (a) Find the minimum cost production quantity.
   (b) Find the minimum cost procurement level if production lead time is 5 days.
   (c) Calculate the total system cost per day.

3. Show that Q becomes infinite and TC approaches C_iD as D approaches R for the production model with infinite shortage cost.

4. The demand for a certain item is 10 units per period. No shortages are to be allowed. Holding cost is $0.01 per unit per period. Demand can be met by either purchasing or manufacturing, with each source described by the following data.

	Purchase	Manufacture
Procurement lead time	16 periods	10 periods
Item cost	$ 8.00	$ 7.40
Procurement cost	$20.00	$80.00
Replenishment rate	∞	25 units per period

(a) Find the minimum cost procurement source and calculate its economic advantage over the alternative source.

(b) Find the minimum cost procurement quantity.

(c) Find the minimum cost procurement level.

5. The army mess sergeant at Camp Swampy is responsible for meeting a demand of 6 bushels of potatoes per day. No shortages are permitted under Technical Order CS-174. Holding cost for potatoes is $0.015 per bushel per day. The demand can be met from one of three government-certified farmers in the immediate area. Farmer Brown requires a lead time of 6 days and attempts to gouge the army to the extent of $4.40 per bushel. Farmer Smith requires 8 days lead time but only charges $4.30 per bushel. The procurement cost from either of these two farmers is $12.00. Farmer Jones sells his wormy potatoes for only $4.10 per bushel. The procurement cost of dealing with Jones is $14.00 and a lead time of 10 days is involved.

(a) Find the minimum cost procurement source.

(b) Find the minimum cost procurement quantity.

(c) Find the minimum cost procurement level.

6. Suppose that the price per bag of cement required by the contractor of Problem 1 is quoted in accordance with the following schedule:

Purchase quantity (bags)	Price per bag
0–1,999	$1.20
2,000–3,999	1.10
4,000–5,999	1.00
6,000 or more	0.90

(a) Find the minimum cost procurement quantity and procurement level.

(b) Calculate the total system cost per day for meeting the demand and compare with the result of Problem 1.

7. Suppose that the learning factor associated with the manufacture of pistons described in Problem 2 is found to be 0.90. The following data describe the manufacturing facility:

$$K = 20 \text{ hr}$$
$$lr = \$3.50 \text{ per hour}$$
$$dm = \$50.00 \text{ per piston}$$
$$fb = 0.60 \text{ of direct labor cost}$$
$$R = 400 \text{ units per period}$$

(a) What is the minimum total system cost per day with and without learning if the total number of units required will be 4,000.

(b) Find the minimum cost procurement quantity and procurement level.

8. A subcontractor has been found that can supply pistons to the manufacturer described in Problem 2. Procurement cost will be $70 per purchase order.

The cost per unit is a function of the purchase quantity as follows:

Purchase quantity	Price per piston
1–249	$105
250–499	100
500 or more	90

(a) Calculate the minimum total system cost per day for purchasing from the subcontractor.

(b) What is the economic advantage of adopting the minimum cost source?

9. The demand for a certain item is 16 units per period. Unsatisfied demand causes a shortage cost of $0.75 per unit short per period. The cost of initiating purchasing action is $15 per purchase and the holding cost is $0.05 per unit per period. Item cost is $8.00 per unit.

(a) Find the minimum cost purchase quantity.

(b) Find the minimum cost procurement level if lead time is 8 periods.

(c) Calculate the total system cost per period.

10. The item described in Problem 9 may be manufactured at the rate of 50 units per period. The cost of initiating manufacturing action is $60 and the production cost per unit is $8.20.

(a) Find the minimum cost purchase quantity.

(b) Find the minimum cost procurement level if production lead time is 4 periods.

(c) Calculate the total system cost per period.

11. A certain fuel is needed at the rate of 2 tons (280 gal per ton) per day. Shortage cost is $0.005 per 100 gal per day and holding cost is $0.02 per 1,000 gal per day. The following data apply to the purchase and manufacture alternatives.

	Purchase	Manufacture
Item cost per ton	$14.00	$ 13.80
Procurement cost	$ 8.00	$100.00
Replenishment rate	∞	6 tons per day

Decide whether it is more economical to purchase or to produce the fuel.

12. Rework Problem 7 if shortage cost is finite and equal to $0.50 per unit short per period.

13. Show that Q becomes infinite and TC approaches $C_i D$ as D approaches R for the production model with finite shortage cost.

14. Show that Equation (10.28) and Equation (10.29) reduce to Equation (10.14) and Equation (10.15), respectively, when R approaches infinity.

15. Show that Equation (10.28) and Equation (10.29) reduce to Equation (10.2) and Equation (10.3), respectively, when both R and C_s approach infinity.

16. Derive expressions for the minimum cost procurement quantity and minimum cost procurement level when C_h is assumed to be infinite. Name a real world situation where such a model would apply.

eleven

PROBABILISTIC

INVENTORY MODELS

*A probabilistic procurement and inventory process
will result if either demand, or procurement lead time, or both
are random variables. Under these conditions, it is not possible to keep both
the procurement quantity and the number of periods per
cycle fixed, as is the case with the deterministic assumption of Chapter 10
The most common inventory system is that in which the procurement quantity is
fixed and the procurement interval is allowed to vary.
This case is treated in this chapter.*

*Models for the probabilistic inventory process will be developed
from expressions for expected values. Thus, they may be
classified as expected value models. Random variable processes can often
be analyzed by the consideration of expected outcomes. This chapter will
avoid the complication of multiple replenishment sources. We shall also adopt
the additional simplification of an infinite replenishment rate.
The resulting inventory models may be used to derive
the minimum cost procurement level and procurement quantity
for a single source. Numerical methods, however, must be used for finding
this minimum in most cases. Mathematical minimization is illustrated
by formulating a simplified system. The probabilistic models of this chapter
can be used to make source decisions if source
parameters are considered.*

11.1. MONTE CARLO ANALYSIS OF INVENTORY FLOW

The probabilistic inventory process may be most easily described by performing a Monte Carlo analysis of inventory flow over time. This does not mean that the simulated flow exactly parallels the real world process that it patterns. The simulation never deviates from the policies established, whereas in the real world such compliance will not occur. Nevertheless, the results provide a useful standard against which expressions for expected values for the probabilistic inventory system can be checked. Thus, Monte Carlo analysis provides the basis for deriving probabilistic inventory models.

Demand and lead time distributions. The probabilistic inventory process usually involves both a demand distribution and a procurement lead time

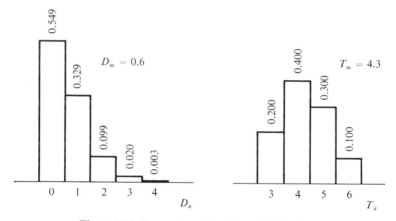

Figure 11.1. Demand and lead time distributions.

distribution. The form and parameters of these distributions must be specified. The cumulative distributions may then be developed and used as a source of demand and lead time data needed in the Monte Carlo analysis.

For the example under consideration, assume that demand has a Poisson distribution with a mean of 0.6 units per period. Lead time will be assumed to have an empirical distribution with a mean of 4.3 periods. Figure 11.1 is an illustration of these distributions giving specific values for the random variables, together with their associated probabilities. Note that D_x and T_x are used to designate demand and lead time random variables, respectively, and that D_m and T_m are mean or expected values of the distributions.

By summing the probabilities from left to right, and plotting the results, cumulative distributions may be developed. Figure 11.2 illustrates the cumulative distributions that result from the demand and lead time distributions

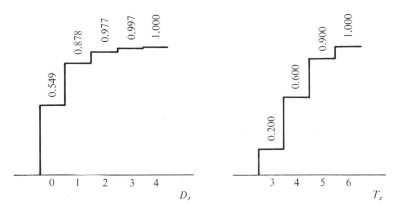

Figure 11.2. Cumulative demand and lead time distributions.

of Figure 11.1. These are used with random rectangular variables to generate demand and lead time data for the simulated inventory flow process.

The Monte Carlo analysis. The inventory flow process operates in accordance with certain policies established by the decision maker. These must be obeyed by the Monte Carlo analysis. For this example, assume that the procurement level is 3 units and that the procurement quantity is 12 units. It will be shown later that these policies lead to a minimum total system cost for the example under consideration.

The simulation process of this example begins with the stock on hand equal to the procurement level. At the beginning of each period, stock on hand plus stock on order is checked against the procurement level. If the procurement level has been reached or exceeded, an order is placed for an amount equal to the procurement quantity. A value is then drawn at random from the lead time distribution and retained.

If the procurement level has not been reached, a value is drawn at random from the demand distribution. This value is subtracted from the stock on hand, resulting in a new stock level at the end of the period. Since one period has passed, 1 is subtracted from all outstanding lead time values. If a lead time value is reduced to zero, an amount equal to the procurement quantity is added to the stock on hand. The statistics for the period are calculated and the next period is considered. If a lead time value is not reduced to zero, period statistics are calculated and the next period is considered. Refer to Table 11.1 and Figure 11.3 in order to get a more complete understanding of the simulation scheme.

Column C of Table 11.1 indicates that the stock on hand at the beginning of the first cycle is 3 units. Since the procurement level has been reached, a

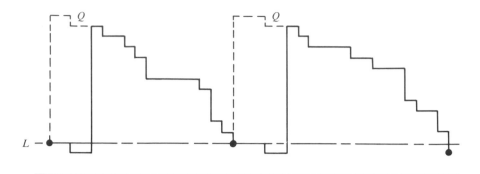

Figure 11.3. Monte Carlo analysis of inventory flow.

procurement order for 12 units is placed. This is shown by the dotted line in Figure 11.3. Next, a value is drawn at random from the cumulative lead time distribution of Figure 11.2 and entered in column D. A value is then drawn at random from the cumulative demand distribution of Figure 11.2 and entered in column E. Since this value was 0 units, the final stock position of column F remains at 3 units.

Since one period is completed, it is now possible to compute three important statistics. First, it is noted that one period is added to the total number of periods for the cycle. This total number will appear in column B just before the beginning of the next cycle. The number of units on hand or short, as the case may be, is recorded in column G or H as required. These data will provide values for the total number of unit periods of stock on hand for the cycle and the total number of unit periods of shortage for the cycle.

The second period of this example begins with 3 units on hand, since the first period ended with 3 units. A random draw from the demand distribution gives a value of 1, which reduces the final stock for the period to 2 units. Since it is assumed that the demand occurs at the end of the period, the number of units on hand for the period is recorded in column G as three. The third period begins with 2 units on hand, experienced no demand, and, therefore, had 2 units on hand. No demand was experienced for the fourth period, thus maintaining the stock on hand at 2 units. As a result of 4 lead time periods having elapsed, 12 units are added to the final stock position in column G. This is shown in Figure 11.3 at the point where the stock on hand rises sharply and the dotted line representing stock on order vanishes. Period 5 begins with 14 units on hand, experiences 1 demand, and ends with 13 units. The units on hand during the period are recorded as fourteen. Two complete cycles of inventory flow are developed and exhibited in Table 11.2. The entries for each period were developed as just outlined.

Output statistics for computer simulation. As the Monte Carlo analysis continues and cycle summary data are developed, a composite picture of the

Table 11.1. Monte Carlo analysis of inventory flow

Cycle (A)	Period (B)	Initial Stock (C)	Lead Time, T_x (D)	Demand, D_x (E)	Final Stock (F)	Units on Hand (G)	Units Short (H)
1	1	3	4	0	3	3	0
	2	3		1	2	3	0
	3	2		0	2	2	0
	4	2		0	14	2	0
	5	14		1	13	14	0
	6	13		0	13	13	0
	7	13		1	12	13	0
	8	12		1	11	12	0
	9	11		2	9	11	0
	10	9		0	9	9	0
	11	9		0	9	9	0
	12	9		0	9	9	0
	13	9		0	9	9	0
	14	9		1	8	9	0
	15	8		3	5	8	0
	16	5		1	4	5	0
	17	4		1	3	4	0
2	1	3	5	0	3	3	0
	2	3		0	3	3	0
	3	3		1	2	3	0
	4	2		0	2	2	0
	5	2		0	14	2	0
	6	14		1	13	14	0
	7	13		1	12	13	0
	8	12		0	12	12	0
	9	12		0	12	12	0
	10	12		0	12	12	0
	11	12		1	11	12	0
	12	11		0	11	11	0
	13	11		1	10	11	0
	14	10		0	10	10	0
	15	10		0	10	10	0
	16	10		3	7	10	0
	17	7		1	6	7	0
	18	6		0	6	6	0
	19	6		2	4	6	0
	20	4		2	2	4	0
3	1	2	4	0	2	2	0
.	.	.	.	.	.	.	.
.	.	.	.	.	.	.	.
.	.	.	.	.	.	.	.

Table 11.2. OUTPUT STATISTICS FOR COMPUTER SIMULATION

Cycle (A)	P_x (B)	P_m (C)	I_x (D)	I_m (E)	S_x (F)	S_m (G)
1	17	17.000	135	135.000	0	0.000
2	20	18.500	163	149.000	0	0.000
3	25	20.667	176	158.000	0	0.000
4	27	22.250	233	176.750	0	0.000
5	17	21.200	115	164.400	0	0.000
6	30	22.667	214	172.667	0	0.000
7	16	21.714	129	166.429	0	0.000
8	17	21.125	108	159.125	0	0.000
9	22	21.222	170	160.333	0	0.000
10	18	20.900	101	154.400	0	0.000
11	12	20.091	44	144.364	7	0.636
12	14	19.583	78	138.833	0	0.583
13	25	20.000	200	143.538	0	0.538
14	18	19.857	112	141.286	0	0.500
15	22	20.000	154	142.133	1	0.533
		Cycles 16 through 985 Omitted				
986	14	20.185	85	140.990	0	0.577
987	35	20.200	325	141.176	0	0.576
988	12	20.191	49	141.083	6	0.582
989	10	20.181	70	141.011	0	0.581
990	47	20.208	410	141.283	0	0.581
991	13	20.201	65	141.206	2	0.582
992	26	20.207	217	141.282	0	0.582
993	25	20.211	162	141.303	0	0.581
994	24	20.215	119	141.281	5	0.586
995	26	20.221	199	141.339	0	0.585
996	20	20.221	137	141.334	0	0.584
997	20	20.221	142	141.335	0	0.584
998	21	20.221	119	141.313	3	0.586
999	21	20.222	140	141.311	0	0.586
1,000	19	20.221	135	141.305	0	0.585

probabilistic inventory process begins to develop. Table 11.2 is an abridged cycle-by-cycle summary of the simulated inventory flow performed on a digital computer for 1,000 cycles. Column A gives the cycle number. Column B gives the number of periods in the cycle, designated P_x, since it is a random variable Column C gives the running average, P_m, of the individual values in column B. Column D gives the total number of unit periods of stock on hand for the cycle. This is designated I_x, since it is also a random variable. Its running average, I_m, is given in column E. Column F gives the total number of unit periods of shortage for the cycle. This is a random variable and is designated S_x. Its running mean, S_m, is given in column G. Table 11.1

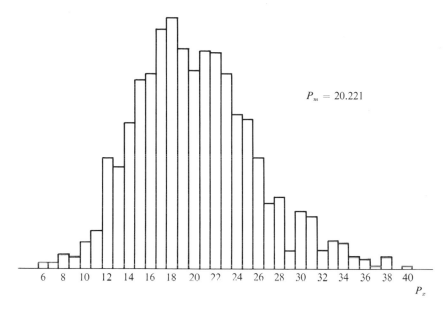

Figure 11.4. Distribution of number of periods per cycle.

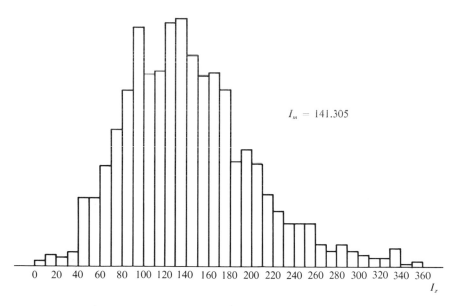

Figure 11.5. Distribution of total number of unit periods of
stock per cycle.

and Figure 11.3 may be used to verify the values for P_x, I_x, and S_x given for cycles 1 and 2 in Table 11.2.

Each of these random variables may be histogramed to describe further the nature of the probabilistic inventory process. These histograms are exhibited in Figure 11.4, Figure 11.5, and Figure 11.6. Although 1,000 cycles are not sufficient to give perfectly smooth histograms, a good idea of the distribution of each random variable is given.

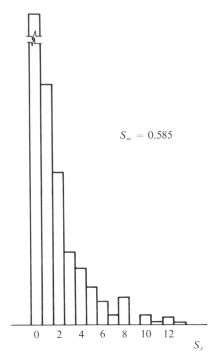

$S_m = 0.585$

Figure 11.6. Distribution of total number of unit periods of shortage per cycle.

The values for P_m, I_m, and S_m given at cycle 1,000 represent estimates of the expected values for P_x, I_x, and S_x, respectively. The relative stability of the mean values may be noted by comparing the terminal cycles with the initial cycles in Table 11.2. Continuing the simulation beyond 1,000 cycles would contribute further to their stability.

11.2. EXPRESSIONS FOR EXPECTED VALUES

The simulation process of the previous section provides expected values for three important random variables associated with the probabilistic inventory system. These values are needed in developing decision models for the process. Use of the simulation method to derive expected values for even a limited number of procurement level and procurement quantity combinations is obviously extremely time-consuming. Hence this section will derive expressions that approximate P_m and I_m. A direct development for S_m is dealt with in the following sections.

The expected inventory geometry. Figure 11.3 illustrates the inventory process as it occurs under the influence of random elements. If variance were not present, the process would operate in accordance with its expected values. Inventory flow over time would appear as in Figure 11.7.

The geometry of the inventory process shown in Figure 11.7 does not differ from that for the deterministic system with instantaneous replenishment. Its orientation, however, is different. Provision is made for safety stock to absorb fluctuations in stock level from cycle to cycle. The need for this extra stock may be attributed to the presence of random elements.

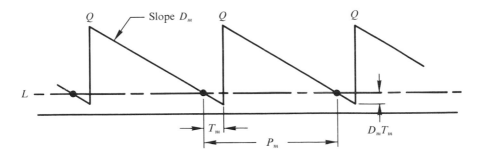

Figure 11.7. Expected inventory flow process.

The expected number of periods per cycle. Referring to Figure 11.7 indicates that the expected number of periods per cycle may be expressed as

$$P_m = T_m + \frac{Q - D_m T_m}{D_m} = \frac{Q}{D_m}, \tag{11.1}$$

The validity of this expression as a measure of the expected number of periods per cycle may be checked by reference to the simulated process. Substituting the values for Q and D_m used in the simulation results in

$$P_m = \frac{12}{0.6} = 20.000 \text{ periods.}$$

Since the value found by simulation was 20.221, it may be concluded that Equation (11.1) gives a good means for approximating the expected number of periods per cycle for the probabilistic inventory process. Intuitive reasoning indicates that this expression yields an exact value; the discrepancy being due to the lack of complete convergence at 1,000 cycles.

The expected total number of unit periods of stock. Figure 11.7 indicates that the expected total number of unit periods of stock on hand during the cycle is the sum of two components which may be approximated as

$$I_m = P_m \left(\frac{Q}{2} \right) + P_m (L - D_m T_m)$$

$$= \frac{Q}{D_m} \left[\frac{Q}{2} + (L - D_m T_m) \right]. \tag{11.2}$$

The validity of Equation (11.2) as an approximation for the total number of unit periods of stock on hand for the cycle may be checked by substituting the values of Q, L, D_m, and T_m used in the simulation. This results in

$$I_m = \frac{12}{0.6}\left[\frac{12}{2} + 3 - 0.6(4.3)\right] = 128.40 \text{ unit periods.}$$

The value found by simulation was 141.305 unit periods. This can be reduced by $\frac{1}{2}P_m D_m = \frac{1}{2}(20)(0.6) = 6$ unit periods to compensate because the simulation charged the entire period for the stock level at the beginning of the period. The simulated result is, therefore, 135.305 unit periods which is comparable with the value found from Equation (11.2).

It may be concluded that Equation (11.2) yields only an approximation for the total number of unit periods of stock on hand for the cycle. This conclusion is supported by intuitive considerations and by the unlikelihood of a discrepancy of seven unit periods being entirely due to the lack of complete convergence at 1,000 cycles. Using expected values to derive an expression for expected area yields a biased result.

11.3. THE DISTRIBUTION OF LEAD TIME DEMAND

Expressions for the expected number of periods per inventory cycle, P_m, and for the expected number of unit periods of stock on hand for the cycle, I_m, were developed in the previous section. The derivation of an expression for the expected number of unit periods of shortage for the cycle, S_m, will deviate from the procedure used there. It requires the development of the distribution of lead time demand as an important intermediate step. The following paragraphs present an exact numerical method for developing this distribution.

Lead time demand. Lead time demand is demand summed over the lead time. When both demand and lead time are random variables, lead time demand may be expressed symbolically as

$$V_x = \sum_{}^{T_x} D_x. \tag{11.3}$$

This expression indicates that lead time demand is the sum of all demand over the lead time. With the distribution of D_x and T_x given, it is possible to develop the distribution of V_x by Monte Carlo analysis. This method, however, requires considerable computational effort to give a good approximation of the actual distribution. For complete generality, it is necessary to have an exact method for developing the lead time demand distribution.

Figure 11.8 illustrates conditional distributions of lead time demand for several specific values of lead time. When viewed as a single distribution, Figure 11.8 may be called a *joint distribution of demand and lead time* if the total probability is adjusted to unity. The probability associated with any specific value of lead time demand may then be found by summing for that value across all lead time values.

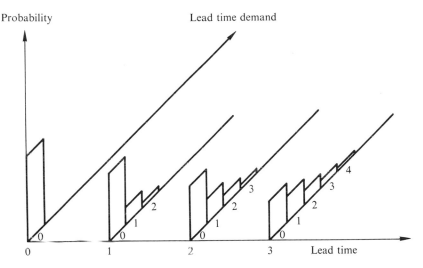

Figure 11.8. Joint distribution of demand and lead time.

The previous qualitative description may be quantified by adopting the following notation:

$V_x \mid T =$ lead time demand random variable, given that lead time is T periods.

$f(V_x \mid T) =$ conditional lead time demand distribution, given that lead time is T periods.

The probability of $V_x \geq V$ for a specific lead time (conditional probability) is

$$P(V_x \geq V \mid T) = \sum_{V_x = V}^{V_{max}} f(V_x \mid T).$$

Multiplying by $f(T_x)$ and summing over all values of T gives

$$P(V_x \geq V) = \sum_{T=0}^{T_{max}} \left[f(T_x) \sum_{V_x = V}^{V_{max}} f(V_x \mid T) \right]. \tag{11.4}$$

The probability associated with each integral value of V_x may be found from Equation (11.4). This procedure is now illustrated with an example based on the distributions of Figure 11.1.

Numerical development of lead time demand. The computational procedure required in developing the distribution of lead time demand may best be explained by reference to Table 11.3. The first section is analogous to

Table 11.3. NUMERICAL DEVELOPMENT OF LEAD TIME DEMAND DISTRIBUTION

V_x	$P[V_x \mid T_x]$				$P(T_x, V_x) = P(T_x) \cdot P(V_x \mid T_x)$				$P(V_x)$
	$T_x = 3$	$T_x = 4$	$T_x = 5$	$T_x = 6$	$P(T_x = 3)$ $= 0.2$	$P(T_x = 4)$ $= 0.4$	$P(T_x = 5)$ $= 0.3$	$P(T_x = 6)$ $= 0.1$	
0	0.1653	0.0907	0.0498	0.0273	0.03306	0.03628	0.01494	0.00273	0.08701
1	0.2975	0.2177	0.1494	0.0984	0.05950	0.08708	0.04482	0.00984	0.20124
2	0.2678	0.2613	0.2240	0.1771	0.05356	0.10452	0.06720	0.01771	0.24299
3	0.1607	0.2090	0.2240	0.2125	0.03214	0.08360	0.06720	0.02125	0.20419
4	0.0723	0.1254	0.1680	0.1912	0.01446	0.05016	0.05040	0.01912	0.13414
5	0.0260	0.0602	0.1008	0.1377	0.00520	0.02408	0.03024	0.01377	0.07329
6	0.0078	0.0241	0.0504	0.0826	0.00156	0.00964	0.01512	0.00826	0.03458
7	0.0020	0.0083	0.0216	0.0425	0.00040	0.00332	0.00648	0.00425	0.01445
8	0.0005	0.0025	0.0081	0.0191	0.00010	0.00100	0.00243	0.00191	0.00544
9	0.0001	0.0007	0.0027	0.0076	0.00002	0.00028	0.00081	0.00076	0.00187
10		0.0002	0.0008	0.0028		0.00008	0.00024	0.00028	0.00060
11			0.0002	0.0009			0.00006	0.00009	0.00015
12			0.0001	0.0003			0.00003	0.00003	0.00004*
13				0.0001				0.00001	0.00001

* Arbitrarily reduced from 0.00006 so that $\Sigma \, P(V_x) = 1.00000$.

Figure 11.8 in that it gives the conditional distribution of lead time demand associated with each lead time value. For the case under consideration, conditional distributions are required for lead time values of 3, 4, 5, and 6. These conditional distributions are selected in accordance with the following rules:

(1) If lead time is 1 period, the basic demand distribution is the lead time demand distribution. The probabilities of each value of D_x would be associated with the respective values of V_x under $T_x = 1$, if $T_x = 1$ were called for.

(2) Enter V_x probabilities under $T_x = 2$, $T_x = 3$, ..., associated with a demand distribution of the same form as the basic demand distribution, but with parameters multiplied by 2, 3, etc. In Table 11.3, this calls for Poisson probabilities for distributions with mean values of 1.8, 2.4, 3.0, and 3.6.

The second section of Table 11.3 involves adjustment of the total probability so it will sum to unity. The procedure is described by Equation (11.4) and is accomplished by multiplying each value of each conditional distribution by the probability of T_x taking its associated value. The result is a joint probability density function from which the lead time demand distribution may be developed.

The probability of lead time demand assuming the specific values specified as V_x in Table 11.3 may be found by summing across all values of $P(T_x, V_x)$

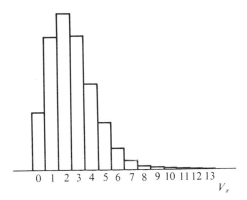

Figure 11.9. Distribution of lead time demand.

in the second section. The results are entered under $P(V_x)$ in the last column and make up a demand marginal distribution. This demand marginal distribution is the required lead time demand distribution for the demand and lead time distribution of Figure 11.1 It is histogramed in Figure 11.9.

The numerical procedure presented in this section is applicable in those cases where demand has a Poisson, normal, or certain other distributions. In selecting the conditional distributions, it is necessary only to increase the parameters of the basic demand distribution by multiplying by the specific conditional lead time value. If demand obeys some other distribution form, this method for selecting the conditional distributions does not hold. The distribution of lead time need not conform to any specific form. Any theoretical or empirical distribution may be used.

11.4. EXPRESSIONS FOR SHORTAGE CONDITION

Lead time demand is independent of the procurement level. A lead time demand distribution simply exhibits the number of demands that may occur during the lead time. The shortage condition at the end of the inventory cycle depends jointly upon the distribution of lead time demand and choice of procurement level. In this section, approximations for the probability of an empty warehouse, the probability of one or more shortages, the expected number of shortages, and the expected number of unit periods of shortage are developed. Completion of this phase will provide the third expected value needed in the derivation of effectiveness functions for the probabilistic inventory process.

The probability of an empty warehouse. An empty warehouse will result if lead time demand is equal to or greater than the procurement level. If the lead time demand distribution is continuous, the probability of an empty warehouse at the end of the inventory cycle may be expressed as

$$P\{\text{empty warehouse}\} = \int_{L}^{\infty} f(V_x)\, dV_x.$$

For the discrete lead time demand distribution of Figure 11.9, the probability of an empty warehouse is

$$P\{\text{empty warehouse}\} = \sum_{L}^{V_{\max}} f(V_x).$$

The second column of Table 11.4 gives the probability of an empty warehouse as a function of the procurement level.

Table **11.4.** SHORTAGE PROBABILITIES AS A FUNCTION OF L

L	$P\{\text{empty warehouse}\}$	$P\{1 \text{ or more short}\}$
0	1.00000	0.91299
1	0.91299	0.71175
2	0.71175	0.46876
3	0.46876	0.26457
4	0.26457	0.13043
5	0.13043	0.05714
6	0.05714	0.02256
7	0.02256	0.00811
8	0.00811	0.00267
9	0.00267	0.00080
10	0.00080	0.00020
11	0.00020	0.00005
12	0.00005	0.00001
13	0.00001	0.00000

The probability of an empty warehouse, as an expression for shortage condition, fails to give a measure of the magnitude of the shortage condition (if any) or the time duration involved. As such, it is very difficult to establish a value for shortage cost. In fact, an empty warehouse is desirable if during this period no demand occurs.

The probability of one or more shortages. One or more shortages will result if lead time demand is greater than the procurement level. If the lead time demand distribution is continuous, the probability of one or more shortages at the end of the inventory cycle may be expressed as

$$P\{1 \text{ or more short}\} = \int_{L+1}^{\infty} f(V_x)\, dV_x.$$

For the discrete lead time demand distribution of Figure 11.9, the probability of one or more shortages is

$$P\{1 \text{ or more short}\} = \sum_{L+1}^{V\text{max}} f(V_x).$$

The third column of Table 11.4 gives the probability of one or more shortages as a function of the procurement level.

The probability of one or more shortages establishes with certainty the existence of a shortage condition. Like the probability of an empty warehouse, however, it does not give a measure of the magnitude of the shortage condition or its time duration. It is, therefore, difficult to establish a value of shortage when using this measure.

The expected number of shortages. If the lead time demand distribution is continuous, the expected number of shortages per inventory cycle may be expressed as

$$E\{\text{number of shortages}\} = \int_{L+1}^{\infty} (V_x - L)f(V_x)\, dV_x.$$

For the discrete lead time demand distribution of Figure 11.9, the expected number of shortages is

$$E\{\text{number of shortages}\} = \sum_{L+1}^{V\text{max}} (V_x - L)f(V_x). \tag{11.5}$$

The application of Equation (11.5) is illustrated in Figure 11.10 and requires the development of one shortage distribution for each procurement level choice. When $L = 0$, the lead time demand distribution is the shortage distribution. This is verified by reasoning as follows: If no demands occur during the lead time, no shortages will result; if one demand occurs, one shortage will result, if two demands occur, two shortages will result, and so forth. The probability of each of these events is given by the lead time demand distribution. Therefore, the expected number of shortages for $L = 0$ is the mean of the shortage distribution for that L choice. This is shown as the first phase of Figure 11.10.

The second phase of Figure 11.10 gives the shortage distribution for the case where $L = 1$. It is developed by reasoning thus: If no demands occur during the lead time, no shortages will result; if one demand occurs, no shortages will result; if two demands occur, one shortage will result; if three demands occur, two shortages will result, and so forth. Again, the probability of each of these events is given by the lead time demand distribution. The mean for the resulting shortage distribution is calculated in Figure 11.10.

The process just outlined is continued for all values of L up to $L = V_{\text{max}}$. For $L = 12$, it is evident that no shortages will occur for all values of lead time demand except 13. If lead time demand is 13, one shortage will occur.

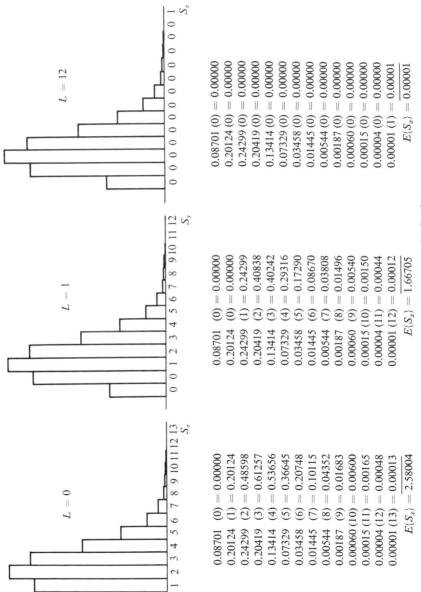

Figure 11.10. Development of shortage distributions.

This is shown in the last phase of Figure 11.10. The expected value for the resulting shortage distribution is calculated as before and is found to be 0.00001. If $L = 13$, it is evident that no shortages will occur for any allowable value of lead time demand up to and including V_{max}. Therefore, the expected number of shortages for this last case will be zero. The second column of Table 11.5 gives the expected number of shortages per inventory cycle as a function of the procurement level.

Table **11.5.** SHORTAGE EXPECTATION AS A
FUNCTION OF L

L	$E\{shortages\}$	S_m
0	2.58004	5.5472
1	1.66705	2.3158
2	0.95530	0.7605
3	0.48654	0.1973
4	0.22197	0.0411
5	0.09154	0.0070
6	0.03440	0.0010
7	0.01184	0.0001
8	0.00373	0.0000
9	0.00106	0.0000
10	0.00026	0.0000
11	0.00006	0.0000
12	0.00001	0.0000
13	0.00000	0.0000

A measure of the magnitude of the shortage condition is provided by an expression for the expected number of shortages. Although the time duration involved is not specified, it is possible to establish a fairly good value of shortage cost when using this expression.

The expected number of unit periods of shortage. By utilizing the values for the expected number of shortages per inventory cycle, it is possible to derive an approximate expression for the expected number of unit periods of shortage. This is the value previously developed by simulation. It is an area which may be approximated by

$$S_m = \frac{[E\{S_x\}]^2}{2D_m}.$$

(11.6)

The third column of Table 11.5 gives specific values for S_m as a function of L. Since these values are based on the same inputs as were used in the simulation, a comparison can be made. The simulated value for S_m given in Table 11.2 is 0.585 unit periods. Since the procurement level was set at three units, this is to be compared to 0.197 given in Table 11.5. The discrepancy may be explained first because using expected values to find an area is bias, as was the case with the expected total number of unit periods of stock. Secondly, the simulation charges the period for the number of shortages at the beginning of the period, whereas Equation (11.6) is based on the average number short for the period. This should almost double the value found by simulation. Finally, procurement action is initiated after the stock level falls below L for some cycles. This occurred on the second cycle of Figure 11.3 and will also contribute to an increase in the simulated value. Its effect is to force a more severe shortage condition than the assumption that procurement action is initiated exactly on the procurement level.

The expected number of unit periods of shortage per cycle gives a measure of the magnitude and time duration of the shortage condition. As a result, assigning a value for shortage cost is not as difficult as for the previous expressions for shortage condition. Although the derived value for S_m does not agree with the simulated value, it deviates to the small side, as does the value of I_m. As such, the errors introduced will tend to cancel, since effectiveness functions utilizing these expected values trade off costs based on their magnitudes. This compensation may be noted in the analysis of the next section.

11.5. THE MINIMUM COST INVENTORY POLICIES

By utilizing the previously derived approximations for P_m, I_m, and S_m, it is possible to develop effectiveness functions that may be used to find the minimum cost inventory policies. This section will present two specific cases: The first deals with an expected total system cost model trading off holding cost per period and shortage cost per period with the procurement quantity fixed. The second deals with an expected total system cost model trading off procurement cost per period, holding cost per period, and shortage cost per period. It will provide a means for finding the minimum cost procurement level and procurement quantity simultaneously.

Expected total variable cost as a function of L given Q. If the procurement quantity is assumed to be fixed, the expected total variable cost per period will be the sum of the expected holding cost per period, and the expected shortage cost per period; that is,

$$TC_m = HC_m + SC_m.$$

The expected holding cost per period will be the holding cost per unit per period multiplied by the expected number of units in stock for the period, or

$$HC_m = \frac{C_h I_m}{P_m}.$$

Substituting Equation (11.1) for P_m and Equation (11.2) for I_m gives

$$HC_m = C_h \left[\frac{Q}{2} + (L - D_m T_m) \right].$$

The expected shortage cost per period will be the shortage cost per unit short per period multiplied by the expected number of unit periods of shortage for the period, or

$$SC_m = \frac{C_s S_m}{P_m}.$$

Substituting Equation (11.1) for P_m gives

$$SC_m = \frac{C_s D_m S_m}{Q}.$$

The expected total system cost per period will be a summation of the two cost components previously developed and may be expressed as

$$TC_m = C_h \left[\frac{Q}{2} + (L - D_m T_m) \right] + \frac{C_s D_m S_m}{Q}. \tag{11.7}$$

Minimization of Equation (11.7) by taking a derivative is not possible because S_m cannot be expressed as a mathematical function of L. It can only be numerically related to L as in Table 11.5.

As an example of the determination of the minimum cost procurement level when the procurement quantity is fixed consider the following situation: Demand and lead time are distributed as shown in Figure 11.1. Holding cost per unit per period is \$0.09 and shortage cost per unit short per period is \$3.50. The procurement quantity is fixed at 10 units. Therefore, the expected total system cost as a function of the procurement level is

$$TC_m = \$0.09 \left[\frac{10}{2} + (L - 2.58) \right] + \$3.50 \left(\frac{0.6}{10} \right) S_m.$$

The expected total system cost as a function of L when Q is fixed at 10 units is given in the second column of Table 11.6. Each value is computed from the foregoing equation by reference to Table 11.5 for values of S_m. Actually, each total cost value shown is an expected value from a total cost distribution. Choosing the L giving a minimum expected cost is equivalent to maximizing the probability of minimizing the sum of holding cost per period and shortage cost per period.

The third column of Table 11.6 gives expected total system cost values for the case where Q is fixed at 14 units. Comparison with the values for $Q = 10$ indicates that the expected minimum total system cost depends on both L and Q. Thus, at this point, it is not certain what value of Q will yield a minimum expected total system cost.

Expected total system cost as a function of L and Q. When the procurement quantity is not restricted to a specific value, the expected total system cost per period will be the sum of the expected procurement cost per period, the expected holding cost per period, and the expected shortage cost per period; that is,

$$TC_m = PC_m + HC_m + SC_m.$$

Table 11.6. EXPECTED TOTAL VARIABLE COST AS A FUNCTION OF L GIVEN Q (dollars)

L	TC_m at $Q = 10$	TC_m at $Q = 14$
0	1.383	1.230
1	0.894	0.835
2	0.558	0.692
3	0.529	0.698
4	0.587	0.764
5	0.669	0.849
6	0.758	0.938

The expected procurement cost per period is the procurement cost per procurement divided by the expected number of periods per inventory cycle, or

$$PC_m = \frac{C_p}{P_m}.$$

Substituting Equation (11.1) for P_m gives

$$PC_m = \frac{C_p D_m}{Q}.$$

The expected holding cost per period and the expected shortage cost per period were derived in the previous paragraphs. Therefore, the expected total system cost per period may be expressed as:

$$TC_m = \frac{C_p D_m}{Q} + C_h \left[\frac{Q}{2} + (L - D_m T_m) \right] + \frac{C_s D_m S_m}{Q}. \qquad (11.8)$$

Minimization of Equation (11.8) by partial differentiation is not possible. Like Equation (11.7), it contains S_m which is only numerically related to L. As an example of the determination of the minimum cost procurement level and procurement quantity, consider the following situation: Demand and lead time are distributed as shown in Figure 11.1. Procurement cost per procurement is $10. Holding cost per unit per period is $0.09 and shortage cost per unit per period is $3.50. Therefore, the expected total system cost as a function of the procurement level and procurement quantity is

$$TC_m = \frac{\$10(0.6)}{Q} + \$0.09\left[\frac{Q}{2} + (L - 2.58)\right] + \$3.50\left(\frac{0.6}{Q}\right)S_m.$$

The expected total system cost as a function of L and Q is given in Table 11.7. Each value is computed from the preceding expression with reference

Table 11.7. EXPECTED TOTAL SYSTEM COST AS A FUNCTION OF L AND Q (dollars)

L \ Q	10	11	12	13	14
0	1.983	1.867	1.779	1.711	1.659
1	1.494	1.340	1.303	1.279	1.264
2	1.158	1.133	1.121	1.118	1.121
3	1.129	1.116	1.113	1.117	1.127
4	1.187	1.176	1.175	1.182	1.193
5	1.269	1.259	1.259	1.266	1.278
6	1.358	1.348	1.348	1.355	1.367

to Table 11.5 for values of S_m. As before, each entry is actually an expected value from a total system cost distribution. Choosing the L and Q giving a minimum expected cost is equivalent to maximizing the probability of minimizing the sum of procurement cost per period, holding cost per period, and shortage cost per period.

The minimum expected cost procurement level and procurement quantity is found by inspection to be 3 and 12, respectively. These are the values that were used in the Monte Carlo analysis. They give an expected total system cost of $1.113 when used with the expressions for expected values. Any error in these values will be reflected in the expected total system cost. Making adjustments in the expected values found by Monte Carlo analysis and using them to compute the expected total system cost gives a value of $1.142.

11.6. MINIMUM COST POLICIES FOR A SIMPLIFIED SYSTEM

The effectiveness functions derived in the previous section could not be minimized by direct mathematical means. This occurred primarily because the term S_m was not a mathematical function of L. This section adopts two simplifications in order to demonstrate the method of finding mathematically minimum cost inventory policies for the probabilistic system. Specifically, this will require that shortage cost be based on the expected number of shortages, and that the lead time demand distribution be a simple continuous function. Although other choices may be made, it is assumed in this section that lead time demand is distributed uniformly in the interval 0 to q units; $f(V_x) = 1/q$.

Expected total variable cost as a function of L given Q. If the procurement quantity is assumed to be fixed, the expected total variable cost per period will be the sum of the expected holding cost per period and the expected shortage cost per period; that is,

$$TC_m = HC_m + SC_m.$$

The expected holding cost was derived in the previous section and was shown to be

$$HC_m = C_h\left[\frac{Q}{2} + (L - D_m T_m)\right].$$

The expected shortage cost per period will be the shortage cost per unit short, designated C_s', multiplied by the expected number of shortages per period, or

$$SC_m = \frac{C_s' E\{S_x\}}{P_m}.$$

Substituting a continuous approximation of Equation (11.5) for $E\{S_x\}$ and Equation (11.1) for P_m gives

$$SC_m = \frac{C_s' D_m}{Q}\int_{L+1}^{q} (V_x - L)f(V_x)\,dV_x.$$

Substituting $f(V_x) = 1/q$ and evaluating gives

$$SC_m = \frac{C_s' D_m}{qQ}\left[\int_{L+1}^{q} (V_x)\,dV_x - \int_{L+1}^{q} (L)\,dV_x\right]$$

$$= \frac{C_s' D_m}{qQ}\left[\frac{V_x^2}{2}\Big|_{L+1}^{q} - L(V_x)\Big|_{L+1}^{q}\right]$$

$$= \frac{C_s' D_m}{qQ}\left[\frac{q^2}{2} - \frac{(L+1)^2}{2} - Lq + L(L+1)\right]$$

$$= \frac{C_s' D_m}{Q}\left[\frac{q}{2} - L + \frac{L^2 - 1}{2q}\right].$$

The expected total system cost per period will be the sum of the expected holding cost for the period and the expected shortage cost for the period and may be expressed as

$$TC_m = C_h\left[\frac{Q}{2} + (L - D_m T_m)\right] + \frac{C_s' D_m}{Q}\left[\frac{q}{2} - L + \frac{L^2 - 1}{2q}\right]. \quad (11.9)$$

The minimum cost procurement level for any given procurement quantity may be found by taking the derivative with respect to L, setting the result equal to zero, and solving for L as follows:

$$\frac{dTC_m}{dL} = C_h - \frac{C_s'(D_m)}{Q} + \frac{L(C_s')(D_m)}{qQ} = 0$$

$$L = -\frac{q(Q)C_h}{C_s'D_m} + q$$

$$= q\left[1 - \frac{(Q)C_h}{C_s'D_m}\right]. \tag{11.10}$$

Equation (11.10) gives the minimum cost procurement level for a fixed procurement quantity as a function of the expected demand, the maximum value of lead time demand, the holding cost, and the shortage cost.

As an example of the application of Equation (11.10), consider the following situation: The expected demand for a certain item is 1 unit per period. Lead time demand is distributed uniformly in the interval 1 to 10 units. Holding cost is \$0.05 per unit per period and shortage cost is \$3 per unit short. The item is procured in lots of 24 units. Under these conditions, the minimum cost procurement level is

$$L = 10\left[1 - \frac{(24)\$0.05}{\$3(1)}\right] = 6 \text{ units.}$$

As before, it is not certain as to what value of L and Q will yield a minimum expected total system cost.

Expected total cost as a function of L and Q. When the procurement quantity is not restricted to a specific value, the expected total system cost per period will be the sum of the expected procurement cost per period, the expected holding cost per period, and the expected shortage cost per period; that is,

$$TC_m = PC_m + HC_m + SC_m.$$

The expected procurement cost per period, the expected holding cost per period, and the expected shortage cost per period were derived previously. Therefore, the expected total system cost per period may be expressed as

$$TC_m = \frac{C_p D_m}{Q} + C_h\left[\frac{Q}{2} + (L - D_m T_m)\right] + \frac{C_s' D_m}{Q}\left[\frac{q}{2} - L + \frac{L^2 - 1}{2q}\right].$$

$$\tag{11.11}$$

The procurement level and procurement quantity resulting in a minimum expected total system cost may be found by taking the partial derivatives of

TC_m with respect to L and Q, setting the results equal to zero, and solving for L and Q as follows:

$$\frac{\partial TC_m}{\partial Q} = -\frac{C_p D_m}{Q^2} + \frac{C_h}{2} - \frac{C_s' D_m}{Q^2}\left[\frac{q}{2} - L + \frac{L^2 - 1}{2q}\right] = 0. \tag{11.12}$$

$$\frac{\partial TC_m}{\partial L} = C_h - \frac{C_s' D_m}{Q} + \frac{L(C_s')(D_m)}{qQ} = 0. \tag{11.13}$$

From Equation (11.13)

$$L = q - \frac{q(C_h)Q}{C_s' D_m}. \tag{11.14}$$

Substituting Equation (11.14) into Equation (11.12) and simplifying gives

$$Q = D_m \sqrt{\frac{C_s'}{qC_h}\left[\frac{C_s' - 2qC_p}{qC_h - C_s' D_m}\right]}. \tag{11.15}$$

Equation (11.15) gives the minimum cost procurement quantity as a function of the expected demand, the maximum value of lead time demand, the procurement cost, the holding cost, and the shortage cost.

The minimum cost procurement level may be found by substituting Equation (11.15) into Equation (11.14) giving

$$L = q - q\sqrt{\frac{C_h}{qC_s'}\left[\frac{C_s' - 2qC_p}{qC_h - C_s' D_m}\right]}. \tag{11.16}$$

As an example of the application of these equations, consider the previous situation and suppose that procurement cost is $6 per procurement. The minimum cost procurement quantity is found from Equation (11.15) as

$$Q = (1)\sqrt{\frac{\$3}{10(\$0.05)}\left[\frac{\$3 - 2(10)(\$6)}{10(\$0.05) - \$3(1)}\right]}$$
$$= \sqrt{280.8} \approx 17 \text{ units}.$$

The minimum cost procurement level is found from Equation (11.16) as

$$L = 10 - 10\sqrt{\frac{\$0.05}{10(\$3)}\left[\frac{\$3 - 2(10)(\$6)}{10(\$0.05) - \$3(1)}\right]}$$
$$= 10 - 10\sqrt{0.078} \approx 7 \text{ units}.$$

QUESTIONS

1. Explain why it is not possible to keep both the number of periods per cycle and the procurement quantity fixed if the inventory process is probabilistic.

2. In the probabilistic inventory process, procurement action is often initiated when the stock on hand is below the procurement level. Explain.

3. Give reasons why Monte Carlo simulation gives a better description of the probabilistic inventory process than mathematical expressions.

4. Name and describe the three expressions for expected values for the probabilistic system and compare with their counterparts for the deterministic system.

5. Why is an inventory policy based on the expected minimum total system cost valid?

6. Although lead time demand is independent of the procurement level, shortages are dependent on the specific procurement level chosen. Explain.

7. Explain why the expected number of unit periods of shortage is a better expression for shortage condition than the probability of one or more shortages.

8. Discuss Equation (11.11) in terms of $E = f(x_i, y_j)$.

PROBLEMS

1. Use Monte Carlo simulation to plot 6 cycles of inventory flow for the case where demand is distributed Poisson with a mean of 10 unit per period and lead time is equal to 3 periods. Set the procurement level at 4 units and the procurement quantity at 8 units.

2. Calculate P_x, I_x, and S_x for each cycle plotted in Problem 1. What are the values of P_m, I_m, and S_m for this 6-cycle sample.

3. The home plate umpire in the game of baseball must maintain an inventory of baseballs in the many pockets of his baggy suit. This inventory is necessary to meet the demands of play when balls must be replaced after they become dirty or misshapen or are boldly hit into the stands of jeering and cheering spectators. One knowledgeable umpire, affectionately referred to by the players as "old four-eyes," concluded that the technique of Monte Carlo analysis might be aptly used to describe this probabilistic inventory system. He found that the pattern of usage followed a Poisson distribution with a mean of 1.2 baseballs per player-at-bat. A deterministic lead time of 3 players at bat was necessary to catch the eye of the ball boy and receive a replenishment quantity of baseballs. With a procurement level of 4 baseballs and a procurement quantity of 10 balls, use Monte Carlo simulation to plot 10 cycles of inventory flow.

4. Use Equation (11.3) and the cumulative distributions of Figure 11.2 to develop the distribution of lead time demand by Monte Carlo simulation. Compare the results obtained after 50 cycles with the exact distribution of Figure 11.9.

5. Specify the distribution of lead time demand if demand is distributed normal with a mean of eight units per period and a standard deviation of two units per period. Lead time is constant and equal to six periods.

6. Specify the distribution of lead time demand if demand is constant and equal to four units per period and lead time is distributed Poisson with a mean of eight periods.

7. Develop the distribution of lead time demand by the exact method if demand is distributed Poisson with a mean of 1 unit per period. Lead time will be 1, 2, 3, or 4 periods with probabilities of 0.10, 0.30, 0.40, and 0.20, respectively.

8. Plot the probability of an empty warehouse and the probability of one or more shortages as a function of the procurement level. (Use the data of Table 11.4.)

9. Plot the expected number of shortages per inventory cycle and the expected number of unit periods of shortage per cycle as a function of the procurement level. (Use the data of Table 11.5.)

10. If the procurement level is set at 12 units, if $D_m = 2$ units per period, and if lead time demand is distributed uniformly in the range 1 to 16 units, what is the probability of an empty warehouse; the probability of one or more shortages; the expected number of shortages; the expected number of unit periods of shortage? (Use the continuous approximations.)

11. If the procurement level is set at 10 units and if lead time demand is distributed Poisson with a mean of 8 periods, what is the probability of an empty warehouse; the probability of one or more shortages; the expected number of shortages; the expected number of unit periods of shortage if $D_m = 2$?

12. The demand and lead time distributions for a certain inventory process are given by Figure 11.1. The holding cost per unit per period is $0.02 and the shortage cost is $2 per unit short. Using the expected number of shortages per cycle given in Table 11.5, plot the expected total cost as a function of the procurement level if the procurement quantity is fixed at 8 units.

13. What is the expected total system cost for the conditions of Problem 12 if the procurement level is 6 units, the procurement quantity is 14 units, and the procurement cost is $6.20 per procurement?

14. The expected demand for a certain item is 1 unit per period and the expected lead time is 6 periods. Lead time demand is distributed uniformly in the range 0 to 12 units. Holding cost is $0.03 per unit per period and shortage cost is $4 per unit short. If the item is being procured in lots of 20 units, what is the minimum cost procurement level?

15. If the procurement cost per procurement in Problem 14 is $10, what is the minimum cost procurement level and procurement quantity? What is the expected minimum total system cost?

Part V

ECONOMY OF WAITING LINE
OPERATIONS

twelve

DETERMINISTIC
WAITING LINE MODELS

The waiting line or queuing system dealt with in this chapter may be described as follows: A facility or group of facilities is maintained to meet the demand for service created by a population of individuals. These individuals form a waiting line or queue and receive service in accordance with a predetermined waiting line discipline. In most cases, the serviced units rejoin the population and again become candidates for the service they received. In other cases, the individuals form a waiting line at the next stage of the system. In either case, the flow of individuals through the system is a discrete process analogous to the procurement and inventory process discussed in the previous chapters.

Systems having the foregoing characteristics are common in many real world operations in which people, materials, or vehicles form waiting lines. In public service, waiting lines are formed at cafeterias, theaters, and doctors' offices. In production, the flow of items in process produces a waiting line at each machine center. In transportation, waiting lines form at toll gates, traffic signals, docks, and landing strips. In each case, the objective is to determine the capacity of the service facility in the light of the relevant costs and the characteristics of the arrival pattern so that the sum of all costs associated with the waiting line system will be minimized. This chapter describes the waiting line system in general terms and presents several deterministic waiting line models.

12.1. THE WAITING LINE SYSTEM

A multiple-channel waiting line system is illustrated schematically in Figure 12.1. It exists because the population shown demands service. In satisfying the demand upon the system, the decision maker must establish the level of service capacity to provide. This will involve increasing or decreasing the service capacity by altering the service rate at existing channels

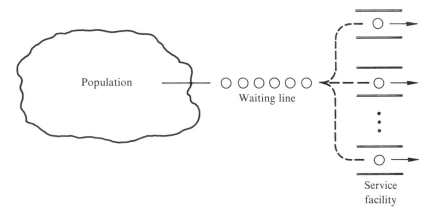

Figure 12.1. A multiple-channel waiting line system.

or by adding or deleting channels. The following paragraphs describe the components of the waiting line system and indicate their importance in the decision-making process.

The arrival population. Waiting line systems come into being because there exists a population of individuals requiring service from time to time. Usually, the arrival population is best thought of as a group of items, some of which depart and join the waiting line. For example, if the population is composed of all airborne aircraft, then flight schedules and random occurrences will determine the number of aircraft that will join the landing pattern of a given airport during a given time interval. If the population is composed of telephone subscribers, then the time of day and the day of the week, as well as many other factors, will determine the number of calls placed upon an exchange. If the population consists of production machines, the deterioration, wearout, and use rates will determine the departure mechanism causing the machines to join a waiting line of machines requiring repair service.

The arrival population, although always finite in size, may be considered infinite under certain conditions. If the departure rate is small relative to the size of the population, the number of units that potentially may require service will not be seriously depleted. Under this condition, the population may be considered infinite. Models used to explain the behavior of such systems are much easier to formulate than models for the finite population. Examples of populations that may usually be treated as infinite are automobiles that may require passage over a bridge, customers who may potentially patronize a theater, telephone subscribers who may place a call, and production orders that may require processing at a specific machine center.

In some cases the proportion of the population requiring service may be fairly large when compared with the population itself. In these cases, the population is seriously depleted by the departure of individuals to the extent that the departure rate will not remain stable. Since models used to explain waiting line systems depend upon the stability of the arrival rate, finite cases must be given special treatment. Examples of waiting line operations that might be classified as finite are production machines that may require repair, semiautomatic production facilities that require operator attention, and company cafeterias that serve a captive population. Waiting line systems for the case where the infinite population assumption does not hold will be treated in the next chapter.

The waiting line. In any waiting line system, a departure mechanism exists which governs the rate at which individuals leave the population and join the queue. This departure mechanism is responsible for the formation of the waiting line and the need to provide service. Formation of the queue is a discrete process. Individuals or items joining the waiting line do so as integer values. The number of units in the waiting line at any point in time is an integer value. Rarely, if ever, is the queuing process continuous.

Individuals or items becoming a part of the waiting line take a position in the queue in accordance with a certain waiting line discipline. The most common discipline is that of first come, first served. Other priority rules that may exist are the random selection process, the head of the line rule, first come last served, and disciplines involving a combination of these. In addition, individuals may remain in the queue for a period of time and rejoin the population. This behavior is called *reneging*.

In an ideal sense, the waiting line may be thought of as a number of items which is increased by arrivals and decreased by services. As such, it is analogous to a stock of items on hand in inventory. The arrivals represent additions to stock and the services represent demands upon the system.

The service facility. Service may be thought of as the process of providing the activities required by the units in the waiting line. It may consist of collecting a toll, filling an order, providing a necessary repair, or completing a manufacturing operation. In each case, the act of providing the service causes a unit decrease in the waiting line. The service mechanism, like the arrival mechanism, is discrete since items are processed on a unit basis.

The service facility may consist of a single channel, or it may consist of several channels in parallel, as in Figure 12.1. If it consists of only a single channel all arrivals must eventually pass through it. If several channels are provided, items may move from the waiting line into the first channel that becomes empty. The rate at which individuals are processed depends upon the service capacity provided at the individual channels and upon the number of channels in the system.

The service may be provided by humans only, by humans aided by tools and equipment, or by equipment alone. For example, collecting a toll is essentially a clerk's task which requires no tools or equipment. Repairing a vehicle, on the other hand, requires a mechanic aided by tools and equipment. Processing a phone call dialed by the suscriber seldom requires human intervention and is usually paced by the automatic equipment. These examples indicate that service facilities can vary widely with respect to the man-machine mix utilized to provide the required service.

12.2. THE DECISION ENVIRONMENT

The waiting line system described in Section 12.1 exists in a decision environment composed of an arrival mechanism, a service mechanism, waiting cost, and service facility cost. This section will describe each of these. The total system cost depends upon the level of service capacity provided. Therefore, this section will also establish the basic structure of decision models that may be used to establish the service capacity so that the sum of all costs associated with the waiting line system is minimized.

The arrival mechanism. The demand for service is the primary stimulus on the waiting line system and the justification for its existence. As previously indicated, the waiting line system may exist to meet the service demand created by people, materials, vehicles, or machines. The characteristics of the arrival pattern depend upon the nature of the population giving rise to the demand for service.

The simplest arrival pattern may be classified as deterministic. In this special case, the future demand for service can be predicted with certainty. The arrival mechanism considered in this restricted sense is only an approximation of reality. All models developed in this chapter are based on the assumption that the arrival mechanism is deterministic.

In the general case, the arrival pattern may be described as a random variable which takes on values in accordance with a specific probability distribution. If the characteristics of the population remain stable over time, the parameters and the form of the distribution will not change. Such steady-state processes are an exception, however, rather than the rule. The probabilistic steady-state waiting line process will be treated in Chapter 13.

The service mechanism. The rate at which units requiring service are serviced is assumed to be a variable directly under the control of the decision maker. This parameter can be assigned a specific value to create a minimum cost waiting line system. For each channel then, the characteristics of the service mechanism may be established.

In the simplest case, service time may be classified as deterministic. Under this assumption the duration of each service is known with certainty. As with the arrival rate, however, the service duration considered in this restricted sense is only an approximation of reality. All models developed in this chapter are based on the assumption of a deterministic service rate.

Most real world service facilities incorporate a service duration that is a random variable, taking on values in accordance with a specific probability distribution. If the characteristics of the service facility remain constant over time, the parameters and the form of the distribution will not change. Those service facilities utilizing a man-machine service element may exhibit learning. In this case the service rate will increase, causing a probabilistic non-steady-state waiting line process. Models based on probabilistic steady-state distributions for service will be treated in the next chapter.

Waiting cost. When a unit joins the waiting line, or is being serviced, a waiting cost is incurred. Waiting cost per unit per period will depend upon the units in question. If expensive production machinery waits for operator attention, the loss of profit may be sizable. Vehicles waiting in queue at a toll gate incur a waiting cost due to interruption of trip progress. Customers waiting at a check-out counter become irritated and the proprietor suffers a loss of good will.

Increasing the level of service capacity will cause a decrease in waiting line length. As a result, the waiting time will be decreased. Since waiting cost to the system is a product of the number of units waiting and the time duration involved, this action will decrease this cost component. But since increasing the service facility capacity increases the service cost, it is appropriate to seek a reduction in waiting cost for the system only up to the point where the saving exceeds the added facility cost.

Service facility cost. Each channel of the service facility represents a capital investment plus operating and maintenance costs. In addition, wages for personnel may be involved, together with associated overhead rates. The capability of the channel to process units requiring service is a function of the resources expended at the channel. For example, the channel may consist of a single repairman with modest tools or it may be a crew of men with complex tools and equipment. The cost of providing such a facility will depend on the characteristics of the personnel and equipment employed.

Since increasing the service capacity will result in a reduction in the waiting line, it is appropriate to adjust service capacity so that the sum of waiting cost and service cost is a minimum. This chapter and the following one consider models useful in establishing the minimum cost service level. The general structure of decision models directed to this objective will be presented next.

The decision model. The primary objective of the waiting line system is to meet the demand for service at minimum cost. This requires the establishment of an appropriate level of service capacity by constructing and manipulating a mathematical model of the form

$$E = f(x_i, y_j)$$

where $E =$ the measure of effectiveness sought (minimize total system cost)
       $x_i =$ the policy variable concerning the level of service capacity to provide
       $y_j =$ the environmental parameters of the arrival pattern, the waiting cost, and the service facility cost.

The following sections are devoted to developing deterministic decision models with the preceding characteristics. We shall use the following symbolism:

$TC =$ total system cost per period.
$A =$ number of periods between arrivals.
$S =$ number of periods to complete one service.
$C_w =$ cost of waiting per unit per period.
$C_f =$ service facility cost for servicing one unit.

Additional notation will be adopted and defined as required for deriving specific decision models.

12.3. MODELS FOR NO INITIAL WAITING LINE

In this section, assume that a queuing situation begins with no units in the system and that arrivals occur at regular intervals of length A periods. The first arrival occurs at the beginning of the process. Service time is constant and equal to S periods. Since each unit serviced will require S periods, it is essential that S be less than or equal to A periods if a single channel is employed. If M channels are to be used, it is required that S be less than or equal to MA periods. If these restrictions are violated, a waiting line will form which will grow beyond bound. This section will treat the simple cases described as an introduction to deterministic waiting line operations.

A single channel model. A single channel waiting line system may be represented schematically as shown in Figure 12.2. The heavy dot represents an arrival every five periods. The slanting path represents a service operation requiring three periods. Since S is less than A, no waiting line will ever form.

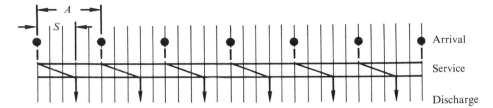

Figure 12.2. Single channel system with no initial queue.

The total system cost per period will be the sum of the waiting cost for the period and the service facility cost for the period; that is,

$$TC = WC + FC.$$

The waiting cost per period will be the product of the cost of waiting per unit per period and the number of units waiting each period, or

$$WC = C_w\left(\frac{S}{A}\right).$$

The service facility cost for the period will be the product of the number of units serviced during the period and the cost of servicing one unit, or

$$FC = C_f\left(\frac{1}{S}\right).$$

Expressing the service facility cost per period as a linear function of the number of units serviced per period may be somewhat unrealistic. It is, however, a convenient means for relating the cost of providing service to the capacity of the service facility. Most of the models derived in this and the following chapter will use this expression for service facility cost per period.

The total system cost per period will be the sum of the waiting cost per period and the facility cost per period, or

$$TC = C_w\left(\frac{S}{A}\right) + C_f\left(\frac{1}{S}\right). \tag{12.1}$$

A minimum cost service interval may be found by differentiating with respect to S, setting the result equal to zero, and solving for S as follows:

$$\frac{dTC}{dS} = \frac{C_w}{A} - \frac{C_f}{S^2} = 0$$

$$S^2 = \frac{C_f A}{C_w} \tag{12.2}$$

$$S = \sqrt{\frac{C_f A}{C_w}}, \qquad S \le A.$$

As an application of the foregoing model, consider the following example: A unit will arrive every five periods. The cost of waiting is $5 per unit per period. One unit can be serviced at a cost of $9. Waiting cost per period, facility cost per period, and total cost per period may be tabulated as a function of S to illustrate the nature of the cost components. The results shown in Table 12.1 were developed from Equation (12.1). Inspection of the tabu-

Table 12.1. COST COMPONENTS FOR SINGLE CHANNEL MODEL

S	WC	FC	TC
0	$0.00	$ ∞	$ ∞
1	1.00	9.00	10.00
2	2.00	4.50	6.50
3	3.00	3.00	6.00
4	4.00	2.25	6.25
5	5.00	1.80	6.80

lated values indicates that waiting cost per period is directly proportional and that facility cost per period is inversely proportional to S. The minimum cost service interval is three periods and may be provided at a facility cost of $3 per period.

The minimum cost service interval may be found directly by substituting into Equation (12.2) as follows:

$$S = \sqrt{\frac{\$9(5)}{\$5}} = 3 \text{ periods.}$$

Under the conditions assumed, the decision maker would provide a single service channel capable of serving one unit every three periods as was shown in Figure 12.2.

In this example, the service interval resulting in a minimum total system cost is a whole number of periods. This occurred because of the cost values assigned. Normally, the minimum service interval will not be an integer. The decision maker will strive to establish a service interval as close to the minimum cost value as possible.

A multiple channel model. A two channel waiting line system may be represented schematically as shown in Figure 12.3. As for Figure 12.2, the heavy dot represents an arrival and the slanting path represents a service operation. The second arrival finds the first service channel busy and goes immediately into the second. The third arrival finds the second channel busy and goes immediately into the first. Since S is less than MA no waiting line will ever form.

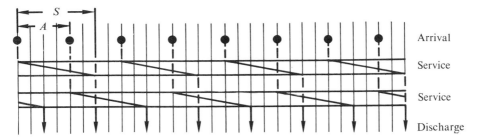

Figure 12.3. A multiple channel system with no initial queue.

The total system cost for the period will be the sum of the waiting cost for the period and the facility cost for the period; that is,

$$TC = WC + FC.$$

The waiting cost per period will be the product of the cost of waiting per unit per period and the number of units waiting per period, or

$$WC = C_w\left(\frac{S}{A}\right).$$

The facility cost for the period will be the product of the number of units served during the period, the cost of serving one unit, and the number of channels in operation, or

$$FC = C_f\left(\frac{1}{S}\right)M.$$

The total system cost per period will be the sum of the waiting cost per period and the facility cost per period, or

$$TC = C_w\left(\frac{S}{A}\right) + C_f\left(\frac{1}{S}\right)M. \qquad (12.3)$$

A minimum cost service interval may be found by differentiating with respect to S, setting the result equal to zero, and solving for S as follows:

$$\frac{dTC}{dS} = \frac{C_w}{A} - \frac{C_f M}{S^2} = 0$$

$$S^2 = \frac{C_f M A}{C_w}$$

$$S = \sqrt{\frac{C_f M A}{C_w}}, \qquad S \le MA. \qquad (12.4)$$

Equation (12.4) reduces to Equation (12.2) for the single channel case; $M = 1$.

To illustrate the application of the foregoing model, consider the following example: A unit will arrive every four periods. The cost of waiting is $2 per

unit per period. A unit can be serviced for a cost of \$9. Two channels are
to be used. The minimum cost service interval may be found by substituting
into Equation (12.4) as follows:

$$S = \sqrt{\frac{\$9(2)(4)}{\$2}} = 6 \text{ periods.}$$

Under the conditions assumed, the decision maker would provide two service
channels, each with the capability of serving one unit every six periods as was
shown in Figure 12.3.

12.4. A MODEL WITH AN INITIAL WAITING LINE

Suppose that a queuing situation made up of repetitive cycles begins with a
finite number of units in the system and that arrivals occur at regular intervals
of length A periods. The first arrival occurs at the beginning of the process.
Service time is constant and equal to S periods. Since each unit serviced will
require S periods, it is essential that S be sufficiently less than A so that the
initial units plus those which arrive will be serviced before the end of the cycle.
If the cycle ends with units waiting, there will be a carry-over to the next cycle
and the waiting line will grow beyond bound. This section will develop an
exact deterministic model for the preceding situation involving a single service
channel.

General system relationships. The waiting line system under consideration
may be represented schematically as shown in Figure 12.4. The small circles
represent initial units in the system, designated k. Assume that these units
accumulated since the termination of the previous cycle. A dot represents an
arrival every five periods and the initial arrival occurs at the beginning of the
cycle. The service operation is of duration two periods. The cycle is composed
of P periods, where $P = 40$ for this example. The final arrival occurs at the
beginning of the forty-first period and becomes part of the initial queue for
the next cycle.

Under the conditions assumed in Figure 12.4, the first units to be serviced
are the initial units in the system. The first of these goes immediately into
service and the others follow in turn, because of a first-come, first-served
queue discipline. The first arrival faces six units in the system and must wait
twelve periods before it can enter the service channel. The second arrival
faces four units in the waiting line and one unit in service. It must wait nine
periods before entering the service channel. The fifth arrival finds no units
in the system and may move immediately into service. From this point on,
each arrival may move directly into the service channel. The service facility
will not be fully utilized beyond this point. The total number of unit periods

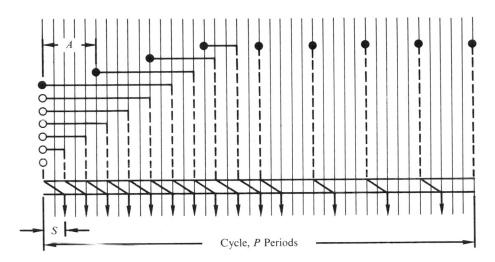

Figure 12.4. A waiting line process with an initial queue.

of waiting for the cycle may be found by observing the length of the horizontal paths.

The number of arrivals up to and including t periods will be the largest integer contained in the ratio t/A plus the unit that arrived at $t = 0$. This may be expressed as

$$\text{number of arrivals} = \left[\frac{t}{A} + 1\right].$$

Therefore, for a cycle of P periods, the total number of arrivals would be

$$\text{total number of arrivals} = \left[\frac{P}{A} + 1\right].$$

The brackets indicate a rounding operation downward to $a < [\ ] \leq a + 1$, where a is an integer expressing the number of arrivals up to and including t periods.

The arrival time in periods for the ith arrival may be expressed as $(i - 1)A$. The service completion time in periods for the ith arrival is $(k + i)S$ if the unit waits. If the unit does not wait, the service completion time in periods is $S + (i - 1)A$. These relationships may be verified by reference to Figure 12.4.

Total waiting time. The total time in periods that the ith unit spends in the queue and in service is given by

$$\max \{(k + i)S - (i - 1)A; S\}$$

which may be written as

$$\max \{kS + A - i(A - S); S\}.$$

There is a number $i*$, such that for every $i \leq i*$ the first term within the brackets will be larger than the second, and for every $i > i*$ the second term will be larger. Therefore,

$$kS + A - i*(A - S) > S$$

$$i* < \frac{kS + A - S}{A - S}$$

or

$$i* = \left[\frac{kS + A - S}{A - S}\right]. \tag{12.5}$$

The brackets indicate a rounding operation downward as previously specified. In effect, $i*$ is the last unit that arrives during the cycle that must wait before entering the service channel. The next unit, $i* + 1$, is the first unit that arrives during the cycle that may be serviced immediately after arrival. The use of Equation (12.5) may be demonstrated for the situation illustrated in Figure 12.4 as

$$i* = \left[\frac{6(2) + 5 - 2}{5 - 2}\right] = [5] = 4 \text{ units.}$$

The waiting time may be expressed as iS if the item is a member of the initial queue, or as $kS + A - i(A - S)$ if $0 \leq i \leq i*$, or S if $i > i*$ and if the item is a new arrival. The total number of unit periods of waiting incurred during the cycle by all units is then

$$W = \sum_{i=1}^{k} iS + \sum_{i=1}^{i*} \{kS + A - i(A - S)\} + \sum_{i=i*+1}^{[(P/A)+1]} S. \tag{12.6}$$

The use of Equation (12.6) may also be demonstrated for the situation illustrated in Figure 12.4 as

$$W = \sum_{i=1}^{6} 2i + \sum_{i=1}^{4} \{6(2) + 5 - i(5 - 2)\} + \sum_{i=5}^{8} 2$$

$$= 42 + 38 + 8 = 88 \text{ unit periods.}$$

A general expression for the total number of unit periods of waiting may be derived from Equation (12.6) as

$$W = \frac{k(k + 1)S}{2} + (kS + A)i* - \frac{A - S}{2} i*(i* + 1) + S\left\{\left[\frac{P}{A} + 1\right] - i*\right\}$$

$$= \frac{k(k + 1)S}{2} + S\left[\frac{P}{A} + 1\right] + (kS + A - S)i* - \frac{A - S}{2} i*(i* + 1)$$

$$= \frac{k(k + 1)S}{2} + S\left[\frac{P}{A} + 1\right] + i*\left\{kS + A - S - \frac{A - S}{2}(i* + 1)\right\}$$

$$= \frac{k(k + 1)S}{2} + S\left[\frac{P}{A} + 1\right] + i*\left\{kS - \frac{A - S}{2}(i* - 1)\right\}.$$

Substituting Equation (12.5) for i^* gives

$$W = \frac{k(k+1)S}{2} + S\left[\frac{P}{A} + 1\right] + \left[\frac{kS + A - S}{A - S}\right]\left\{kS - \frac{A - S}{2}\left[\frac{kS}{A - S}\right]\right\}.$$

$$(12.7)$$

Total system cost. The total system cost for the period will be the sum of the waiting cost for the period and the facility cost per period; that is,

$$TC = WC + FC.$$

The waiting cost per period will be the product of the cost of waiting per unit per period and the average number of unit periods of waiting per period, or

$$WC = C_w\left(\frac{W}{P}\right).$$

The facility cost for the period will be the product of the number of units served during the period and the cost of serving one unit, or

$$FC = C_f\left(\frac{1}{S}\right).$$

The total system cost per period will be the sum of the waiting cost per period and the facility cost per period, or

$$TC = C_w\left(\frac{W}{P}\right) + C_f\left(\frac{1}{S}\right).$$

Substituting Equation (12.7) for W gives

$$TC = \frac{C_w}{P}\left(\frac{k(k+1)S}{2} + S\left[\frac{P}{A} + 1\right] + \left[\frac{kS + A - S}{A - S}\right]\right.$$
$$\left. \times \left\{kS - \frac{A - S}{2}\left[\frac{kS}{A - S}\right]\right\}\right) + C_f\left(\frac{1}{S}\right). \quad (12.8)$$

For the case where there is no initial queue, $k = 0$, Equation (12.8) reduces to

$$TC = \frac{C_w}{P}\left(S\left[\frac{P}{A} + 1\right]\right) + C_f\left(\frac{1}{S}\right).$$

By considering the rounding operation, this becomes

$$TC = C_w\left(\frac{S}{A}\right) + C_f\left(\frac{1}{S}\right)$$

which was shown previously to be the total system cost when there is no initial queue.

An example application. Mathematical minimization of Equation (12.8) to find the least cost service interval, S, is not possible. The quantities in brackets are not differentiable making a numerical procedure necessary.

Consider the following example: A waiting line process begins with 6 units in the system at the beginning of a cycle 40 periods long. A unit will arrive every 5 periods, with the first arrival occurring at the beginning of the cycle. The cost of waiting is $5 per unit per period. A unit can be serviced for a facility cost of $40. The objective is to determine the minimum cost service interval.

Substituting each system and cost parameter into Equation (12.8) gives

$$TC = \frac{\$5}{40}\left(\frac{6(7)S}{2} + S\left[\frac{40}{5} + 1\right]\right.$$

$$\left. + \left[\frac{6S + 5 - S}{5 - S}\right]\left\{6S - \frac{5 - S}{2}\left[\frac{6S}{5 - S}\right]\right\}\right) + \frac{\$40}{S}.$$

Waiting cost per period, facility cost per period, and total cost per period may be tabulated as a function of S. By performing the rounding operations specified by the brackets, the values given in Table 12.2 may be found. The

Table 12.2. COST COMPONENTS FOR INITIAL QUEUE MODEL

S	WC	FC	TC
0	$ 0.00	$ ∞	$ ∞
1	4.63	40.00	44.63
2	11.00	20.00	31.00
3	22.13	13.33	35.46
4	52.00	10.00	62.00
5	∞	8.00	∞

minimum cost service interval is two periods and may be provided at a cost of $20 per period. Under the conditions assumed, the decision maker would provide a single service channel capable of serving one unit every two periods, as was shown in Figure 12.4.

12.5. AN APPROXIMATION FOR TOTAL WAITING TIME

The number of units in the waiting line system is an integer value at any point in time. This occurs because both the formation of the waiting line and the completion of service are normally discrete processes. Only if the system involves the flow of a fluid material can continuous analysis be accurately applied. Nevertheless, use of continuous analysis for discrete processes often leads to a simplification resulting in more complete understanding. This section, for comparison with earlier results, treats the queuing situation described in Section 12.4 as though it were continuous.

Approximate total waiting time. In addition to the notation already presented, let n be the number of units in the system at any point in time. The number of units in the system at any point will be the sum of the initial units in the system, and cumulative arrivals up to time t, minus the cumulative services up to time t, or

$$n = k + 1 + \left(\frac{1}{A}\right)t - \left(\frac{1}{S}\right)t$$

$$= k + 1 + t\left(\frac{1}{A} - \frac{1}{S}\right).$$

When $n = 0$, waiting in the queue ceases and utilization of the service facility becomes intermittent. This occurs after 22 periods in Figure 12.4 and is approximated by

$$0 = k + 1 + t\left(\frac{1}{A} - \frac{1}{S}\right)$$

$$t = -\frac{k + 1}{1/A - 1/S}.$$

This approximation gives 23 periods for the condition assumed.

Cumulative waiting time up to the point where waiting in queue ceases is approximated by

$$\int_0^{[-(k+1)/1/A-1/S]} \left[k + 1 + t\left(\frac{1}{A} - \frac{1}{S}\right)\right] dt.$$

And, the cumulative waiting time from this point to the end of the cycle is approximated by

$$\int_{[-(k+1)/1/A-1/S]}^{P} \left(\frac{S}{A}\right) dt.$$

Therefore, the cumulative waiting time for the cycle is approximated by

$$W = \int_0^{[-(k+1)/1/A-1/S]} \left[k + 1 + t\left(\frac{1}{A} - \frac{1}{S}\right)\right] dt + \int_{[-(k+1)/1/A-1/S]}^{P} \left(\frac{S}{A}\right) dt$$

$$= (k + 1)t + \frac{t^2}{2}\left(\frac{1}{A} - \frac{1}{S}\right)\Big|_0^{[-(k+1)/1/A-1/S]} + \left(\frac{S}{A}\right)t\Big|_{[-(k+1)/1/A-1/S]}^{P}$$

$$= -\frac{(k + 1)^2}{1/A - 1/S} + \frac{(k + 1)^2}{2(1/A - 1/S)} + \left(\frac{S}{A}\right)P + \left(\frac{S}{A}\right)\frac{k + 1}{1/A - 1/S}$$

$$= -\frac{(k + 1)^2}{2(1/A - 1/S)} + \frac{S}{A}\left(P + \frac{k + 1}{1/A - 1/S}\right). \tag{12.9}$$

This result is an approximation for Equation (12.7) but is much easier to work with.

Comparison of exact and approximate expressions. Figure 12.5 is a plot of the number of units in the system at any point in time for the queuing situation described in the previous section. The solid line represents the actual number in the system resulting from the waiting line process illustrated in Figure 12.4. The dotted line represents the approximate number in the system based on the continuous approximation of this section.

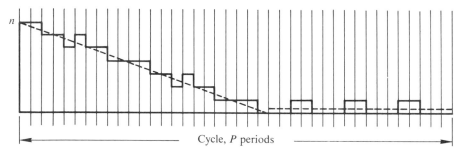

Figure 12.5. Actual and approximate number in the system.

The total number of unit periods of waiting during the cycle may be found exactly from Equation (12.7) as

$$W = \frac{6(6+1)2}{2} + 2\left[\frac{40}{5} + 1\right] + \left[\frac{6(2)+5-2}{5-2}\right]\left\{6(2) - \frac{5-2}{2}\left[\frac{6(2)}{5-2}\right]\right\}$$

$$= 42 + 16 + 30 = 88 \text{ unit periods.}$$

The approximate number of unit periods of waiting for the cycle may be found from Equation (12.9) as

$$W = -\frac{(6+1)^2}{2(1/5-1/2)} + \frac{2}{5}\left(40 + \frac{6+1}{1/5-1/2}\right)$$

$$= 81.67 + 6.67 = 88.34 \text{ unit periods.}$$

The discrepancy between the actual and the approximate total waiting time is only 0.34 unit periods for this example. This discrepancy will be even less for cycles of longer duration. Therefore, Equation (12.9) may be substituted for W into Equation (12.8) in place of Equation (12.7). It is unlikely that this simplification will affect the minimum cost service interval significantly.

12.6. A GENERAL NUMERICAL SOLUTION METHOD

The waiting line situations presented in the previous sections assumed that arrivals occur at regular intervals. A more general system is allowed if it is assumed that arrivals occur in some irregular pattern during the cycle. The deterministic assumption of this chapter requires, however, that this pattern be known with certainty. Nevertheless, the ability to analyze waiting line operations with deterministic non-steady-state arrivals adds considerable generality. As before, the queuing system will be viewed in terms of a cycle made up of P periods. Instead of an arrival occurring every A periods, the system will be viewed as accepting a number of arrivals per period with the number depending upon the period. It is assumed that the cycle repeats itself and that no carry-over is permitted from one cycle to the next. The objective will be to determine the minimum cost service capacity.

Total waiting time. Suppose that a waiting line system is to be subjected to the arrival pattern shown in Figure 12.6. It is anticipated that this pattern

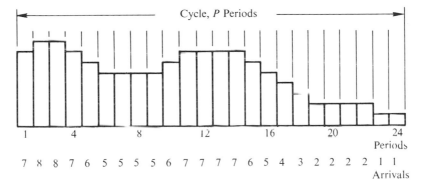

Figure 12.6. Deterministic non-steady-state arrival pattern.

will repeat itself for the cycles which follow. The number of units that can be serviced per period may vary in increments of one unit with a cost of $1 per unit serviced. Waiting cost is $0.30 per unit per period.

The total number of unit periods of waiting for the cycle will be a function of the number of units serviced per period. The "no carry-over" restriction requires that the service rate be sufficiently large to process all units before the end of the cycle. Table 12.3 gives the computations necessary to establish the total number of unit periods of waiting in the queue. It begins with the case where $S = 1/5$, providing a cumulative service capacity sufficient to process all arrivals for the cycle. The number of units in the queue for each period is found by subtracting the cumulative services from the cumulative arrivals. Any error introduced because of services and arrivals occurring during the period is neglected.

The total waiting time in the queue is found by adding the number in queue for all periods. This was found to be 284, 69, and 6 unit periods, respectively for $S = 1/5$, $1/6$, and $1/7$ periods. The total waiting time in queue

Table 12.3. CALCULATING TOTAL WAITING TIME IN QUEUE

Period	Arrivals	Σ Arrivals	$S=\frac{1}{5}$ Services	Σ Services	Queue	$S=\frac{1}{6}$ Services	Σ Services	Queue	$S=\frac{1}{7}$ Services	Σ Services	Queue
1	7	7	5	5	2	6	6	1	7	7	0
2	8	15	5	10	5	6	12	3	7	14	1
3	8	23	5	15	8	6	18	5	7	21	2
4	7	30	5	20	10	6	24	6	7	28	2
5	6	36	5	25	11	6	30	6	7	35	1
6	5	41	5	30	11	6	36	5	6	41	0
7	5	46	5	35	11	6	42	4	5	46	0
8	5	51	5	40	11	6	48	3	5	51	0
9	5	56	5	45	11	6	54	2	5	56	0
10	6	62	5	50	12	6	60	2	6	62	0
11	7	69	5	55	14	6	66	3	7	69	0
12	7	76	5	60	16	6	72	4	7	76	0
13	7	83	5	65	18	6	78	5	7	83	0
14	7	90	5	70	20	6	84	6	7	90	0
15	6	96	5	75	21	6	90	6	6	96	0
16	5	101	5	80	21	6	96	5	5	101	0
17	4	105	5	85	20	6	102	3	4	105	0
18	3	108	5	90	18	6	108	0	3	108	0
19	2	110	5	95	15	2	110	0	2	110	0
20	2	112	5	100	12	2	112	0	2	112	0
21	2	114	5	105	9	2	114	0	2	114	0
22	2	116	5	110	6	2	116	0	2	116	0
23	1	117	5	115	2	1	117	0	1	117	0
24	1	118	3	118	0	1	118	0	1	118	0
Unit periods of waiting				284			69				6

and in service (in the system) may be found by adding the service time incurred by all units in each case. For $S = 1/5$ the total waiting time is $284 + 118/5$ or approximately 308 unit periods. For $S = 1/6$ it is approximately $69 + 118/6$ or 89 unit periods. And for $S = 1/7$ the total number of unit periods of waiting is approximately $6 + 118/7$ or 23. The result of increasing the service rate is a reduction in the total number of unit periods of waiting for the cycle.

The minimum cost service rate. The total system cost per period given by the expression

$$TC = C_w\left(\frac{W}{P}\right) + C_f\left(\frac{1}{S}\right)$$

may be used to determine a minimum cost service rate, $1/S$. With the costs given and the total number of unit periods calculated, the total cost per period for a service rate of five units per period is

$$TC = \$0.30\left(\frac{308}{24}\right) + \$1(5) = \$8.85.$$

For a service rate of six units per period,

$$TC = \$0.30\left(\frac{89}{24}\right) + \$1(6) = \$7.11.$$

And for a service rate of seven units per period,

$$TC = \$0.30\left(\frac{23}{24}\right) + \$1(7) = \$7.29.$$

Therefore, the minimum cost service rate for this situation is six units per period. If the service rate can be established as a continuous variable, the minimum cost might be found to be between six and seven units per period.

QUESTIONS

1. Name and briefly describe the components of the waiting line system.

2. Describe the essential facets of the decision environment relative to waiting line operations.

3. Name and describe a parallel channel service facility; a random queue discipline.

4. Contrast a deterministic and a probabilistic arrival mechanism. Give an example of each.

5. Contrast a deterministic and a probabilistic service mechanism. Give an example of each.

6. Describe how learning would cause the service interval to be a non-steady-state process.

7. Explain how the cost of a service facility is related to its capacity.

8. Explain how an increased resource expenditure on the service facility reduces the cost of waiting.

9. Describe the general effectiveness function for the waiting line system, $E = f(x_i, y_j)$.

10. Explain the conditions under which a deterministic waiting line system might become explosive.

PROBLEMS

1. A single channel waiting line system receives a unit every eight periods. The waiting cost is $2.50 per unit period and the cost to service one unit is $10.
   (a) Plot total system cost as a function of the service interval.
   (b) Calculate the minimum cost service interval.

2. Suppose that the waiting cost for the system described in Problem 1 drops to $1 per unit per period.
   (a) Plot the total system cost as a function of the service interval.
   (b) Indicate the zone of explosive condition.
   (c) What is the minimum cost service interval under this condition?

3. Suppose that two channels are provided for the waiting line system described in Problem 1.
   (a) Calculate the minimum cost service interval.
   (b) Calculate the minimum total system cost and compare with the minimum total system cost for one channel.

4. Use Equation (12.4) to calculate the minimum number of channels for which the minimum cost service interval lies outside the explosive zone. Express M in terms of C_f, C_w, and A. If $C_f = \$40$, $C_w = \$2.00$, and $A = 5$ periods, calculate the minimum number of channels required.

5. A waiting line process begins with 12 units in the system at the beginning of a cycle 60 minutes long. A unit will arrive every 6 minutes with the first arrival occurring at the beginning of the hour. A unit can be inspected at a cost of $0.20. Due to spoilage, the cost of waiting is $0.03 per unit per minute. Determine the minimum cost number of units that should be inspected per minute.

6. Waiting line models have recently received widespread attention in a number of leading popular medical journals. This theory has been found to be useful in studying and minimizing patient waiting time which has always been of great concern to the medical fraternity. One such enterprising physician, Thaddeus Quack, M.D., D.V.M., specialist in pediatrics, pathology, and small animals, reported a startling breakthrough in the study of patient waiting time. He found that by adding nursing assistants, he could reduce patient service time and thus reduce total patient waiting time. With no nurses, he found it took him exactly 12 minutes to process each animal or human patient. Adding two nurses reduced this service time to 8 minutes, adding two more nurses reduced the service time to 6 minutes. The doctor worked a 10-hour day and found there were always 20 patients, evenly divided between people and animals, waiting to be treated at the start of the day. He treated these patients on a democratic first-come, first-served basis. Patients arrived during the work day at the rate of one every 30 minutes. The doctor estimated that patient waiting time was worth $0.60 per patient-hour. Nurses must be paid at the rate of $3.00 per hour.

(a) What is the average patient waiting time under the three conditions described?

(b) Which operational policy will result in a minimum total system cost?

7. A purchasing department receives 100 requisitions during the day from other departments in the plant. In addition, 40 requisitions are received from the night shift and are waiting to be processed at the beginning of the day. It costs the company $5.00 for each hour of delay in processing a requisition. One clerk can process requisitions at the rate of four per hour. If a clerk costs $30 per 8-hour day, how many clerks should be hired? Use the approximate expression for W.

8. A waiting line process begins with 6 units in the system and a unit will arrive every 5 periods. The first arrival occurs at the beginning of the cycle. It takes 3 periods to service one unit. Calculate the minimum value of P required to avoid an explosive condition.

9. Under the condition assumed in Problem 8, calculate the cumulative waiting time up to the point where waiting in queue ceases. Plot the number of units in the system as a function of time. Use approximate expressions.

10. Plot cumulative waiting time as a function of S if a waiting line process begins with 20 units in the system, a unit arrives every 6 periods with the first arrival occurring at the beginning of the cycle, and if the cycle is 60 periods long. Use the approximate expression of Equation (12.9).

11. Suppose that 8 arrivals occur per hour during the first 6 hours of a 24-hour cycle. During the next 8 hours, 6 arrivals occur per hour. During the remaining 10 hours, the arrival pattern is as follows: 5, 4, 3, 2, 2, 2, 2, 2, 1, 1. This cycle will repeat itself exactly each day. Waiting cost is $0.10 per unit per hour and it costs $0.50 per unit serviced. Find the minimum cost number of units to service per hour.

12. Rework the example of Section 12.4 by the method of Section 12.6. Compare the results obtained with those given in Table 12.2.

thirteen

PROBABILISTIC

WAITING LINE MODELS

*In this chapter, the deterministic restriction on arrival time and
service time does not apply. Ordinarily, both the arrival
rate and the service rate are expected values from specified
probability distributions. A probabilistic waiting line system will result,
however, if either the arrival time and/or the service time is a random
variable. For simplicity, the arrival rate is often assumed to be an expected
value from a Poisson distribution. This assumption is mathematically
convenient and has a sound practical basis in many situations. Most models
presented in this chapter assume that the number of arrivals per period
obey the Poisson distribution.*

*Two types of waiting line systems are dealt with in the following sections.
The first is based on the assumption of
an infinite population, in that the size of the population is large relative to
the arrival rate. In this case, individuals leaving the population do not
significantly affect the arrival potential of the remaining units.
The second involves a finite population, in that the population is small relative
to the arrival rate. In this system, individuals leaving the
population significantly change the characteristics of the population and the
arrival pattern. This chapter presents probabilistic waiting line
models for each of these systems.*

13.1. MONTE CARLO ANALYSIS OF WAITING LINES

Decision models for probabilistic waiting line systems are usually based upon certain assumptions regarding the mathematical forms of the arrival and service time distributions. Monte Carlo analysis, however, does not require that the arrival and service time distributions obey certain theoretical forms. Waiting line data are produced as the system is simulated over time. Conclusions can be reached from the output statistics whatever the form of the distributions assumed. In addition, the detailed numerical description which results from Monte Carlo analysis assists greatly in understanding the probabilistic queuing process. This section illustrates the application of Monte Carlo analysis to an infinite population, single channel waiting line system.

Arrival and service time distributions. The probabilistic waiting line system usually involves both an arrival time and a service time distribution. Monte Carlo analysis requires that the form and parameters of these distributions be specified. The cumulative distributions may then be developed and used as a means for generating arrival and service time data.

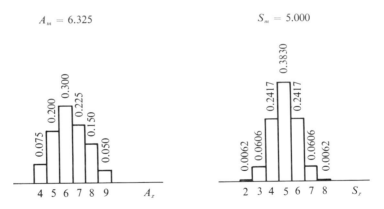

Figure 13.1. Arrival and service time distributions.

For the example under consideration, assume that the time between arrivals, A_x, has an empirical distribution with a mean of 6.325 periods. Service time, S_x, will be assumed to have a normal distribution with a mean of 5.000 periods and a standard deviation of one period. These distributions are exhibited in Figure 13.1. The probabilities associated with each value of A_x and S_x are indicated. By summing these individual probabilities from left to right, the cumulative distributions of Figure 13.2 result. These distributions may be used with a table of random rectangular variates to generate arrival and service time random variables.

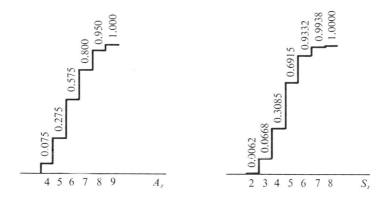

Figure 13.2. Cumulative arrival and service time distributions.

The Monte Carlo analysis. The queuing process under study is assumed to begin when the first arrival occurs. A unit will move immediately into the service facility if it is empty. If the service facility is not empty, the unit will wait in the queue. Units in the waiting line will enter the service facility on a first-come, first-served basis. The objective of the Monte Carlo analysis is to simulate this process over time. The number of unit periods of waiting in the queue and in service may be observed for each of several service rates. The service rate resulting in a minimum cost system may then be adopted.

The waiting line process resulting from the arrival and service time distributions of Figure 13.1 is shown in Figure 13.3. The illustration reads from left to right, with the second line being a continuation of the first, and so forth. The interval between vertical lines represents two periods, the heavy dots represent arrivals, the slanting path a unit in service, and the arrows a service completion. When a unit cannot move directly into the service channel, it waits in the queue which is represented by a horizontal path. This graphical representation is identical to that used for the deterministic process in Figure 12.2.

The probabilistic waiting line process of Figure 13.3 involves 400 periods and was developed in the following manner: First, the sequence of arrivals was established by the use of random rectangular variates and the cumulative arrival distribution of Figure 13.2. Next, each arrival was moved into the service channel if it was available. This availability is a function of the arrival pattern and the service durations selected with the aid of random rectangular variates and the cumulative service time distribution of Figure 13.2.

Specifically, the Monte Carlo analysis proceeded as follows: Random rectangular variates from Appendix A, Table A.2 were chosen as 5668, 3513, 2060, 7804, 0815, 2639, 9845, 6549, 6393, 7941, and so on. These correspond

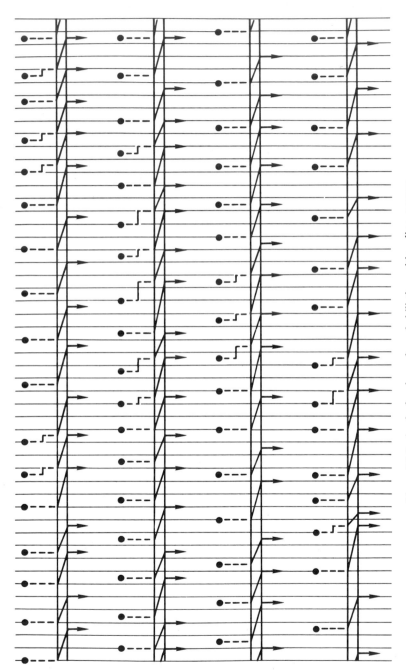

Figure 13.3. A single channel probabilistic waiting line process.

to arrival intervals of 6, 6, 5, 7, 5, 5, 9, 7, 7, 7, and so forth. Next, random rectangular variates were chosen as 323, 249, 404, 275, 879, 404, 740, 779, 441, 384, and so on. These correspond to service durations of 5, 4, 5, 4, 6, 5, 6, 6, 5, 5, and so forth. These service times determine the time an arrival enters the service channel and the time it is discharged. By proceeding in this manner, the results of Figure 13.3 are obtained.

Economic analysis of output results. The 400 periods simulated produced a waiting pattern involving 337 unit periods of waiting in service and 23 unit periods of waiting in the queue. The total number of unit periods of waiting for the 400 period sample was 360.

Suppose that waiting cost per unit per period is $0.04 and that it costs $0.065 to provide the service capability indicated by the service time distribution of Figure 13.1. The total system cost for the study period is therefore $0.04(360) + $0.065(400) = $40.40. This total system cost may be compared with the total system cost for alternate service policies by performing a Monte Carlo simulation for the alternate policies. Although this process is time-consuming, it is applicable to many situations that cannot be treated by mathematical means.

13.2. POISSON ARRIVALS WITH EXPONENTIAL SERVICE

In this section, assume that both the arrival rate and the service rate are expected values from independent Poisson distributions. This assumption holds when the rates are independent of time, queue length, or any other property of the waiting line system. The expected number of arrivals per period may be expressed as $1/A_m$ or λ. The expected number of service completions per period may be expressed as $1/S_m$ or μ. If the number of arrivals per period or the number of services per period have a Poisson distribution, then the time between arrivals, A_x, or the service duration, S_x, will have an exponential distribution.[1] (We assume that μ is greater than λ, and that the arrival population is infinite.)

The probability of n units in the system. Under the foregoing assumptions, the probability that an arrival occurs between time t and time $t + \Delta t$ is $\lambda \Delta t$.[2] Likewise, the probability that a service is completed in the time interval from t to $t + \Delta t$, given that a unit is being serviced at time t (conditional

---

[1] For a mathematical proof see C. W. Churchman, R. L. Ackoff, and E. L. Arnoff, *Introduction to Operations Research* (New York: John Wiley & Sons, Inc.), 1957, pp. 398–400.

[2] See W. Feller, *An Introduction to Probability Theory and Its Applications*, 2nd ed., (New York: John Wiley and Sons, Inc.,) 1957, p. 400.

probability), is $\mu \Delta t$. Let

$$n = \text{number of units in the system at time } t$$
$$P_n(t) = \text{probability of } n \text{ units in the system at time } t.$$

If it is assumed that the probabilities of more than one unit arriving or being served during the small time interval Δt are negligible, and if $n \geq 1$, the probability that there will be n units in the system at time $t + \Delta t$ may be expressed as the sum of three independent compound probabilities as follows:

(1) The product of the probabilities that there are n units in the system at time t, no arrivals occur during time Δt, and no services are completed during time Δt, which is $[P_n(t)][1 - \lambda(\Delta t)][1 - \mu(\Delta t)]$.

(2) The product of the probabilities that there are $n + 1$ units in the system at time t, there is one unit serviced during time Δt, and there are no arrivals during time Δt, which is $[P_{n+1}(t)][\mu(\Delta t)][1 - \lambda(\Delta t)]$.

(3) The product of the probabilities that there are $n - 1$ units in the system at time t, there is one arrival during time Δt, and there are no units serviced during Δt, which is $[P_{n-1}(t)][\lambda(\Delta t)][1 - \mu(\Delta t)]$.

All other possibilities that might be enumerated will yield terms in Δt of higher order. These are assumed to be negligible.

The probability of n units in the system, for $n \geq 1$, at time $t + \Delta t$ is obtained by adding the preceding probabilities.

$$P_n(t + \Delta t) = [P_n(t)][1 - \lambda(\Delta t)][1 - \mu(\Delta t)] + [P_{n+1}(t)][\mu(\Delta t)]$$
$$\times [1 - \lambda(\Delta t)] + [P_{n-1}(t)][\lambda(\Delta t)][1 - \mu(\Delta t)].$$

Since the time interval Δt is small, the probabilities at time $t + \Delta t$ are equivalent to those at time t. By substituting $P_n(t)$ for $P_n(t + \Delta t)$, expanding, and dropping terms in Δt of higher order, the foregoing expression becomes

$$P_n(t) = P_n(t)[1 - \lambda(\Delta t) - \mu(\Delta t)] + P_{n+1}(t)[\mu(\Delta t)] + P_{n-1}(t)[\lambda(\Delta t)]$$

$$P_{n+1}(t)[\mu(\Delta t)] = P_n(t) - P_n(t)[1 - \lambda(\Delta t) - \mu(\Delta t)] - P_{n-1}(t)[\lambda(\Delta t)]$$

$$P_{n+1}(t) = P_n(t)\frac{\lambda + \mu}{\mu} - P_{n-1}(t)\frac{\lambda}{\mu}. \tag{13.1}$$

The probability of no units in the system, $n = 0$, at time $t + \Delta t$ is the sum of two independent probabilities as follows:

(1) The product of the probability that there are no units in the system at time t, and the probability that there are no arrivals during time Δt, which is $P_0(t)[1 - \lambda(\Delta t)]$.

(2) The product of the probabilities that there is one unit in the line at time t, that one unit is serviced during time Δt, and that there are no arrivals during time Δt, which is $P_1(t)[\mu(\Delta t)][1 - \lambda(\Delta t)]$.

All other possibilities that might be enumerated will yield terms in Δt of higher order. As before, these are assumed to be negligible.

The probability of no units in the system at time $t + \Delta t$ is obtained by adding the foregoing probabilities.

$$P_0(t + \Delta t) = P_0(t)[1 - \lambda(\Delta t)] + P_1(t)[\mu(\Delta t)][1 - \lambda(\Delta t)].$$

Since the time interval Δt is small, the probabilities at time $t + \Delta t$ are equivalent to those of time t. By substituting $P_n(t)$ for $P_n(t + \Delta t)$, expanding, and dropping terms in Δt of higher order, the foregoing expression becomes

$$P_0(t) = P_0(t) \qquad P_0(t)[\lambda(\Delta t)] + P_1(t)[\mu(\Delta t)]$$

$$P_1(t) = P_0(t)\frac{\lambda}{\mu}. \qquad (13.2)$$

Equations (13.1) and (13.2) may be solved by successive substitution for P_0 in terms of P_0, P_1, P_2, ..., and P_n. Assuming that $P_n(t)$ is independent of t, and equal to P_n, results in

$$P_0 = P_0$$

$$P_1 = P_0\left(\frac{\lambda}{\mu}\right) \qquad \text{from Equation (13.2)}$$

$$P_2 = P_0\left(\frac{\lambda}{\mu}\right)^2 \qquad \text{letting } n - 1 \text{ in Equation (13.1) and substituting for } P_1$$

$$P_3 = P_0\left(\frac{\lambda}{\mu}\right)^3 \qquad \text{letting } n = 2 \text{ in Equation (13.1) and substituting for } P_2$$

.

.

.

$$P_n = P_0\left(\frac{\lambda}{\mu}\right)^n \qquad \text{letting } n = n - 1 \text{ in Equation (13.1) and substituting for } P_{n-1}.$$

Summing the left and the right sides of the preceding series results in the equality

$$\sum_{n=0}^{\infty} P_n = P_0 \sum_{n=0}^{\infty} \left(\frac{\lambda}{\mu}\right)^n.$$

But it is obvious that

$$\sum_{n=0}^{\infty} P_n = 1.$$

And from the sum of an infinite geometric series

$$\sum_{n=0}^{\infty} \left(\frac{\lambda}{\mu}\right)^n = \frac{1}{1 - (\lambda/\mu)}.$$

Therefore,

$$P_0\left[\frac{1}{1 - (\lambda/\mu)}\right] = 1$$

$$P_0 = 1 - \frac{\lambda}{\mu}.$$

Substituting this expression for P_0 into the previous relationship for P_n gives

$$P_n = \left(1 - \frac{\lambda}{\mu}\right)\left(\frac{\lambda}{\mu}\right)^n. \tag{13.3}$$

As an example of the significance of Equation (13.3) in waiting line operations, suppose that a queue is experiencing Poisson arrivals with a mean rate of 1/10 unit per period and that the service duration is distributed exponentially with a mean of four periods. The service rate is, therefore, 1/4, or 0.25 units per period. Probabilities associated with each value of n may be calculated as follows:

$$P_0 = (0.6)(0.4)^0 = 0.600$$
$$P_1 = (0.6)(0.4)^1 = 0.240$$
$$P_2 = (0.6)(0.4)^2 = 0.096$$
$$P_3 = (0.6)(0.4)^3 = 0.039$$
$$P_4 = (0.6)(0.4)^4 = 0.015$$
$$P_5 = (0.6)(0.4)^5 = 0.006$$
$$P_6 = (0.6)(0.4)^6 = 0.003$$
$$P_7 = (0.6)(0.4)^7 = 0.001$$

Figure 13.4 exhibits the probability distribution of n units in the system. Certain important characteristics of the waiting line system can be extracted

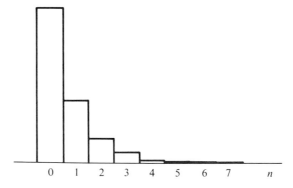

Figure 13.4. Probability distribution of n units in the system.

from this distribution. For example, the probability of one or more units in the system is 0.4, the probability of no units in the system is 0.6, the probability of more than four units in the system is 0.01, and so forth. Such information as this is useful when there is a restriction on the number of units in the system. By altering the arrival population or the service rate or both, the probability of the number of units in the system exceeding a specified value may be controlled.

The mean number of units in the system. The mean number of units in the system, n_m, may be expressed as

$$n_m = \sum_{n=0}^{\infty} n P_n$$

$$= \sum_{n=0}^{\infty} n \left(1 - \frac{\lambda}{\mu}\right) \left(\frac{\lambda}{\mu}\right)^n$$

$$= \left(1 - \frac{\lambda}{\mu}\right) \sum_{n=0}^{\infty} n \left(\frac{\lambda}{\mu}\right)^n$$

$$= \left(1 - \frac{\lambda}{\mu}\right) \left[\frac{\lambda}{\mu} + 2\left(\frac{\lambda}{\mu}\right)^2 + 3\left(\frac{\lambda}{\mu}\right)^3 + \cdots\right]. \tag{13.4}$$

Let $g = \frac{\lambda}{\mu} + 2\left(\frac{\lambda}{\mu}\right)^2 + 3\left(\frac{\lambda}{\mu}\right)^3 + \cdots$

And let $g\left(\frac{\lambda}{\mu}\right) = \left(\frac{\lambda}{\mu}\right)^2 + 2\left(\frac{\lambda}{\mu}\right)^3 + \cdots$

Subtracting the second series from the first gives

$$g\left(1 - \frac{\lambda}{\mu}\right) = \frac{\lambda}{\mu} + \left(\frac{\lambda}{\mu}\right)^2 + \left(\frac{\lambda}{\mu}\right)^3 + \cdots$$

Adding 1 to each side gives

$$g\left(1 - \frac{\lambda}{\mu}\right) + 1 = 1 + \frac{\lambda}{\mu} + \left(\frac{\lambda}{\mu}\right)^2 + \left(\frac{\lambda}{\mu}\right)^3 + \cdots$$

The right side is now an infinite geometric series, therefore

$$g\left(1 - \frac{\lambda}{\mu}\right) + 1 = \frac{1}{1 - (\lambda/\mu)}$$

$$g = \frac{\lambda/\mu}{[1 - (\lambda/\mu)]^2}.$$

Substituting for g in Equation (13.4) gives

$$n_m = \frac{\lambda}{\mu}\left[\frac{1}{1 - (\lambda/\mu)}\right]$$

$$= \frac{\lambda}{\mu - \lambda}. \tag{13.5}$$

For the example given previously, the mean number of units in the system is

$$n_m = \frac{0.10}{0.25 - 0.10} = 0.667.$$

The mean waiting time. The expected time an arrival spends in the system, w_m, can be shown to be

$$w_m = \frac{n_m}{\lambda}.$$

Substituting Equation (13.5) for n_m gives

$$w_m = \frac{1}{\mu - \lambda}. \tag{13.6}$$

For the previous example, the expected time an arrival spends in the system is

$$w_m = \frac{1}{0.25 - 0.10} = 6.67 \text{ periods.}$$

As a further example of the use of Equation (13.6), assume that the maximum expected time in the system that can be tolerated is six periods. The service rate required under these conditions can be found as follows:

$$\frac{1}{\mu - 0.1} = 6.0$$
$$\mu = 0.267 \text{ units per period.}$$

The minimum cost service rate. The expected total system cost per period is the sum of the expected waiting cost per period and the expected facility cost per period; that is,

$$TC_m = WC_m + FC_m.$$

The expected waiting cost per period is the product of the cost of waiting per unit per period and the mean number of units in the system during the period or   ,

$$WC_m = C_w(n_m)$$
$$= \frac{C_w \lambda}{\mu - \lambda}.$$

The expected service cost per period is the product of the cost of servicing one unit and the service rate in units per period, or

$$FC_m = C_f(\mu).$$

The expected total system cost per period is the sum of these cost components and may be expressed as

$$TC_m = \frac{C_w \lambda}{(\mu - \lambda)} + C_f(\mu). \tag{13.7}$$

A minimum cost service rate may be found by differentiating with respect to μ, setting the result equal to zero, and solving for μ as follows:

$$\frac{dTC_m}{d\mu} = -C_w\lambda(\mu - \lambda)^{-2} + C_f = 0$$

$$(\mu - \lambda)^2 C_f = \lambda C_w$$

$$\mu = \lambda + \sqrt{\frac{\lambda C_w}{C_f}}. \tag{13.8}$$

As an application of the preceding model, consider the following Poisson arrival, exponential service time illustration. The mean time between arrivals is eight periods, the cost of waiting is $0.10 per unit per period, and the facility cost for serving one unit is $0.165. The expected waiting cost per period, the expected facility cost per period, and the expected total system cost per period is exhibited as a function of μ in Table 13.1. The expected

Table 13.1. COST COMPONENTS FOR EXPONENTIAL SERVICE DURATION

μ	WC_m	FC_m	TC_m
0.125	$ ∞	$0.0206	$ ∞
0.150	0.5000	0.0248	0.5248
0.200	0.1667	0.0330	0.1997
0.250	0.1000	0.0413	0.1413
0.300	0.0714	0.0495	0.1209
0.400	0.0455	0.0660	0.1115
0.500	0.0333	0.0825	0.1158
0.600	0.0263	0.0990	0.1253
0.800	0.0185	0.1320	0.1505
1.000	0.0143	0.1650	0.1793

waiting cost per period is infinite when $\mu = \lambda$ and decreases as μ increases. The expected facility cost per period increases with increasing values of μ. The minimum expected total system cost occurs when μ is 0.4 units per period.

The minimum cost service rate may be found directly by substituting into Equation (13.8) as follows:

$$\mu = 0.125 + \sqrt{\frac{(0.125)(\$0.10)}{0.165}}$$

$$= 0.125 + 0.275 = 0.400 \text{ units per period.}$$

13.3. POISSON ARRIVALS WITH NON-EXPONENTIAL SERVICE

The assumption that the number of arrivals per period obeys a Poisson distribution has a sound practical basis. Although it cannot be said that the

Poisson distribution always adequately describes the distribution of the number of arrivals per period, much evidence exists to indicate that this is often the case. Intuitive considerations add support to this assumption since arrival rates are usually independent of time, queue length, or any other property of the waiting line system. Evidence in support of the exponential distribution of service durations is not as strong. Often, this distribution is assumed for mathematical convenience, as in Section 13.2. When the service time distribution is non-exponential, the development of decision models is quite difficult. Therefore, this section will present models with non-exponential service without proof. The assumptions that μ is greater than λ and that the population is infinite are retained.

Poisson arrivals with constant service times. When service is provided automatically by mechanical means, or when the service operation is mechanically paced, the service duration might be a constant. Under these conditions, the service time distribution has a variance of zero. The mean number of units in the system is given by

$$n_m = \frac{(\lambda/\mu)^2}{2[1 - (\lambda/\mu)]} + \frac{\lambda}{\mu}.$$ (13.9)

And the mean waiting time is

$$w_m = \frac{\lambda/\mu}{2\mu[1 - (\lambda/\mu)]} + \frac{1}{\mu}.$$ (13.10)

The expected total system cost per period is the sum of the expected waiting cost per period and the expected facility cost per period; that is,

$$TC_m = WC_m + FC_m.$$

The expected waiting cost per period is the product of the cost of waiting per unit per period and the mean number of units in the system during the period, or

$$WC_m = C_w(n_m)$$
$$= C_w \left\{ \frac{(\lambda/\mu)^2}{2[1 - (\lambda/\mu)]} + \frac{\lambda}{\mu} \right\}.$$

The expected facility cost per period is the product of the cost of servicing one unit and the service rate in units per period, or

$$FC_m = C_f(\mu).$$

The expected total system cost per period is the sum of these cost components and may be expressed as

$$TC_m = C_w \left\{ \frac{(\lambda/\mu)^2}{2[1 - (\lambda/\mu)]} + \frac{\lambda}{\mu} \right\} + C_f(\mu).$$ (13.11)

Table 13.2. COST COMPONENTS FOR CONSTANT SERVICE DURATION

μ	WC_m	FC_m	TC_m
0.1250	$ \infty$	$0.0206	$ \infty$
0.1500	0.2913	0.0248	0.3161
0.2000	0.1145	0.0330	0.1475
0.2500	0.0750	0.0413	0.1163
0.3000	0.0566	0.0495	0.1061
0.4000	0.0383	0.0660	0.1043
0.5000	0.0292	0.0825	0.1117
0.6000	0.0236	0.0990	0.1226
0.8000	0.0170	0.1320	0.1490
1.0000	0.0134	0.1650	0.1784

As an application of the foregoing model, consider the example of the previous section. Instead of the parameter μ being the expected value from an exponential distribution, however, assume that it is a constant. The expected waiting cost per period, the expected service cost per period, and the expected total system cost per period is exhibited as a function of μ in Table 13.2. Although the expected waiting cost function differs from the previous example, the minimum cost service interval is still 0.4 units per period.

These examples may be more easily compared by graphing the expected total cost functions as shown in Figure 13.5. The upper curve is the expected total system cost function when μ is an expected value from an exponential distribution. The lower curve is the expected total system cost when μ is a constant. No significant difference in the minimum cost policy is evident for the example considered.

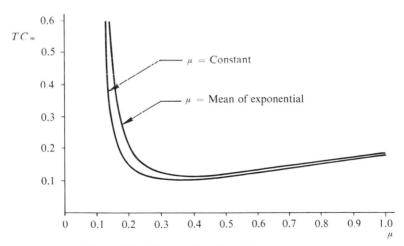

Figure 13.5. TC_m as a function of the service rate.

Poisson arrivals with any service time distribution. For further generality, it is desirable to have expressions for pertinent system characteristics regardless of the form of the service time distribution. If σ^2 is the variance of the service time distribution, the mean number of units in the system is given by

$$n_m = \frac{(\lambda/\mu)^2 + \lambda^2\sigma^2}{2[1 - (\lambda/\mu)]} + \frac{\lambda}{\mu}. \tag{13.12}$$

And, the mean waiting time is

$$w_m = \frac{(\lambda/\mu^2) + \lambda\sigma^2}{2[1 - (\lambda/\mu)]} + \frac{1}{\mu}. \tag{13.13}$$

Equation (13.12) reduces to Equation (13.9) and Equation (13.13) reduces to Equation (13.10) when $\sigma^2 = 0$. In addition, since the variance of an exponential distribution is $(1/\mu)^2$, Equation (13.12) reduces to Equation (13.5) and Equation (13.13) reduces to Equation (13.6) when this substitution is made.

The expected total system cost per period is the sum of the expected waiting cost per period and the expected facility cost per period; that is,

$$TC_m = WC_m + FC_m.$$

The expected waiting cost per period is the product of the cost of waiting per unit per period and the mean number of units in the system during the period. The expected facility cost per period may be taken as the product of the cost of serving one unit and the service rate in units per period. Therefore, the expected total system cost per period is

$$TC_m = C_w\left\{\frac{(\lambda/\mu)^2 + \lambda^2\sigma^2}{2[1 - (\lambda/\mu)]} + \frac{\lambda}{\mu}\right\} + C_f(\mu). \tag{13.14}$$

As an example of the application of this model, consider the following situation: The number of arrivals per hour has a Poisson distribution with a mean of 0.2 units. The cost of waiting per unit per hour is \$2.10 and the cost of servicing one unit is \$4.05. The decision maker may choose one of two service policies. The first will result in a service rate of 0.4 units per hour with a service time variance of three hours. The second will result in a service rate of 0.5 units per hour with a service time variance of four hours. The first policy will result in an expected total system cost of

$$TC_m = \$2.10\left\{\frac{(0.2/0.4)^2 + (0.2)^2(3)}{2[1 - (0.2/0.4)]} + \frac{0.2}{0.4}\right\} + \$4.05(0.4)$$

$$= \$1.83 + \$1.62 = \$3.45.$$

The second policy will result in an expected total system cost of

$$TC_m = \$2.10\left\{\frac{(0.2/0.5)^2 + (0.2)^2(4)}{2[1 - (0.2/0.5)]} + \frac{0.2}{0.5}\right\} + \$4.05(0.5)$$

$$= \$1.40 + \$2.03 = \$3.43.$$

From these results, it is evident that it makes little difference which policy is adopted.

13.4. FINITE POPULATION MODELS

Finite waiting line models must be applied to those waiting line systems where the population is small relative to the arrival rate. In these systems, units leaving the population significantly affect the characteristics of the population and the arrival probabilities. It is assumed that both the time between calls for service for a unit of the population, and the service times are distributed exponentially. As a result of the changing arrival probabilities, mathematical formulations are difficult. Tables describing important facets of the finite waiting line systems are, however, available.[3] The use of these tables for systems having the characteristics described above will be presented in this and the following section.

The finite queuing tables. For convenience, the notation used in the tables will be adopted. Let

$N =$ number of units in the population
$M =$ number of service channels
$T =$ mean service time
$U =$ mean time between calls for service
$H =$ mean number of units being serviced
$L =$ mean number of units waiting for service
$J =$ mean number of units running or productive.

Appendix D gives a portion of the Finite Queuing Tables (for populations of 10, 20, and 30 units). Each set of values is indexed by N, the number of units in the population. Within each set, data are classified by X, the service factor, and M, the number of service channels. Two values are listed for each value of N, X, and M. The first is D, the probability of a delay, expressing the probability that an arrival will have to wait. The second is F, an efficiency factor needed in the calculation of H, L, and J.

[3] L. G. Peck and R. N. Hazelwood, *Finite Queuing Tables* (New York: John Wiley & Sons, Inc., 1958).

The service factor is a function of the mean service time and the mean time between calls for service,

$$X = \frac{T}{T + U}. \qquad (13.15)$$

The mean number of units being serviced is a function of the efficiency factor, the number of units in the population, and the service factor,

$$H = FNX. \qquad (13.16)$$

The mean number of units waiting for service is a function of the number of units in the population and the efficiency factor,

$$L = N(1 - F). \qquad (13.17)$$

Finally, the mean number of units running or productive is a function of the number of units in the population, the efficiency factor, and the service factor,

$$J = NF(1 - X). \qquad (13.18)$$

A knowledge of N, T, and U for the waiting line system under study, together with a set of tabular values and these expressions makes possible the derivation of optimum waiting line policies. This will be illustrated by several examples:

Number of service channels under control. As a first example, assume that a population of 20 units exists, with each unit having a mean time between required service of 32 minutes. Each service channel provided will have a mean service time of 8 minutes. Both the time between arrivals and the service interval are distributed exponentially. The number of channels to be provided is under management control. The cost of providing one channel with a mean service time capacity of 8 minutes is $10 per hour. The cost of waiting is $5 per unit per hour. The service factor for this system is

$$X = \frac{T}{T + U} = \frac{8}{8 + 32} = 0.200.$$

Table 13.3 provides a systematic means for finding the minimum cost number of service channels. The values in column A and column B are entered from Appendix D, Table D.2 with $N = 20$ and $X = 0.200$. The mean number of units being serviced is found from Equation (13.16) and entered in column C. The mean number of units waiting for service is found from Equation (13.17) and is entered in column D. The mean number of units waiting in queue and in service is given in column E. The data of column A and column E may be multiplied by their respective costs to give the total system cost.

Table 13.3. COST AS A FUNCTION OF THE NUMBER OF SERVICE CHANNELS

M (A)	F (B)	H (C)	L (D)	H + L (E)	Waiting Cost (F)	Service Cost (G)	Total Cost (H)
8	0.999	4.00	0.02	4.02	$20.10	$80	$100.10
7	0.997	3.99	0.06	4.05	20.25	70	90.25
6	0.988	3.95	0.24	4.19	20.95	60	80.95
5	0.963	3.85	0.74	4.59	22.95	50	72.95
4	0.895	3.58	2.10	5.68	28.40	40	68.40
3	0.736	2.94	5.28	8.22	41.10	30	71.10
2	0.500	2.00	10.00	12.00	60.00	20	80.00

First, multiplying $5 per unit per hour by the mean number of units waiting gives the waiting cost per hour in column F. Second, multiplying $10 per channel per hour by the number of channels gives the service cost per hour in column G. Finally, adding the expected waiting cost and the service cost gives the expected total system cost in column H. The minimum cost number of channels is found to be four.

In this example, the cost of waiting was taken to be $5 per unit per hour. If this is due to lost profit, resulting from unproductive units, the same solution may be obtained by maximizing profit. As before, the values in column A and column B of Table 13.4 are entered from Appendix D, Table D.2 with $N = 20$ and $X = 0.200$. The mean number of units running or productive is found from Equation (13.18) and entered in column C.

The profit per hour in column D is found by multiplying the mean number of productive units by $5 profit per productive unit per hour. The cost of service per hour in column E is obtained by multiplying the number of channels by $10 per channel per hour. Finally, the net profit in column F is found by subtracting the service cost per hour from the profit per hour. As before, the number of channels that should be used is four. This example illustrates

Table 13.4. PROFIT AS A FUNCTION OF THE NUMBER OF SERVICE CHANNELS

M (A)	F (B)	J (C)	Gross Profit (D)	Service Cost (E)	Net Profit (F)
8	0.999	15.98	$79.90	$80	$-0.10
7	0.997	15.95	79.75	70	9.75
6	0.988	15.81	79.05	60	19.05
5	0.963	15.41	77.05	50	27.05
4	0.895	14.32	71.60	40	31.60
3	0.736	11.78	58.90	30	28.90
2	0.500	8.00	40.00	20	20.00

that either the minimum cost or the maximum profit approach may be used with equivalent results.

Mean service time under control. Assume that a population of 10 units is to be served by a single service channel. The mean time between calls for service is 30 minutes. If the mean service rate is 60 units per hour, the service cost will be $100 per hour. The service cost per hour is inversely proportional to the time in minutes to service one unit, expressed as $100/T$. Both the time between calls for service and the service duration are distributed exponentially. Lost profit due to units waiting in the system is $15 per hour.

Column A in Table 13.5 gives the capacity of the channel expressed as the mean service time in minutes per unit processed. The service factor for each

Table 13.5. PROFIT AS A FUNCTION OF THE MEAN SERVICE TIME

T (A)	X (B)	F (C)	J (D)	Gross Profit (E)	Service Cost (F)	Net Profit (G)
1	0.032	0.988	9.56	$143.20	$100.00	$43.20
2	0.062	0.945	8.86	132.90	50.00	82.90
3	0.091	0.864	7.85	117.75	33.33	84.42
4	0.118	0.763	6.73	101.00	25.00	76.00
5	0.143	0.674	5.77	86.51	20.00	66.51

service time is found from Equation (13.15) and entered in column B. The efficiency factors in column C are found by interpolation in Appendix D, Table D.1 for $N = 10$ and the respective service factors of column B. The mean number of units running is found from Equation (13.18) and entered in column D. The data given in column A and column D may now be used to find the service capacity that results in a maximum net profit.

The expected profit per hour in column E is found by multiplying the mean number of units running by $15 per hour. The cost of service per hour is found by dividing $100 by the value for T in column A. These costs are entered in column F. By subtracting the cost of service per hour from the expected gross profit per hour, the expected net profit per hour in column G is found. The mean service time resulting in an expected maximum profit is three periods.

13.5. FINITE POPULATION MODELS AND MAINTENANCE

Suppose that a population of production equipment is under study with the objective of deriving minimum cost maintenance policy. It is assumed that both the time between calls for maintenance for a unit of the population and the service times are distributed exponentially. Two parameters of the system are subject to management control: First, by increasing the repair capability (reducing T) the average machine down time will be reduced. Secondly, alternative policies of preventive maintenance will alter the mean time between breakdowns, U. Therefore, the problem of machine maintenance reduces to one of determining the service factor, X, that will result in a minimum cost system. This section will present methods for establishing and controlling the service factor in maintenance operations.

Machine downtime as a function of the service factor. As machines break down they become unproductive with a resulting economic loss. This loss may be reduced by reducing the service factor. But a decrease in the service factor requires either a reduction in the repair time or a more expensive policy of preventive maintenance or both. Therefore, the objective is to find an economic balance between the cost of unproductive machines and the cost of maintaining a specific service factor.

The analysis of this situation is facilitated by developing curves giving the percentage of machines not running as a function of the service factor. Figure 13.6 gives curves for selected populations when one service channel is provided. Each curve is developed from Equation (13.18) and the Finite Queuing Tables. As was expected, the percentage of machines not running increases as the service factor increases.

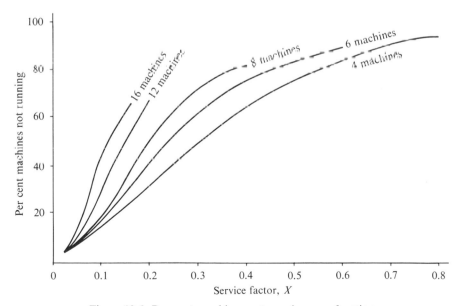

Figure 13.6. Per cent machines not running as a function of the service factor.

As an example of the determination of the minimum cost service factor, consider the following situation: Eight machines are maintained by a mechanic and his helper. Each machine produces a profit of $2.20 per hour while it is running. The mechanic and his assistant cost the company $4.80 per hour. Three policies of preventive maintenance are under consideration. The first will cost $8 per hour. After considering the increase in the mean time between breakdowns and the effect on service time, it is estimated that the resulting service factor will be 0.04. The second policy of preventive maintenance will cost only $1.80 per hour, but will result in a service factor of 0.10. The third alternative involves no preventive maintenance at all; hence it will cost nothing, but a service factor in excess of 0.2 will result. The time between

Table 13.6. THREE POLICIES OF PREVENTIVE MAINTENANCE

Maintenance Policy	Service Factor, X	Machines Not Running	Cost of Lost Profit	Cost of Maintenance	Cost of Mechanic	Total Cost
1	0.04	0.5	$1.10	$8.00	$4.80	$13.90
2	0.10	1.6	3.52	1.80	4.80	10.12
3	0.20	4.1	9.02	0.00	4.80	13.82

calls for service and the service times are distributed exponentially. By reference to Figure 13.6, the results of Table 13.6 are developed. From the results of the last column, it is evident that the second alternative should be adopted.

Service factor control by chart. Once the service factor resulting in a minimum cost system has been established, it may be desirable to implement a control model for detecting the effects of a shift in the arrival rate or the service rate or both. This may be accomplished by constructing a control chart for the number of machines not running. The statistical control models presented in Chapter 8 cannot be applied directly to this variable, since its distribution is badly skewed. The expected form of the distribution is known in advance, however, a factor usually missing in other control model applications.

As an example of the application of control charts in waiting line operations, consider a one-man N machine situation.[4] Suppose that 20 automatic machines are to be run by one man, and that the minimum cost service factor was found to be 0.03. It is assumed that the machines require service at randomly distributed times, that the service times are distributed exponentially, and that machines are serviced on a first-come, first-served basis. The

---

[4] Adapted from R. W. Llewellyn, "Control Charts for Queueing Applications," *Journal of Industrial Engineering*, **XI**, No. 4, July–August, 1960.

probability of n machines in the queue and in service (not running) is given by

$$P_n = \frac{N!}{(N-n)!} X^n P_0 \qquad (13.19)$$

where P_n = probability that n machines are not running at any point in time
P_0 = probability that all machines are running at any point in time
X = service factor
N = number of machines assigned
n = number of machines not running at any point in time.

Values for P_n are given in column C of Table 13.7 for $0 \le n \le N$. The first entry is found by dividing the first entry in column B by 2.30005387. The second results from dividing the second entry in column B by the same value, etc. The results for P_n are plotted in Figure 13.7. The distribution of n is seen to be extremely skewed, being completely convex. Unlike some

Table 13.7. CALCULATION OF P_n AND ΣP_n

n (A)	$\dfrac{P_n}{P_0}$ (B)	P_n (C)	ΣP_n (D)
0	1.000000000	0.434772422	0.434772422
1	0.600000000	0.260863453	0.695635875
2	0.342000000	0.148692168	0.844328043
3	0.184680000	0.080293771	0.924621814
4	0.094186800	0.040949823	0.965571637
5	0.045209664	0.019655915	0.985227552
6	0.020344349	0.008845162	0.994072714
7	0.008544627	0.003714968	0.997787682
8	0.003332405	0.001448838	0.999236520
9	0.001199666	0.000521582	0.999758102
10	0.000395890	0.000172122	0.999930224
11	0.000118767	0.000051637	0.999981861
12	0.000032067	0.000013942	0.999995803
13	0.000007696	0.000003346	0.999999149
14	0.000001616	0.000000703	0.999999852
15	0.000000291	0.000000127	0.999999979
16	0.000000044	0.000000019	0.999999998
17	0.000000005	0.000000002	1.000000000
18	0.000000000	0.000000000	1.000000000
19	0.000000000	0.000000000	1.000000000
20	0.000000000	0.000000000	1.000000000

2.300053887

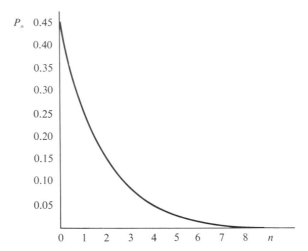

Figure 13.7. Probability distribution of the number of machines not running.

control chart applications, the distribution of the variable to be controlled is known. It may be used to determine the control limits.

Since the probability that all machines are running is approximately 0.435, the lower control limit is obviously zero. The upper control limit is all that needs to be determined, since the variable n can go out of control only at the top. Thus, the entire critical range will be at the upper end of the distribution. It will be desirable to set this limit so that it will not be violated too frequently. Since n is an integer, the magnitude of the critical range can be observed as a function of n from column D in Table 13.7. If six machines not running is chosen as a point in control and seven is a point out of control, the probability of designating the system out of control when it is really in control is

$$1 - \sum_{n=0}^{6} P_n = 0.0059.$$

Therefore, a control limit set at 6.5 should be satisfactory. The control chart applied to a period of operation might appear as in Figure 13.8. It would be concluded that the service factor has not changed during this period of observation.

In order for the application of this control model to be valid, two conditions must be met. First, the observation must be made at random times. Second, the observations must be spaced far enough apart so that the results are independent. For example, if the service time averages 5 minutes, and if

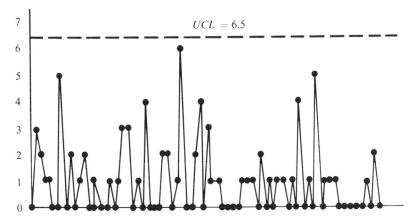

Figure 13.8. Control chart for the number of machines not running

6 machines are idle in an observation, then an observation taken 10 minutes later would probably indicate at least four idle. The readings should be far enough apart for a waiting line to be dissipated. To insure both randomness and spacing, all numbers from 45 to 90 could be taken from a random number table with their order preserved; numbers from 00 to 44 and from 91 to 99 would be dropped. These numbers can then be used to space the observations. This would yield an average of 8 random observations per day with a minimum spacing of 45 minutes and a maximum spacing of 90 minutes.

If the control chart indicates that n is no longer in control, corrective action must be taken. This will require investigation to determine whether the service factor has changed because of a change in the mean time between calls, or a change in the mean service time, or both. Specific items that might be studied are the policy of preventive maintenance, the age of the machines, the capability of the operator, or material characteristics. Once the assignable cause for the out-of-control condition is located, it may be corrected so that the system will return to a minimum cost position.

13.6. A GENERAL SOLUTION METHOD

The analysis of waiting line operations presented thus far required derived expressions and/or tabulated values describing system characteristics. These decision models and tabulated values were based upon certain assumptions regarding the empirical or theoretical forms of the arrival and service time distributions. In this section, we present a general solution method that may be applied in any waiting line situation. It makes no assumption about the arrival and service time distributions, but does require historical data describing the system under study.

As an example of the general solution method, consider the following example:[5] In petroleum production, heavy equipment is used to pump oil to the surface. When this equipment fails, it is necessary to remove it from the well. The required repairs are made by a crew of three to five men who are equipped with portable machinery to pull the pumping equipment from the well. Between the failure of the pumping equipment and its repair, the well is idle. This results in lost production equal to the amount of oil that would have been produced. In some cases, lost production may be only production that is deferred to a later data. In other cases, lost production is partially lost because of drainage to competitor's wells. Down time of the well is made up of the time that the well is idle before the repair crew arrives and the time it is idle while the repair is in progress. Loss is reduced by cutting the time a well is idle awaiting a repair crew. This is done at the expense of maintaining excess repair crews. Thus, the problem is to balance the cost of repair crews with the cost of lost production resulting from repair delays.

Operation with a single repair crew. Suppose that the hourly cost of a repair crew with its associated repair equipment is $13.80. The cost of lost production due to drainage to competitors' wells, together with the time value of lost revenue, is estimated to be $170 per day. This repair crew requires an average of 12 hours per repair. Wells are operated 24 hours per day, 7 days per week.

At present, analysis has shown that operation of the equivalent of one repair crew 24 hours per day can keep up with the repair work in the long run. Serious losses are arising, however, from delays in getting to wells after a breakdown. Delays are due to the chance bunching of well failures. For instance, one period during which no wells fail may be followed by a period of an above average number of failures. Since repairs cannot be made before failures occur, it is evident that a number of crews sufficient to take care of the average number of failures will have a backlog of failures most of the time.

In the solution of this example, the pattern of well failures of a previous 30-day period selected at random will be considered to be representative of the future. Although a larger sample is ordinarily needed for reliable results, the data given by line A in Figure 13.9 will be used as an illustration. The number of wells failing during any one day ranged between 0 and 5, and their total was 57. Since the crew can repair two wells per day when operating three 8-hour shifts per day, unrepaired wells will be carried over one day each day that the number of failures plus the carry-over from the previous day exceeds two. Line B gives the number of wells repaired each day with a single crew. During the 30-day period, 55 wells were repaired. Thus, even though there were periodic backlogs, idle time sufficient to repair five wells occurred

---

[5] Adapted from H. G. Thuesen and W. J. Fabrycky, *Engineering Economy*, 3rd ed. (Englewood Cliffs, N.J.: Prentice-Hall, Inc., 1964).

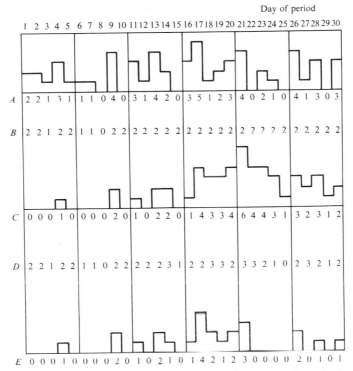

Figure 13.9. Pattern of oil well failure with two repair methods.

on the days numbered 3, 6, 7, and 8. The carry-over of unrepaired wells is given in line C. The total carry-over for the 30-day period was 52 well days.

With the present method of operation, the cost associated with lost production during the 30-day period was 52($170) = $8,840. The cost of maintaining the equivalent of one repair crew 24 hours per day during the 30-day period was $13.80(24)(30) = $9,936. Therefore, the total cost for the study period was $18,776.

A proposed method of operation. Analysis of the pattern of unrepaired wells reveals that once a backlog has accumulated, wells may remain unrepaired and unproductive for many days. As a remedy, the feasibility of hiring an additional crew whenever this backlog of unrepaired wells reaches two is under consideration. Because the hired crew is not under the control of the organization and is called on short notice, it will cost $18 per hour. Because of greater travel distances and unfamiliarity with the oil field, the hired crew requires an average of 16 hours to repair a well. The crew is paid for a minimum of 16 hours each time it is asked to report, whether or not it is in use.

If this policy had been in effect during the 30-day study period, the additional repair crew would have been hired for 16 hours on the days numbered

10, 14, 18, 19, 21, 22, and 27. The number of wells repaired each day would have been as given in line D. The total carry-over would have been 24 well-days as is shown in line E. Idle time would have occurred on the days numbered 3, 6, 7, 8, 10, 15, 24, 25, and 29, sufficient to repair 11 wells.

Under the proposed policy, the cost associated with lost production during the 30-day period would have been 24($170) = $4,080. The cost of maintaining the equivalent of one repair crew 24 hours per day during the 30-day period would be $9,936 as before. The cost of the hired crew for seven calls would be $18(16)(7) = $2,016. Therefore, the total cost for the study period under the proposed policy would have been $16,032. Thus, a decision to hire an additional crew on days when there is a carry-over of two or more unrepaired wells from a previous day would be economically advantageous. This is based on the assumption that the pattern of failure is typical and representative of the future.

QUESTIONS

1. Contrast the deterministic waiting line system and the probabilistic waiting line system.

2. Name and describe an infinite population; a finite population.

3. Under what conditions is it mandatory that Monte Carlo analysis be used in the study of a waiting line system?

4. Why is it essential that μ be greater than λ in a probabilistic waiting line process?

5. What conditions must be met for the Poisson distribution adequately to describe the number of arrivals per period?

6. Name and describe a situation in which the assumption of a constant service rate would be valid.

7. Describe a situation in which it is possible to alter the service rate; the service factor.

8. Why might it be desirable to apply a control chart to the number of machines not running?

PROBLEMS

1. Suppose that the time between arrivals is distributed exponentially with a mean of 4 minutes and that service time is constant and equal to 3 minutes. Service is provided on a first-come, first-served basis. No units are in the system at 8:00 A.M. Use Monte Carlo analysis to estimate the total number of unit minutes of waiting between 8:00 A.M. and 12:00 noon.

2. Rework the example of Section 13.1 if the service time distribution of Figure 13.1 has a mean of six periods with the same standard deviation. Compare the total system cost with that found in the text if the cost of providing this service capacity is $0.06 per period and the waiting cost per unit per period remains the same.

3. Use Monte Carlo analysis to verify Equation (13.5) if the number of arrivals per period has a Poisson distribution with a mean of 0.10 and if the service duration is distributed exponentially with a mean of four periods. Plot the histogram of the number of units in the system and compare with Figure 13.4.

4. Suppose that arrivals are distributed according to the Poisson distribution with a mean of 0.125 units per period and that the service duration is distributed exponentially with a mean of four periods. Develop the probability distribution of n units in the system. What is the probability of there being more than six units in the system?

5. The arrival rate for a certain waiting line system obeys a Poisson distribution with a mean of 0.5 units per period. It is required that the probability of one or more units in the system not exceed 0.25. What is the minimum service rate that must be provided if the service duration will be distributed exponentially?

6. What is the expected number of units in the system for the conditions of Problem 4; the expected waiting time?

7. The expected number of units in a waiting line system experiencing Poisson arrivals with a rate of 0.4 units per period must not exceed eight. What is the minimum service rate that must be provided if the service duration will be distributed exponentially? What will be the expected waiting time?

8. Plot the mean number of units in the system, and the mean waiting time, as a function of λ/μ if the number of arrivals per period obey the Poisson distribution and if the service duration is distributed exponentially. What is the significance of this illustration?

9. The number of arrivals per period is distributed according to the Poisson with an expected value of 0.8 units per period. The cost of waiting per unit per period is $3.20. The facility cost for serving one unit per period is $5.15. What expected service rate should be established if the service duration will be distributed exponentially? What is the expected total system cost?

10. The expected waiting time in a waiting line system with Poisson arrivals at a rate of 1.5 units per day must not exceed five days. What is the minimum constant service rate that must be provided? What is the expected number in the system?

11. Trucks arrive at a loading dock in a Poisson manner at the rate of 3.5 per day. The cost of waiting per truck per day is $42. A three-man crew that can load at a constant rate of four trucks per day costs $56 per day. Compute the total system cost for the operation.

12. Enrolling and advising new students at Sharecropper State University is currently accomplished through the services of a graduate assistant who is paid $1.90 per hour. Each student requires an average of 5 minutes, but there is a variance of 12 minutes in the distribution of advisement times. An associate professor can be hired to accomplish this same task at $2.00 per hour. He will spend all of 6 minutes with each student, but because of the rigor of his academic

preparation, there will be no variance in this time. Students arrive for enrollment and advice in a Poisson manner with an average interval of 8 minutes. The cost of student waiting is estimated at $3.80 per student per hour. Is there an economic advantage in using the associate professor?

13. Plot the waiting cost, service cost, and total cost given in Table 13.3. Also, plot the gross profit, service cost, and net profit given in Table 13.4.

14. Each truck in a fleet of 30 delivery trucks will return to a warehouse for reloading at an average interval of 160 minutes. An average of 20 minutes is required by the driver and one warehouseman to load the next shipment. If the warehouse personnel are busy loading previous arrivals, the driver and his unit must wait in queue. Both the time between arrivals and the loading time are distributed exponentially. The cost of waiting in the system is $6.75 per hour per truck and the total cost per warehouseman is $2.35 per hour. Find the minimum cost number of warehousemen to employ.

15. A population of 10 cargo ships each produces a profit of $1,360 per 24-hour period when not waiting to be unloaded. The time between arrivals is distributed exponentially with a mean of 144 hours. The unloading time at the dock is distributed exponentially with a mean of 21 hours. It costs $42 per hour to lease a dock with this unloading capacity. How many docks should be leased?

16. Each machine in a semiautomatic group of 20 machines requires operator attention at an average interval of 18 minutes. Each operator assigned can service the machine in an average of 4 minutes. Both the time between calls for service and the service duration approximate the exponential distribution. Each minute a machine is idle produces a lost profit of $0.18. Operators cost the firm $0.42 per operator per minute which includes overhead. How many operators should be assigned for maximum profit?

17. A population of 30 chemical processing units is to be unloaded and loaded by a single crew. The mean time between calls for this operation is 68 minutes. If the mean service rate is one unit per minute, the cost of the crew and equipment will be $1.60 per minute. This cost will decrease to $1.20, $0.90, and $0.70, for service intervals of 2, 3, and 4 minutes, respectively. The time between calls for service and the service duration are distributed exponentially. If it costs $28 per hour for each unit that is idle, find the minimum cost service interval.

18. Plot the percentage of machines not running as a function of the service factor for a population of 20 machines with exponential arrivals and services if a single channel is employed; if two channels are employed.

19. A group of 12 machines are repaired by a single repairman when they break down. Each machine yields a profit of $1.82 per hour while running. The mechanic costs the firm $3.20 per hour, including overhead. At the present time no preventative maintenance is utilized. It is proposed that one mechanic be employed to perform certain routine maintenance and adjustment tasks.

This will cost $2.80 per hour, but will reduce the service factor from 0.12 to 0.08. What is the economic advantage of implementing preventive maintenance?

20. One operator is assigned to run 14 automatic machines. The minimum cost service factor is 0.2. The machines require attention at random, and the service duration is distributed exponentially. Machines receive service on a first-come, first-served basis. Specify the upper control limit if the probability of designating the system out of control when it is really in control must not exceed 0.05.

21. A certain population of machines produced the following 30-day pattern of machine failures: 7, 5, 8, 4, 6, 6, 6, 7, 2, 9, 6, 8, 7, 6, 6, 9, 7, 5, 5, 3, 5, 4, 8, 7, 6, 6, 5, 6, 5, 6. Assume that all breakdowns occurred at the beginning of each day. A repair crew requires one day to repair a machine and costs $90 per day. A loss of $80 per day is incurred for each day a machine is carried over unrepaired. Find the minimum cost number of crews to employ if it is assumed that this failure pattern is representative of the future.

22. The number of jobs that arrive at a certain production facility is either 0, 1, 2, 3, or 4 per day, with each number being equally likely. Use a table of random rectangular variates to generate a 60-day pattern of arrivals. If each job requires one day to complete, and if it costs $4 for each day a job is carried over unfinished, what is the minimum cost service rate if the cost of processing a job is $14.

Part VI

PROGRAMMING FOR ECONOMY
OF OPERATIONS

fourteen

DISTRIBUTION MODELS

OF LINEAR PROGRAMMING

Linear programming is a mathematical means for providing the decision maker with a basis for resolving complex operational alternatives. It is applicable to a general category of optimization problems involving the interaction of many variables subject to certain constraints. These constraints usually arise because the activities under consideration compete for scarce resources. A basic supposition in linear programming is the existence of linearity. The objective is to optimize some linear effectiveness function subject to linear constraints. This may require minimization of time, of cost, or of distance, or it may require maximization of profit, depending upon the problem under consideration.

This chapter presents two distribution models of linear programming The first deals with the problem which arise when it is desired to assign each of a number of means to an equal number of requirements on a one-for-one basis. This special case of the general linear programming problem is known as the assignment model. The second deals with the problem which arises when a number of origins possess units needed by a number of destinations. The quantity of units from each origin to be allocated to each destination is to be determined. This special case of the general linear programming problem is known as the transportation model. Development of the general linear programming model is deferred until the next chapter.

14.1. THE ASSIGNMENT MODEL

The assignment model of linear programming may be described as follows: There exist n requirements together with n means for satisfying them. Associated with the assignment of the ith means to be the jth requirement, x_{ij}, is a certain effectiveness coefficient, e_{ij}. It is required that $x_{ij} = 1$ if the ith means is used to satisfy the jth requirement, and that $x_{ij} = 0$ if the ith means is not used to satisfy the jth requirement. Since one means can be associated with only one requirement, the assignment problem can be stated mathematically as that of optimizing the effectiveness function

$$E = \sum_{i=1}^{n} \sum_{j=1}^{n} e_{ij} x_{ij}$$

subject to

$$\sum_{i=1}^{n} x_{ij} = 1 \qquad j = 1, 2, \ldots, n$$

$$\sum_{j=1}^{n} x_{ij} = 1 \qquad i = 1, 2, \ldots, n.$$

Optimization will require either minimization or maximization, depending upon the measure of effectiveness involved. The decision maker has control of a matrix of assignments, x_{ij}. Not directly under his control is the matrix of effectiveness coefficients, e_{ij}.

The assignment matrix. The assignment matrix will contain $n \times n$ elements with $n!$ possible arrangements. Solution by direct enumeration is ordinarily not possible. For example, if eight requirements are to be satisfied by eight means, there will be 40,320 possible arrangements. The following paragraphs present the Hungarian method for finding the optimal assignment.

Consider the following application of the assignment model: Four different assemblies are to be produced by four contractors. Each contractor is to receive only one assembly to produce. The cost of each assembly is determined by bids submitted by each contractor. This information, when arranged in tabular form, gives an effectiveness matrix shown in Table 14.1. The differences in the bid prices are due to differences in the work to be done and

Table 14.1. COSTS FOR PROCURING ASSEMBLIES
(thousands of dollars)

		Contractor			
		A	B	C	D
	1	16	14	15	18
Assembly	2	12	13	16	14
	3	14	13	11	12
	4	16	18	15	17

preferences for certain assemblies. The objective is to determine the assignment of assemblies to contractors that will result in a minimum cost.

The first step in the Hungarian method is to alter the effectiveness matrix
to obtain a reduced matrix. This is accomplished by subtracting the minimum
element in each row from all elements in the row, and then by subtracting the
minimum element in each column from all elements in the column. The first
reduced matrix for the procurement problem of Table 14.1 is shown in Table
14.2. An assignment that minimizes the total for a matrix reduced in this
manner also minimizes the total for the original effectiveness matrix.

Table 14.2. FIRST REDUCED COST MATRIX FOR
PROCUREMENT

		Contractor			
		A	B	C	D
Assembly	1	2	0	1	3
	2	0	1	4	1
	3	3	2	0	0
	4	1	3	0	1

The elements of the first reduced matrix will always be zero or positive.
As a result, the total cannot be negative for any assignment. Therefore, all
assignments that might be made will have a total that is zero or positive. If
an assignment can be made that has a zero total, there cannot be an assignment with a lower total.

Reference to Table 14.2 indicates that an assignment with a zero total can
be made. This requires assigning assembly 1 to contractor B, assembly 2 to
contractor A, assembly 3 to contractor D, and assembly 4 to contractor C.
The resulting assignment matrix is shown in Table 14.3. Its total cost may

Table 14.3. ASSIGNMENT MATRIX FOR PRO-
CUREMENT

		Contractor			
		A	B	C	D
Assembly	1	0	1	0	0
	2	1	0	0	0
	3	0	0	0	1
	4	0	0	1	0

be found from Table 14.1 and Table 14.3 as $14,000 + $12,000 + $12,000 +
$15,000 = $53,000. No other assignment will result in a lower total cost.

The problem just described conforms exactly to the assignment model.
Sometimes, however, a problem can be made to conform to the assignment
model by adding dummy rows or dummy columns. Consider the following
example: At the end of a cycle of schedules, a trucking firm has a surplus of

one vehicle in cities 1, 2, 3, 4, and 5, and a deficit of one vehicle in cities A, B, C, D, E, and F. The distances between cities with a surplus and the cities with a deficit are shown in Table 14.4. The objective is to find the assignment of surplus vehicles to deficit cities that will result in a minimum total distance.

Table 14.4. DISTANCES FOR MOVING VEHICLES (miles)

		To City					
		A	B	C	D	E	F
	1	13	11	16	23	19	9
	2	11	19	26	16	17	13
From City	3	12	11	4	9	6	10
	4	7	15	9	14	14	13
	5	9	13	12	8	14	11

Inspection of Table 14.4 indicates that there exist more requirements than means. When this is the case, an $n \times n$ effectiveness matrix will result by adding a dummy row, or dummy rows if required. Elements in the dummy row are zeros since no cost is associated with not moving a vehicle. The adjusted effectiveness matrix is shown in Table 14.5. If there had been more

Table 14.5. ADJUSTED COST MATRIX FOR MOVING VEHICLES

		To City					
		A	B	C	D	E	F
	1	13	11	16	23	19	9
	2	11	19	26	16	17	13
From City	3	12	11	4	9	6	10
	4	7	15	9	14	14	13
	5	9	13	12	8	14	11
	Dummy	0	0	0	0	0	0

means than requirements, dummy columns would have been added with zeros as elements. Dummy rows mean that some requirements are not met, and dummy columns mean that some means are not used. Adjustment of the effectiveness matrix in this manner makes the problem conform to the assignment model.

Table 14.6. FIRST REDUCED COST MATRIX FOR MOVING VEHICLES

		To City					
		A	B	C	D	E	F
	1	4	2	7	14	10	0
	2	0	8	15	5	6	2
From City	3	8	7	0	5	2	6
	4	0	8	2	7	7	6
	5	1	5	4	0	6	3
	Dummy	0	0	0	0	0	0

The first reduced matrix for this problem is shown in Table 14.6. Inspection indicates that an assignment with a zero total cannot be made. When this is the case, additional computations are necessary to produce more zeroes.

Iteration toward an optimal assignment. The following iterative scheme may be employed when the first reduced matrix does not yield an assignment with a zero total:

(1) Draw the minimum number of lines that will pass through all zeros in the reduced matrix. There may be several minimum sets. A set is known to be minimum when the number equals the number of independent zeros used in constructing an assignment. Any minimum set may be chosen.

(2) Select the smallest element in the reduced matrix that does not have a line through it. Add this element to all elements that occur at the intersection of two lines and subtract it from all elements that do not have a line through them. The other elements of the matrix remain unchanged.

Application of step 1 to the first reduced matrix of the vehicle assignment example results in Table 14.7. The minimum number of lines that can be

Table 14.7. STEP ONE, THE MINIMUM SET OF LINES

		To City					
		A	B	C	D	E	F
	1	4	2	7	14	10	0
	2	0	8	15	5	6	2
From City	3	8	7	0	5	2	6
	4	0	8	2	7	7	6
	5	1	5	4	0	6	3
	Dummy	0	0	0	0	0	0

drawn is four. An assignment with a zero total cannot be made when the minimum number of lines is less than the matrix size. Application of step 2 gives the matrix shown in Table 14.8. It may be called a *modified reduced*

Table 14.8. STEP TWO, MODIFIED REDUCED MATRIX

		To City					
		A	B	C	D	E	F
	1	4	0	7	14	8	0
	2	0	6	15	5	4	2
From City	3	8	5	0	5	0	6
	4	0	6	2	7	5	6
	5	1	3	4	0	4	3
	Dummy	2	0	2	2	0	2

Table 14.9. STEP ONE, A MINIMUM SET OF LINES

To City

From City	A	B	C	D	E	F
1	4	0	7	14	8	0
2	0	6	15	5	4	2
3	8	5	0	5	0	6
4	0	6	2	7	5	6
5	1	3	4	0	4	3
Dummy	2	0	2	2	0	2

matrix. An assignment with a zero total still cannot be made as is indicated by the application of step 1 shown in Table 14.9. Step 2 now yields the final reduced matrix shown in Table 14.10.

Table 14.10. STEP TWO, FINAL MODIFIED REDUCED MATRIX

To City

From City	A	B	C	D	E	F
1	6	0	7	14	8	0
2	0	4	13	3	2	0
3	10	5	0	5	0	6
4	0	4	0	5	3	4
5	3	3	4	0	4	3
Dummy	4	0	2	2	0	2

An optimal assignment can now be made as is shown in Table 14.11. This will require assigning vehicle 1 to city B, vehicle 2 to city F, vehicle 3 to city C, vehicle 4 to city A, vehicle 5 to city D, and no vehicle to city E. The total distance for this assignment may be found from Table 14.5 and Table 14.11

Table 14.11. ASSIGNMENT MATRIX FOR MOVING VEHICLES

To City

From City	A	B	C	D	E	F
1	0	1	0	0	0	0
2	0	0	0	0	0	1
3	0	0	1	0	0	0
4	1	0	0	0	0	0
5	0	0	0	1	0	0
Dummy	0	0	0	0	1	0

as $11 + 13 + 4 + 7 + 8 + 0 = 43$ miles. No other assignment will result in less total distance for moving the surplus vehicles. An alternate assignment with the same total distance, however, is revealed by Table 14.10. It involves assigning vehicle 1 to city F, vehicle 2 to city A, vehicle 3 to city E, vehicle 4 to city C, vehicle 5 to city D, and no vehicle to city B. There may be some reason why this alternate optimal solution would be preferred.

It can be shown that iteration, as demonstrated with this example, will always lead to an optimal assignment in a finite number of cycles. The optimum assignment will occur when the minimum number of lines that can be drawn is equal to the matrix size. This optimum assignment is guaranteed by the existence of one or more assignments with a zero total in the reduced effectiveness matrix.

Finding a maximum profit assignment. Effectiveness is often expressed in terms of profit instead of cost. This requires maximizing the effectiveness function. Maximization may be accomplished by replacing each element of the effectiveness matrix by its negative and proceeding as for minimization. This procedure is valid, since minimizing the negative of a function is equivalent to maximizing the function.

Table 14.12. PROFITS FOR SALESMAN ASSIGN-
MENT (dollais)

		District			
		A	B	C	D
Salesman	1	14	8	12	9
	2	12	9	13	13
	3	13	13	11	10
	4	11	10	12	13

Consider the following maximization problem: A sales manager has four salesmen and four sales districts. After considering the capabilities of the salesmen and the nature of the districts, he estimates that the profit per day for each salesman in each district would be as shown in Table 14.12. The objective is to find the assignment of salesmen to districts that will result in a maximum profit.

The first step is to replace each element in Table 14.12 by its negative. Next, the most negative element in each row is subtracted from all elements in the row, and then the most negative element in each column is subtracted from all elements in the column. The resulting first reduced matrix is shown in Table 14.13.

Inspection indicates that an assignment with a zero total can be made, as is shown in Table 14.14. This requires assigning salesman 1 to district A,

Table 14.13. FIRST REDUCED MATRIX FOR
SALESMAN ASSIGNMENT

		District			
		A	B	C	D
Salesman	1	0	6	2	5
	2	1	4	0	0
	3	0	0	2	3
	4	2	3	1	0

Table 14.14. ASSIGNMENT MATRIX FOR SALES-
MAN ASSIGNMENT

		District			
		A	B	C	D
	1	1	0	0	0
Salesman	2	0	0	1	0
	3	0	1	0	0
	4	0	0	0	1

salesman 2 to district C, salesman 3 to district B, and salesman 4 to district D. The total profit from this assignment may be found from Table 14.12 and Table 14.14 as \$14 + \$13 + \$13 + \$13 = \$53. No other assignment will result in a greater profit. If an assignment with a zero total was not produced at this point, it would have been necessary to use the iterative scheme described previously.

When the effectiveness matrix is not square, dummy rows or dummy columns can be added as before. Elements in the dummy rows or dummy columns are zeroes since no profit is associated with them. The maximization process then proceeds as previously outlined.

14.2 THE TRANSPORTATION MODEL

The transportation model of linear programming is a generalization of the assignment model. It may be described thus: There exist m origins, with the ith origin possessing a_i units, and n destinations, with the jth destination requiring b_j units. It is not required that m be equal to n, but the sum of the units available at the origins must equal the sum of the requirements at the destinations. Associated with the allocation of one unit from the ith origin to the jth destination is a certain effectiveness coefficient, e_{ij}. If x_{ij} is the number of units allocated from the ith origin to the jth destination, the transportation problem may be stated mathematically as that of optimizing the effectiveness function

$$E = \sum_{i=1}^{m} \sum_{j=1}^{n} e_{ij} x_{ij}$$

subject to

$$\sum_{i=1}^{m} x_{ij} = b_j \qquad j = 1, 2, \ldots, n$$

$$\sum_{j=1}^{n} x_{ij} = a_i \qquad i = 1, 2, \ldots, m$$

where

$$\sum_{i=1}^{m} a_i = \sum_{j=1}^{n} b_j.$$

Optimization will require either minimization or maximization, depending on the measure of effectiveness involved. The decision maker has under his control the allocation matrix, x_{ij}. Not directly under his control is the matrix of effectiveness coefficients, e_{ij}.

The transportation matrix. The transportation matrix will contain $m \times n$ non-negative allocations. Selection of that set of allocations that optimizes the effectiveness function is sought. The paragraphs which follow will present a solution improvement algorithm. It starts with any initial allocation and terminates with an optimal allocation.

Consider the following application of the transportation model: Four dealers place orders for new automobiles that are to be shipped from three

Table 14.15. COSTS FOR SHIPPING AUTO-
MOBILES (dollars)

		Dealer			
		A	B	C	D
Plant	1	50	80	60	70
	2	80	50	60	60
	3	70	60	80	60

plants. Dealer A requires six automobiles, dealer B requires five, dealer C requires four, and dealer D requires four. Plant 1 has seven automobiles in stock, plant 2 has thirteen, and plant 3 has three. The cost of shipping one automobile from the ith plant to the jth dealer is shown in Table 14.15. For this situation to be classified as a linear programming problem, the assumption is made that the cost of shipping more than one automobile is proportional to the number shipped.

The number of automobiles available at the three plants is twenty-three, whereas the number required by the four dealers is only nineteen. Therefore, to make this problem conform to the transportation model, it is necessary to add a dummy destination. This means that some of the available automobiles will not be shipped. The costs associated with the dummy destination are zero.

A transportation matrix exhibiting all information relevant to the situation described is shown as Table 14.16. The number of automobiles available at the respective plants are given in the last column, and the number required at each dealer are given in the last row. The dummy destination is indicated by the next to last column and receives four units. As a result, the number of automobiles available is made equal to the number required. The cost per unit shipped for each possible route is entered in the small squares from Table 14.15. The objective is to find the allocation of automobiles to dealers that will satisfy the requirements and will result in a minimum total cost.

Table 14.16. TRANSPORTATION MATRIX FOR SHIPPING AUTOMOBILES

Plant \ Dealer	A	B	C	D	Dummy	Available
1	50	80	60	70	0	7
2	80	50	60	60	0	13
3	70	60	80	60	0	3
Required	6	5	4	4	4	23

Finding an initial allocation. One formal means for finding an initial allocation is to employ the northwest corner rule. This requires allocating units to the northwest cell in the transportation matrix in such a magnitude that either the origin capacity is exhausted, or the destination requirement is satisfied or both. If the origin capacity is exhausted first, an allocation is made to column 1 from the second origin. This will either exhaust the origin capacity of row 2 or satisfy the remaining requirement of column 1. If the first allocation satisfies the requirement of column 1, an allocation is made in column 2. This will either exhaust the capacity of row 1 or satisfy the requirement of column 2 or both. Continuing in this manner, satisfying the destination requirements and exhausting the origin capacities, one at a time, results in a movement toward the southeast corner with all row and column requirements being satisfied in the process.

Application of the northwest corner rule to the transportation matrix of Table 14.16 results in the allocations shown in Table 14.17. Since seven automobiles were available at plant 1, dealer A has his requirements completely satisfied from this source. The remaining unit at plant 1 is allocated to dealer B. Four automobiles from plant 2 are used to finish satisfying the requirement of dealer B. Of the remaining nine units at plant 2, four are allocated to dealer C, four to dealer D, and one to the dummy destination. The three automobiles available at plant 3 are allocated to the dummy destination. The resulting solution contains seven allocations. The total cost of this solution may be found from Table 14.17 as $6(\$50) + 1(\$80) + 4(\$50) + 4(\$60) + 4(\$60) + 1(\$0) + 3(\$0) = \$1,060$.

The northwest corner rule does not take into consideration the cost of each allocation. Therefore, it is likely that a scheme considering these costs will result in a lower total cost. One method is to make an allocation to the cell with the lowest cost, up to the maximum allowed by the origin and

Table 14.17. INITIAL ALLOCATION BY THE NORTHWEST CORNER RULE

Dealer / Plant	A	B	C	D	Dummy	Available
1	50 / 6	80 / 1	60	70	0	7
2	80	50 / 4	60 / 4	60 / 4	0 / 1	13
3	70	60	80	60 / 3	0	3
Required	6	5	4	4	4	23

destination involved. Then, an allocation is made to the next lowest-cost cell in view of the remaining capacities and requirements. This process is continued until all origins are emptied and all destinations are filled. If a tie occurs between lowest-cost cells, judgment may be used in making the allocation. For small problems, this procedure may result in an optimum solution.

Applying this procedure to the transportation matrix of Table 14.16 results in the allocations shown in Table 14.18. Six units were allocated to dealer A and five units were allocated to dealer B since each involves a minimum shipping cost. The requirement of dealer D is then satisfied from plant 3 at a cost of $60 per unit. Four units from plant 2 are allocated to the dummy destination at no cost. Finally, the remaining requirements are satisfied by allocating one unit from plant 1 and three units from plant 2 to dealer C,

Table 14.18. INITIAL ALLOCATION BY INSPECTION

Dealer / Plant	A	B	C	D	Dummy	Available
1	50 / 6	80	60 / 1	70	0	7
2	80	50 / 5	60 / 3	60 / 1	0 / 4	13
3	70	60	80	60 / 3	0	3
Required	6	5	4	4	4	23

and one unit from plant 2 to dealer **D**. The total cost of this inspection allocation is 6($50) + 1($60) + 5($50) + 3($60) + 1($60) + 4($0) + 3($60) =
$1,030. This scheme resulted in a $30 improvement over the northwest corner
rule.

Testing for optimality. A basic feasible solution to the transportation
problem is one that contains $m + n - 1$ positive allocations. When a basic
feasible solution has been obtained, it may be tested to see whether a lower
cost allocation can be made. This can be accomplished as follows:

(1) Set up a matrix containing the costs associated with the cells for which
allocations have been made.
(2) Enter a set of numbers, v_j, across the top of the matrix and a set of
numbers, u_i, down the left side so that their sums equal the costs
entered in step 1.
(3) Fill the vacant cells in step one with the sums of the u_i and v_j.
(4) Subtract the u_i plus v_j values from the original unit cost matrix.
(5) If any of the cell evaluations are negative, the basic feasible solution
is not optimal.

Table 14.19 illustrates the application of this optimality test to the initial
solution of the automobile shipment problem in Table 14.18. The u_i plus v_j
matrix was constructed by entering costs in those cells for which allocations

Table 14.19. TESTING TABLE 14.18 FOR OPTIMALITY

u_i \ v_j	0	0	10	10	-50
50	50	50		60 · 60	0
50	50	50	60	60	0
50	50	50	60	60	0

u_i plus v_j matrix.

·	30	·	10	0
30	·	·	·	·
20	10	20	·	0

Cell evaluation matrix.

were made. These are the boxed values shown. Next, v_1 was arbitrarily set equal to zero to begin the determination of u_i and v_j numbers. This action forces u_1 to be 50 which, in turn, forces v_3 to be 10, u_2 to be 50, v_2 to be 0, v_4 to be 10, v_5 to be -50, and u_3 to be 50. The vacant cells were then filled with the sum of the u_i and v_j giving the u_i plus v_j matrix shown. By subtracting the elements of the u_i plus v_j matrix from those in the unit cost matrix of Table 14.5, the cell evaluation matrix results. Since no elements in the cell

Table 14.20. TESTING TABLE 14.17 FOR OPTIMALITY

u_i \ v_j	0	30	40	40	-20
50	50 ⃞	80 ⃞	90	90	30
20	20	50 ⃞	60 ⃞	60 ⃞	0 ⃞
20	20	50	60	60	0 ⃞

u_i plus matrix

.	.	-30	-20	-30
60	.	.	.	.
50	10	20	0	.

Cell evaluation matrix.

evaluation matrix are negative, the initial solution by the inspection allocation is optimal.

If the solution by inspection is optimal, the solution by the northwest corner rule cannot be, since it has a higher total cost. This fact is demonstrated by the optimality test illustrated in Table 14.20. Here three cells in the cell evaluation matrix are negative. When this is the case, an iterative scheme may be used to find an optimal allocation.

Iteration toward an optimal allocation. Since the northwest corner rule did not yield an optimal allocation, the following iterative scheme can be employed:

(1) From the cell evaluation matrix, identify the cell with the most negative entry. Make a choice when a tie is involved.

(2) Trace a path in the transportation matrix consisting of a series of segments which are alternately horizontal and vertical. The path begins and terminates in the cell identified in step 1. All corners of the path occur in cells for which allocations have been made.

(3) Mark the cell identified in step 1 plus and each cell at a corner of the path alternatively minus, plus, minus, and so forth.

(4) Make a new allocation in the cell identified in step 1 by entering the smallest allocation on the path which has been given a minus sign.

(5) Add and subtract the quantity of the new allocation in step 4 to all cells at the corners of the path maintaining all row and column requirements.

Table 14.21. TRACING THE "PLUS-MINUS" PATH

Plant \ Dealer	A	B	C	D	Dummy	Available
1	50 6	80 --1--	60	70	0 +	7
2	80 +-4	50 -4	60 -4	60	0 1	13
3	70	60	80	60	0 3	3
Required	6	5	4	4	4	23

Table 14.21 illustrates the application of step one and step two to the initial solution of Table 14.17. The "plus-minus" path begins and terminates with the cell that was evaluated to be minus 30. Table 14.22 shows the allocation of one unit into this cell. This is the maximum amount that could be reallocated among the members of the loop and still maintain the row and column requirements. The new solution has a total cost of $6(\$50) + 1(\$0) + 5(\$50) + 4(\$60) + 4(\$60) + 3(\$0) = \$1,030$. This is equal to the optimal cost found by the inspection allocation and is also optimal. Whenever the cell evaluation matrix contains zero elements, alternate optimal solutions exist.

Treating degeneracy. The allocation given in Table 14.22 is a degenerate basic feasible solution, since it contains less than $m + n - 1$ allocations. When degeneracy exists, a "plus-minus" path cannot begin in all cells for which allocations have not been made. If further iteration had been necessary, this degeneracy would have had to be resolved before applying the optimality test.

Table 14.22. REALLOCATION BY ADDING AND SUBTRACTING

Dealer \\ Plant	A	B	C	D	Dummy	Available
1	50 \ 6	80	60	70	0 \ 1	7
2	80	50 \ 5	60 \ 4	60 \ 4	0	13
3	70	60	80	60	0 \ 3	3
Required	6	5	4	4	4	23

Consider the degenerate solution of Table 14.23 obtained by the northwest corner rule. It is possible to trace a "plus-minus" path only for cells 1-B and 4-C. In Table 14.22 degeneracy occurred because the reallocation of one unit caused two previous allocations to become zero.

Degeneracy can be resolved at any stage in the solution by placing an infinitesimally small allocation, ε, in an appropriate cell. This small allocation is made by inspection and assumed not to affect the row and column totals. In Table 14.23, "plus-minus" paths can be traced for all open cells if ε is placed in any cell other than 1-B or 4-C. The ε allocation is then manipulated in accordance with the rules established previously. It is treated no differently than any other allocation. When an optimal solution is found, ε is set equal to zero, thus regaining the original problem.

Table 14.23. A DEGENERATE BASIC FEASIBLE SOLUTION

To \\ From	A	B	C	D	Available
1	5				5
2	3	6			9
3			5	1	6
4				6	6
Required	8	6	5	7	26

Table 14.24. PERTURBATION TO ELIMINATE DEGENERACY

From \ To	A	B	C	D	Available
1	$5 + \varepsilon$				$5 + \varepsilon$
2	$3 - \varepsilon$	$6 + 2\varepsilon$			$9 + \varepsilon$
3		-2ε	5	$1 + 3\varepsilon$	$6 + \varepsilon$
4				$6 + \varepsilon$	$6 + \varepsilon$
Required	8	6	5	$7 + 4\varepsilon$	$26 + 4\varepsilon$

It can be shown that degeneracy can occur only if the sum of some subset of the row requirements equals the sum of some subset of the column requirements. Since degeneracy can exist only when this condition occurs, any adjustment that makes this equality impossible also makes degeneracy impossible. This can be accomplished by making a small perturbation of the row requirements and one of the column requirements before any calculations are made. Applying the perturbation technique to the problem given by Table 14.23 results in the nondegenerate basic feasible solution of Table 14.24. The optimality test and the iterative process can now be applied. Again, the ε and the multiples of ε are treated no differently than other allocations. When an optimal solution is reached, ε is set equal to zero.

Finding a maximum profit allocation. Consider the following maximization problem: A carpet manufacturer has two plants and produces three styles of carpet. For the coming week, plant A has a capacity of 8,400 yd and plant B has a capacity of 5,800 yd. This total capacity is to be used to produce 4,200 yd of style 1, 6,100 yd of style 2, and 3,900 yd of style 3 for the week. The estimated profit per yard for each style at each plant is given in Table 14.25. The profit per yard depends upon the style and upon the plant at which it is manufactured.

Minimizing the negative of a function is equivalent to maximizing the function. Therefore, the first step in finding a maximum profit allocation of

Table 14.25. PROFITS FOR
CARPET MANUFACTURING
(dollars)

		Plant A	B
	1	0.82	0.76
Style	2	0.34	0.41
	3	0.66	0.60

Table 14.26. TRANSPORTATION MATRIX FOR CARPET MANUFACTURING

Plant / Style	A	B	Production
1	−0.82 4,200	−0.76	4,200
2	−0.34 300	0.41 5,800	6,100
3	−0.66 3,900	0.60	3,900
Capacity	8,400	5,800	14,200

styles to plants is making all elements in the profit matrix of Table 14.25 negative. The transportation method may then be applied as for minimization.

Table 14.26 exhibits the transportation matrix applicable to the carpet manufacturing problem. Since the required total production equals the total capacity available, no dummy origins or destinations are needed. Each profit element carries a negative sign since profit is to be maximized. The basic feasible solution shown was determined by judgement. It represents a total profit of $4,200(\$0.82) + 300(\$0.34) + 5,800(\$0.41) + 3,900(\$0.66) = \$8,498$. Application of the optimality test is shown in Table 14.27. Since all

Table 14.27. TESTING TABLE 14.26 FOR OPTIMALITY

u_i \ v_j	0	−0.07
−0.82	−0.82	−0.89
−0.34	−0.34	−0.41
−0.66	−0.66	−0.73

u_i plus v_j matrix.

.	0.13	
.	.	
.	0.13	

Cell evaluation matrix.

cells in the cell evaluation matrix are positive this solution is optimal. No other allocation will result in a higher profit for the coming week.

14.3. VOGEL'S APPROXIMATION METHOD

Vogel's approximation method is offered as an alternative to the method presented previously. The procedure is simple and fast by comparison. Its advocates claim that it will give an optimal allocation for a majority of problems and that the approximation is very good for the remainder. In some applications, the final result of this approximation method may be accepted as is. In others it might be desirable to apply the optimality test and then iterate toward an optimal solution if needed. Normally, use of this scheme to find an initial solution will reduce the number of iterations required by the conventional method.

An example application. Suppose that there are three machine centers in a job shop that can process any one of four orders. The capacities of each machine center, as well as the time needed by each order, are expressed in standard machine hours. The capacity for machine center A is 95 standard hours; for machine center B, 115 standard hours; and for machine center C, 50 standard hours. Order 1 needs 66 standard machine hours; order 2, 45 standard hours; order 3, 82 standard hours; and order 4, 44 standard hours. The cost per standard machine hour for each order at each machine center is given in Table 14.28. Costs are a function of the order and the nature of the machine center relative to the order.

Table 14.28. COSTS PER STANDARD MACHINE HOUR (dollars)

| | | Machine Center | |
	A	B	C
1	8.40	7.90	7.60
2	9.20	6.10	8.70
3	6.00	7.50	9.10
4	7.80	8.00	6.90

Order labels rows 1–4.

Table 14.29 exhibits the transportation matrix for this production problem. Since there are 260 standard machine hours available and only 237 required by the four orders, it is necessary to add a dummy order. This dummy order will absorb the extra capacity, thus making the problem conform to the transportation model. Elements in the dummy row are set equal to zero, since no cost is associated with a dummy order that will not be processed.

Table 14.29. TRANSPORTATION MATRIX FOR VOGEL'S APPROXIMATION METHOD

Machine \ Order	A	B	C	Needed					
1	8.40 X	7.90 66	7.60 X	66	0.30 ✓	0.30 ✓	0.30 ✓	0.30 ✓	0.50 ✓
2	9.20 X	6.10 45	8.70 X	45	2.60	2.60 ✓	—	—	—
3	6.00 82	7.50 X	9.10 X	82	1.50 ✓	1.50 ✓	1.50 ✓	—	—
4	7.80 13	8.00 4	6.90 27	44	0.90 ✓	0.90 ✓	0.90 ✓	0.90 ✓	0.20 ✓
Dummy	0 X	0 X	0 23	23	0.00 ✓	—	—	—	—
Available	95	115	50	260					

6.00 ✓	6.10 ✓	6.90 ✓
1.80 ✓	1.40 ✓	0.70 ✓
1.80 ✓	0.40 ✓	0.70 ✓
0.60 ✓	0.10 ✓	0.70 ✓
0.60 ✓	0.10	—

The solution procedure. The solution procedure for Vogel's approximation method may be pursued with the aid of the original transportation matrix. It is not necessary to develop a new matrix for each cycle. Each cycle involves a series of steps repeated in exactly the same manner until the final allocation is made.

Since a minimum cost assignment is required, the first step in the cycle is to inspect the costs in each row and take the difference between the two smallest of these. (If the problem is one of maximization, the difference between the two highest values is taken.) These differences form the first column of values to the right of the matrix in Table 14.29. This difference process is now applied to each column in the matrix and the results form the first row of values across the bottom.

The second step involves identification of the largest difference in the column and row just developed. This occurs in column 3 for the problem under consideration. Thus, column 3 is the first candidate for an allocation.

Step 3 involves the allocation of needed standard machine hours to the column with the largest difference, up to the maximum allowed by the row and column totals. This allocation is made in the row with the lowest cost or highest profit. Since this row is the dummy with zero cost, 23 hours are allocated. Since all needed machine hours have been allocated, all cells in the row are marked out. If the largest difference had occurred in a row instead of a column, the assignment would have been made to the cell in that row with the lowest cost or highest profit. The procedure is the same in either case. This completes the first cycle.

Each cycle follows the steps just outlined and is applied to the reduced matrix; that is, the matrix remaining after some rows or columns or both are marked out. The difference column and difference row from the previous cycle are disregarded. A new difference column and row are developed for the reduced matrix at the beginning of each cycle. This is shown for each cycle in Table 14.29. Allocations are made in accordance with the largest differences until all allocations are completed. The resulting solution may now be tested for optimality if desired.

PROBLEMS

1. Three customers in a certain sales territory have requested technical assistance. Three technicians are available for assignment with the distance in miles from each technician to each customer being as follows:

		Customer		
		A	B	C
Technician	1	470	580	410
	2	385	920	740
	3	880	550	430

If it costs $0.10 per mile for travel, find the assignment of technicians to customers that will result in a minimum travel cost. Compare this cost with the cost of the next best assignment.

2. A lead draftsman has five drafting tasks to accomplish and five idle draftsmen. Each draftsman is estimated to require the following number of hours for each task.

		Task				
		A	B	C	D	E
Draftsman	1	65	40	90	80	90
	2	60	35	100	85	85
	3	60	38	105	90	95
	4	70	45	120	90	100
	5	65	40	105	87	90

If each draftsman costs the company $4.60 per hour including overhead, find each assignment of draftsmen to tasks that will result in a minimum total cost. What is this total cost?

3. Five jobs are to be processed and five machines are available. Any machine can process any job, with the resulting profits in dollars as follows:

		Machines				
		A	B	C	D	E
Jobs	1	32	38	40	28	40
	2	40	24	28	21	36
	3	41	27	33	30	37
	4	22	38	41	36	36
	5	29	33	40	35	39

What is the maximum profit that may be expected if an optimum assignment is made?

4. The owner of a small machine shop has four machinists available to assign to jobs for the day. Five jobs are offered with the expected profit in dollars for each machinist on each job being as follows:

		Job				
		A	B	C	D	E
Machinist	1	6.20	7.80	5.00	10.10	8.20
	2	7.10	8.40	6.10	7.30	5.90
	3	8.70	9.20	11.10	7.10	8.10
	4	4.80	6.40	8.70	7.70	8.00

Find the assignment of machinists to jobs that will result in a maximum profit. Which job should be declined?

5. Three buildings are to be added to a university campus. Bids are submitted by five contractors. The bid figures are given in millions of dollars and are as follows:

		Building		
		A	B	C
Contractor	1	2.90	1.62	3.11
	2	3.10	1.74	2.82
	3	3.05	1.80	2.92
	4	2.87	1.57	2.78
	5	3.11	1.68	2.99

Find the assignment of buildings to contractors that will result in a minimum total cost for the building program.

6. Three new automatic feed devices have been made available for existing punch presses. Six presses in the plant can be fitted with this equipment. The plant superintendent estimates that the increased output, together with the labor saved, will result in the following dollar increase in profits per day.

		Press					
		A	B	C	D	E	F
Device	1	20	20	19	22	18	17
	2	21	17	20	22	20	19
	3	22	18	20	23	19	14

Determine which presses should receive which feed devices so that the benefit to the plant is maximized.

7. Three plants, 1, 2, and 3, produce 760, 650, and 810 refrigerators per week, respectively. These are to be distributed equally to six warehouses. The cost of shipping in dollars per unit is as follows:

		Warehouse					
		A	B	C	D	E	F
Plant	1	12	14	21	11	16	27
	2	18	24	16	12	34	13
	3	13	12	11	19	13	22

Determine the allocation that will result in a minimum shipping cost. What is the shipping cost per week?

8. A company has three warehouses, 1, 2, and 3, containing 8,000, 14,000, and 9,000 units of a certain product. In the next week, 4,200, 6,700, 6,000, 5,700, and 4,800 units must be shipped to retail centers A, B, C, D, and E, respectively. The cost in dollars of shipping one unit from each warehouse to each retail center is as follows:

		Retail Center				
		A	B	C	D	E
Warehouse	1	0.70	0.62	0.84	1.20	0.92
	2	0.94	0.74	0.78	1.10	0.81
	3	0.72	1.20	0.61	0.90	0.72

Find the shipping schedule that will result in a minimum shipping cost.

9. A company has factories in cities 1, 2, and 3, and supplies warehouses in cities A, B, C, D, E, and F. Monthly factory capacities are 30, 25, and 42 units, respectively. Monthly warehouse requirements are 15, 15, 12, 30, 10, and 15 units, respectively. Unit shipping costs in dollars are as follows:

		Warehouse					
		A	B	C	D	E	F
Factory	1	6	9	7	14	9	21
	2	20	8	7	6	11	18
	3	8	6	14	9	7	8

Use the northwest corner rule to determine the initial solution and then find the optimum distribution for the company.

10. At the beginning of next week there will be a surplus of 6, 9, 7, and 5 trailers in cities 1, 2, 3, and 4, respectively. Cities A, B, and C will have a deficit of 8, 7, and 9 trailers, respectively. The cost for moving trailers from each surplus city to each deficit city is given in dollars in the following matrix.

		Deficit		
		A	B	C
Surplus	1	26	32	28
	2	19	27	16
	3	39	21	32
	4	18	24	23

Use the perturbation technique to eliminate degeneracy and find the optimum allocation.

11. Two garment plants are available for the production of six styles of a basic men's shirt. Next month, plant A has a capacity of 124,000 units and plant B has a capacity of 160,000 units. The number of units required of styles 1 through 6 is 48,000, 32,000, 50,000, 44,000, 38,000, and 46,000. The profit in dollars per shirt at each plant for each style is estimated as follows:

		Plant	
		A	B
Style	1	0.24	0.22
	2	0.18	0.19
	3	0.26	0.24
	4	0.16	0.15
	5	0.25	0.26
	6	0.20	0.24

Find the production allocation for the month that will result in a maximum profit.

12. During the Second Punic War, one of the most terrible in antiquity, Hanibal crossed the Alps into Liguria in what is now Italy. In planning this campaign Hanibal decided to procure 250 elephants to carry supplies and for use in battle against the Romans. Hanibal required a hundred of these for his own phalanx. Hasdrubal, the brother of Hanibal (not to be confused with Hanibal's brother-in-law of the same name) also required a hundred. The remaining fifty were to be put at the disposal of Mago, a younger brother of Hanibal, who was given 200,000 gold florins and told to procure the elephants. Mago realized that if he economized on elephants, he could pocket the difference to spend on anticipated pleasures when they reached Rome. He contacted Mutafa-et-Al, a sheik and elephant dealer in Alexandria, and received a firm quotation

of 900, 875, and 910 florins for the delivered cost per elephant to Hanibal, Hasdrubal, and Mago, respectively. Snuff-en-Stuff, the elephant trader in Begasi, quoted Mago prices of 750, 790, and 820 florins respectively, but told Mago that he would be unable to deliver any elephants to Hasdrubal for some time because of an earlier commitment of the available transportation to the slave market in Carthage. The dealers in Cairo and Damascus quoted Mago prices of 800, 900, and 740 florins; and 740, 525, and 600 florins, respectively. Each dealer can supply no more than 100 elephants. If Mago bought his elephants optimally, how much money did he have available to spend in Rome?

13. In the event of a certain limited conflict, eight fully loaded cargo aircraft must be dispatched to point A, fourteen to point B, and eleven to point C. Five bases are within range of the danger spot and each has eight aircraft with the needed payload. The air mileage from each base to each point is as follows:

		Point		
		A	B	C
	1	820	940	1,420
	2	910	1,100	890
Base	3	720	650	630
	4	1,300	810	950
	5	700	920	1,050

Determine how the aircraft should be dispatched so as to deliver the required cargo in a minimum time.

14. Work centers A through F have capacities of 620, 410, 540, 770, 650, and 820 units of a certain product per day. Work centers 1 through 6 will produce exactly 635 units per day each. The distance in feet from centers 1 through 6 to centers A through F is as follows:

		To					
		A	B	C	D	E	F
	1	92	67	84	78	56	64
	2	67	92	63	57	62	81
From	3	84	76	79	83	92	99
	4	64	78	97	58	82	65
	5	53	64	67	74	92	81
	6	89	76	97	87	80	69

How should the production of work centers 1 through 6 be allocated so as to minimize material handling costs? Use Vogel's approximation method.

15. A dealer stocks and sells four styles of carpet which he may procure from three different suppliers. His anticipated sales in yards for styles A through D for the coming month are 410, 680, 310, and 550 yd. He can obtain 900 yd of brand, 600 yd of brand 2, and 560 yd of brand 3 at suitable prices. The profit per yard

in dollars for each brand and each style is as follows.

		Style			
		A	B	C	D
Brand	1	2.15	2.60	1.95	2.10
	2	2.05	2.40	2.00	2.10
	3	1.80	1.95	1.90	1.95

Use Vogel's approximation method to obtain an initial feasible solution. Test for optimality and iterate toward an optimal solution if required.

16. Use the transportation method to find the minimum cost assignment for the situation presented in Problem 1.

17. Use the transportation method to find the maximum profit assignment for the situation presented in Problem 4.

fifteen

THE GENERAL
LINEAR PROGRAMMING MODEL

*The initial mathematical formulation of the general linear programming
model, together with the simplex method for its solution,
was developed by Dantzig and his associates in 1947.
The simplex method is significant because it is applicable to the general category
of problems requiring the optimization of a linear effectiveness function subject
to linear constraints. Distribution problems may be
solved by the simplex method if properly formulated. The simplex method may,
however, be used where distribution methods cannot, making
it more universal in application.*

*The general linear programming problem may be stated symbolically as
that of optimizing the effectiveness function*

$$E - \sum_{j=1}^{n} e_j x_j \qquad \textit{subject to the constraints}$$

$$\sum_{j=1}^{n} a_{ij} x_j = b_i \qquad i = 1, 2, \ldots, m$$

$$x_j \geq 0 \qquad j = 1, 2, \ldots, n.$$

*Optimization requires either maximization or minimization,
depending on the measure of effectiveness involved. The decision
maker has control of the vector of variables, x_j. Not directly under his control
is the vector of effectiveness coefficients, e_j, the matrix of constants, a_{ij}, and
the vector of constants, b_i.*

397

15.1. GRAPHICAL SOLUTION METHODS

The symbolic statement of the general linear programming model may be explained in graphical terms. There exist n variables that define an n-dimensional space. Each restriction corresponds to a hyperplane in this space. These restrictions surround the region of feasible solution by hypersurfaces so that the region is the interior of a convex polyhedron. Since the effectiveness function is linear in the n variables, the requirement that this function have some constant value gives a hyperplane that may or may not cut through the polyhedron. If it does, one or more feasible solutions exist. By changing the value of this constant, a family of hyperplanes, parallel to each other, is generated. The distance from the origin to a member of this family is proportional to the value of the effectiveness function.

Two limiting hyperplanes may be identified: One corresponds to the largest value of the effectiveness function for which the hyperplane just touches the polyhedron; the other corresponds to the smallest value which just touches. In most cases, the limiting members just touch a vertex of the limiting polyhedron. This outermost limiting point is the solution that optimizes the effectiveness function. Although this is a graphical description, a graphical solution is not convenient when more than three variables are involved. The following paragraphs illustrate the general linear programming problem by graphical means for problems having two and three activities.

Graphical maximization for two activities. When two activities compete for scarce resources, a two-dimensional space is defined. Each restriction corresponds to a line on this surface. These restrictions identify a region of feasible solutions. The effectiveness function is also a line, its distance from the origin being proportional to its value. The optimum value for the effectiveness function occurs when it is located so that it just touches an extreme point of the region.

Consider the following production example: Two products are to be manufactured. A single unit of product A requires 2.4 minutes of punch press time and 5.0 minutes of assembly time. The profit for product A is $0.60 per unit. A single unit of product B requires 3.0 minutes of punch press time and 2.5 minutes of welding time. The profit for product B is $0.70 per unit.

Table 15.1. MANUFACTURING AND MARKETING DATA FOR TWO PRODUCTS

Department	Product A	Product B	Capacity
Punch press	2.4	3.0	1,200
Welding	0.0	2.5	600
Assembly	5.0	0.0	1,500
Profit	$0.60	$0.70	

The capacity of the punch press department available for these products is 1,200 minutes per week. The welding department has idle capacity of 600 minutes per week; the assembly department can supply 1,500 minutes of capacity per week. The manufacturing and marketing data for this production situation are summarized in Table 15.1.

In this example, two products compete for the available production time. The objective is to determine the quantity of product A and the quantity of product B to produce so that total profit will be maximized. This will require maximizing

$$TP = \$0.60A + \$0.70B$$

subject to

$$2.4A + 3.0B \leq 1,200$$
$$0.0A + 2.5B \leq 600$$
$$5.0A + 0.0B \leq 1,500$$
$$A \geq 0 \quad \text{and} \quad B \geq 0.$$

The graphical equivalent of the algebraic statement of this two-product problem is shown in Figure 15.1. The set of linear restrictions define a region of feasible solutions. This region lies below $2.4A + 3.0B = 1,200$ and is restricted further by the requirements that $B \leq 240$, $A \leq 300$, and that both A and B be non-negative. Thus, the scarce resources determine which combinations of the activities are feasible and which are not feasible.

The production quantity combinations of A and B that fall within the region of feasible solutions constitute feasible production programs. That

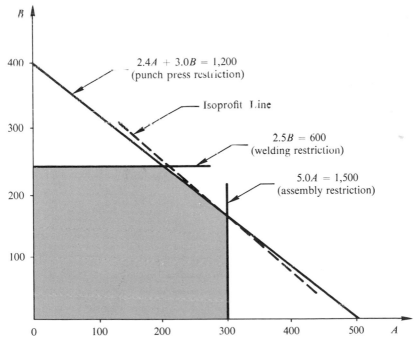

Figure 15.1. Maximizing profit for two products.

combination or combinations of A and B which maximize profit are sought. The relationship between A and B is $A = 1.167B$. This relationship is based on the relative profit of each product. The total profit realized will depend upon the production quantity combination chosen. Thus, there is a family of isoprofit lines, one of which will have at least one point in the region of feasible production quantity combinations and be a maximum distance from the origin. The member that satisfies this condition intersects the region of feasible solutions at the extreme point $A = 300$, $B = 160$. This is shown as a broken line in Figure 15.1, and represents a total profit of $0.60(300) + 0.70(160) = 292$. No other production quantity combination would result in a higher profit.

Alternate production programs with the same profit might exist in some cases. This occurs when the isoprofit line lies parallel to one of the limiting restrictions. For example, if the relative profits of product A and product B were $A = 1.25B$, the isoprofit line in Figure 15.1 would coincide with the restriction $2.4A + 3.0B = 1,200$. In this case, the isoprofit line would touch the region of feasible solutions along a line instead of at a point. All production quantity combinations along the line would maximize profit.

Graphical maximization for three activities. When three activities compete for scarce resources, a three-dimensional space is defined. Each restriction is a plane in this space, and all restrictions taken together identify a volume of feasible solutions. The effectiveness function is also a plane, its distance from the origin being proportional to its value. The optimum value for the effectiveness function occurs when this plane is located so that it is at the extreme point of the volume of feasible solutions.

As an example, suppose that the production operations for the previous example are to be expanded to include a third product designated C. A single unit of product C will require 2.0 minutes of punch press time, 1.5 minutes of welding time, and 2.5 minutes of assembly time. The profit associated with product C is $0.50 per unit. Manufacturing and marketing data for this revised production situation are summarized in Table 15.2.

In this example, three products compete for the available production time. The objective is to determine the quantity of product A, the quantity of product B, and the quantity of product C to produce so that total profit will be maximized. This will require maximizing

$$TP = \$0.60A + \$0.70B + \$0.50C$$

subject to

$$2.4A + 3.0B + 2.0C \leq 1,200$$
$$0.0A + 2.5B + 1.5C \leq 600$$
$$5.0A + 0.0B + 2.5C \leq 1,500$$
$$A \geq 0, B \geq 0, \quad \text{and} \quad C \geq 0.$$

Table 15.2. MANUFACTURING AND MARKETING DATA FOR THREE PRODUCTS

Department	Product A	Product B	Product C	Capacity
Punch Press	2.4	3.0	2.0	1,200
Welding	0.0	2.5	1.5	600
Assembly	5.0	0.0	2.5	1,500
Profit	$0.60	$0.70	$0.50	

The graphical equivalent of the algebraic statement of this three-product production situation is shown in Figure 15.2. The set of restricting planes defines a volume of feasible solutions. This region lies below $2.4A + 3.0B + 2.0C = 1,200$ and is restricted further by the requirement that $2.5B + 1.5C \leq 600$, $5.0A + 2.5C \leq 1,500$, and that A, B, and C be non-negative. Thus, the scarce resources determine which combinations of the activities are feasible and which are not feasible.

The production quantity combinations of A, B, and C that fall within

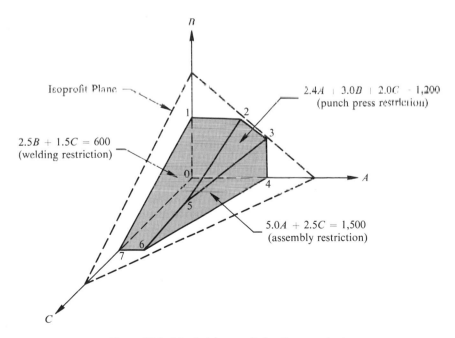

Figure 15.2. Maximizing profit for three products.

problem requires minimization. The region lies above $0.1A + 0.2B = 2.0$ and $0.2A + 0.1B = 1.8$, and is further restricted by $A \geq 4$, $B \geq 6$, and the requirements that A and B be non-negative. Thus, the minimum nutrient requirements specify which combinations of feed A and feed B are feasible and which are not feasible.

The quantity combinations of feed A and feed B that fall within the region of feasible solutions constitute feasible feed mixes. That combination or combinations of A and B which minimize total cost is sought. There is

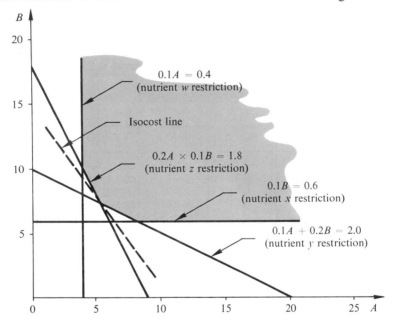

Figure 15.3. Minimizing cost for feed mixing.

a family of isocost lines one of which will have at least one point in the region of feasible solutions and will be a minimum distance from the origin. The member that satisfies this condition intersects the region of feasible solutions at the extreme point $A = 5.33$, $B = 7.34$. This is shown as a broken line in Figure 15.3 and represents a total cost of $\$0.07\,(A) + \$0.05\,(B) = \$0.74$. No other feed mixture will yield a lower total cost. Also, no alternate optimum solutions exist.

15.2. MAXIMIZING BY THE SIMPLEX METHOD

The simplex method is an algorithm that makes possible the numerical solution of the general linear programming problem. It is not restricted to problems involving three activities or fewer, as are the graphical solution methods. The simplex method is an iterative process that begins with a feasible solution, tests for optimality, and proceeds toward an improved solution. It can be shown that the algorithm will finally lead to an optimal solution if such a solution exists. In this section, the simplex method will be applied to the three-product maximization problem presented graphically. Reference to the graphical solution will explain certain facets of the computational procedure.

The simplex matrix for maximization. The three-product production problem under consideration requires the maximization of a total profit equation subject to certain restrictions. These restrictions must be converted to equalities of the form specified by the general linear programming model. This requires the addition of three "slack" variables to remove the inequalities. Thus, the restrictions become

$$2.4A + 3.0B + 2.0C + S_1 = 1{,}200$$
$$0.0A + 2.5B + 1.5C + S_2 - 600$$
$$5.0A + 0.0B + 2.5C \mid S_3 - 1{,}500.$$

The amount of departmental time not used in the production program is represented by a slack variable. Thus, each slack variable takes on whatever value is necessary for the equality to exist. If nothing is produced, the slack variables assume values equal to the total production time available in each department. This gives an initial feasible solution expressed as $S_1 = 1{,}200$, $S_2 = 600$, and $S_3 = 1{,}500$. Each slack variable is one of the x_j variables in the model. Since, however, no profit can be derived from idle capacity, total profit may be expressed as

$$TP = \$0.60A + \$0.70B + \$0.50C + \$0S_1 + \$0S_2 + \$0S_3.$$

The initial matrix required by the simplex algorithm may now be set up as shown in Table 15.5. The first column is designated e_i and gives the

Table 15.5. INITIAL MATRIX FOR A THREE-PRODUCT PRODUCTION PROBLEM

e_j			0	0	0	0.60	0.70	0.50	
e_i	Sol	b	S_1	S_2	S_3	A	B	C	θ
0	S_1	1,200	1	0	0	2.4	3.0	2.0	400
0	S_2	600	0	1	0	0	2.5	1.5	240
0	S_3	1,500	0	0	1	5.0	0	2.5	∞
E_j		0	0	0	0	0	0	0	
$e_j - E_j$			0	0	0	0.60	0.70	0.50	

r

k

profit coefficients applicable to the initial feasible solution. These are all zero since the initial solution involves the allocation of all production time to the slack variables. The second column is designated *Sol* and gives the variables in the initial solution. These are the slack variables that were introduced. The third column is designated *b* and gives the number of minutes of production time associated with the solution variables of the previous column. These reflect the total production capacity in the initial solution. Each of the next three columns is headed by slack variables with elements of zero or unity depending upon which equation is served by which slack variable. The e_j heading for these columns carries an entry of zero, corresponding to a zero profit. The last three columns are headed by the activity variables with elements entered from the restricting equations. The e_j heading for these columns is the profit associated with each activity variable. The last column, designated θ, is utilized during the computational process.

Testing for optimality. After an initial feasible solution has been obtained, it must be tested to see if a program with a higher profit can be found. The optimality test is accomplished with the aid of the last two rows in Table 15.5. The required steps are:

(1) Enter values in the row designated E_j from the expression $E_j = \Sigma\, e_i a_{ij}$, where a_{ij} are the matrix elements in the ith row and the jth column.

(2) Calculate $e_j - E_j$ for all positions in the row designated $e_j - E_j$.

(3) If $e_j - E_j$ is positive for at least one j, a better program is possible.

Application of the optimality test to the initial feasible solution is shown in the last two rows of Table 15.5. The first element in the E_j row is calculated as $0(1,200) + 0(600) + 0(1,500) = 0$. The second is $0(1) + 0(0) + 0(0) = 0$. All values in this row will be zero since all e_i values are zero in the initial feasible solution. The first element in the $e_j - E_j$ row is $0 - 0 = 0$, the second is $0 - 0 = 0$, the third is $0 - 0 = 0$, the fourth is $0.60 - 0 = 0.60$, and so forth. Since $e_j - E_j$ is positive for at least one j, this initial solution is not optimal. This will always be the case when the initial feasible solution is obtained by allocating all capacity to the slack variables.

Iteration toward an optimal program. If the optimality test indicates that an optimal program has not been found, the following iterative procedure may be employed:

(1) Find the maximum value of $e_j - E_j$ and designate this column k. The variable at the head of this column will be the incoming variable.

(2) Calculate entries for the column designated θ from $\theta_i = b_i / a_{ik}$.

(3) Find the minimum positive value of θ_i and designate this row r. The variable to the left of this row will be the outgoing variable.

(4) Set up a new matrix with the incoming variable substituted for the outgoing variable. Calculate new elements, a'_{ij}, as $a'_{rj} = a_{rj}/a_{rk}$ for $i = r$ and $a'_{ij} = a_{ik}a'_{rj}$ for $i \neq r$.

(5) Perform the optimality test.

Apply steps 1, 2, and 3 of the foregoing procedure to the initial matrix. In Table 15.5 step 1 designates B as the incoming variable. Values for θ_i are calculated from step 2. Step 3 designates S_2 as the outgoing variable. The affected column and row are marked with a k and an r, respectively, in Table 15.5.

Steps 4 and 5 require a new matrix as is shown in Table 15.6. The

Table 15.6. FIRST ITERATION FOR A THREE-PRODUCT PRODUCTION PROBLEM

e_j			0	0	0	0.60	0.70	0.50	
e_i	Sol	b	S_1	S_2	S_3	A	B	C	θ
0	S_1	480	1	−1.20	0	2.40	0	0.20	200	r
0.70	B	240	0	0.40	0	0	1	0.60	∞
0	S_3	1,500	0	0	1	5.00	0	2.50	300
	E_i	168	0	0.28	0	0	0.70	0.42	
$e_j - E_j$			0	−0.28	0	0.60	0	0.08	

k

incoming variable B, together with its associated profit, replaces the outgoing variable S_2 with its profit. All other elements in this row are calculated from the first formula of step 4. Elements in the remaining two rows are calculated from the second formula of step 4. The optimality test indicates that an optimal solution has not yet been reached. Note that after this iteration, the profit at point 1 of Figure 15.2 appears. Comparison of the results in Table 15.5 and Table 15.6 with the total profit computations in Table 15.3 indicates that the isoprofit plans which began at the origin has now moved away from this initial position to point 1. The gain from this iteration was $168 − $0 = $168.

Since the first iteration did not yield an optimal solution, it is necessary to repeat steps 1 through 5. Steps 1, 2, and 3 are applied to Table 15.6 designating A as the incoming variable and S_1 as the outgoing variable.

The incoming variable, together with its associated profit, replaces the outgoing variable as shown in Table 15.7. All other elements in this new matrix are calculated from the formulas of step 4. Application of the optimality test indicates that the solution indicated is still not optimal. Table

Table 15.7. SECOND ITERATION FOR A THREE-PRODUCT PRODUCTION PROBLEM

e_j			0	0	0	0.60	0.70	0.50		
e_i	Sol	b	S_1	S_2	S_3	A	B	C	θ	
0.60	A	200	0.416	−0.50	0	1	0	0.084	2,381	
0.70	B	240	0	0.40	0	0	1	0.60	400	
0	S_3	500	−2.08	2.50	1	0	0	2.08	240	r
E_j		288	0.25	−0.02	0	0.60	0.70	0.47		
$e_j − E_j$			−0.25	0.02	0	0	0	0.03		

k

15.3 and Figure 15.2 show that the isoprofit plane is now at point 2. The gain from this iteration was $288 − $168 = $120.

Table 15.7 did not yield an optimal solution, requiring the application of steps 1 through 5 again. Steps 1, 2, and 3 designate C as the incoming variable and S_3 as the outgoing variable. This incoming variable, together

Table 15.8. THIRD ITERATION FOR A THREE-PRODUCT PRODUCTION PROBLEM

e_j			0	0	0	0.60	0.70	0.50	
e_i	Sol	b	S_1	S_2	S_3	A	B	C	θ
0.60	A	180	0.50	−0.60	−0.04	1	0	0	
0.70	B	96	0.60	−0.32	−0.29	0	1	0	
0.50	C	240	−1	1.20	0.48	0	0	1	
E_j		295.20	0.22	0.016	0.016	0.60	0.70	0.50	
$e_j − E_j$			−0.22	−0.016	−0.016	0	0	0	

with its associated profit, replaces the outgoing variable as shown in Table 15.8. All other elements in the matrix are calculated from the formulas of step 4. Application of the optimality test indicates that the solution exhibited by Table 15.8 is optimal. Table 15.3 and Figure 15.2 indicate that the isoprofit plane is now at point 5. The gain from this iteration was $295.20 − $288 = $7.20.

15.3. MINIMIZING BY THE SIMPLEX METHOD

The computational scheme of Section 15.2 may be used without modification for problems requiring minimization if the signs of the cost coefficients are changed from positive to negative. The principle that maximizing the negative of a function is the same as minimizing the function then applies. If these coefficients are entered in the simplex matrix with their negative signs, the value of the solution will decrease as the computations proceed. In this section, the feed-mixing problem presented graphically will be solved by the simplex method.

The simplex matrix for minimization. The problem under consideration requires the minimization of a total cost equation subject to certain restrictions. Changing the sign of each cost coefficient in the total cost equation gives

$$TC = -\$0.07A - \$0.05B.$$

As before, the restrictions must be converted to equalities so the problem will conform to the general linear programming model. This is accomplished by subtracting a slack variable from the left-hand side of each. The restrictions then become

$$0.1A + 0.0B - S_1 = 0.4$$
$$0.0A + 0.1B - S_2 = 0.6$$
$$0.1A + 0.2B - S_3 = 2.0$$
$$0.2A + 0.1B - S_4 = 1.8.$$

Although the restrictions are now equalities, a feasible solution does not exist. If A and B are set equal to zero, $S_1 = -0.4$, $S_2 = -0.6$, $S_3 = -2.0$, and $S_3 = -1.8$. An initial feasible solution of the correct algebraic form can be forced by adding artificial variables resulting in

$$0.1A + 0.0B - S_1 + A_1 = 0.4$$
$$0.0A + 0.1B - S_2 + A_2 = 0.6$$
$$0.1A + 0.2B - S_3 + A_3 = 2.0$$
$$0.2A + 0.1B - S_4 + A_4 = 1.8.$$

Artificial variables with a value greater than zero destroy the equality required by the general linear programming model. Therefore, they must not appear in the final solution. To assure that they are forced out of the solution, a large penalty will be associated with each. This penalty will be larger than any other effectiveness coefficient and is designated $-M$. With these changes, the total cost equation becomes

$$TC = -\$0.07A - \$0.05B - \$0S_1 - \$0S_2 - \$0S_3$$
$$\$0S_4 - \$MA_1 - \$MA_2 - \$MA_3 - \$MA_4.$$

The initial matrix required by the simplex algorithm may now be set up as shown in Table 15.9. The initial solution variables are the artificial variables. Effectiveness coefficients for each artificial variable, slack variable, and activity variable are entered in the second row. All other matrix elements are entered from the restrictions. The simplex method may be applied to this matrix in the manner outlined for the maximization problem.

Performing the calculations for minimization. The last two rows of Table 15.9 are used in the optimality test. Since at least one $e_j - E_j$ is positive, the initial feasible solution is not optimal. Therefore, B becomes the incoming variable. Computation of θ_i identifies A_2 as the outgoing variable. The incoming variable and the outgoing variable are designated k and r, respectively, in Table 15.9. They provide the basis for the first iteration.

The incoming variable B is entered in place of the outgoing variable A_2 in Table 15.10, together with its associated effectiveness coefficient. Each element in this new matrix is calculated from step 4 of the iterative procedure outlined in the previous section. Application of the optimality test indicates that the solution is still not optimal. This makes the second iteration given in Table 15.11 necessary. Proceeding in this manner results in the third iteration given in Table 15.12, the fourth iteration given in Table 15.13, and the fifth iteration given in Table 15.14. The program indicated by the fifth iteration is optimal. This final table indicates that 5.33 lb of feed A and 7.34 lb of feed B should be used in the mixture. The total cost of the mixture will be $0.74, neglecting the negative sign. These results agree with the solution found graphically.

15.4. DUALITY, DEGENERACY, AND EQUALITY CONSTRAINTS

This section presents three topics that add further versatility to the general linear programming model. *Duality* is a property of the simplex method that allows a maximization problem to be viewed as a minimization problem. *Degeneracy* is a condition that may occur during the computational process of some problems that may prevent further progress toward an optimal program. Finally, *equality constraints* may be employed when no slack is allowed in the utilization of certain resources.

Duality in linear programming. The simplex examples of the previous sections may be called *primal problems*. These same examples may be solved by transposing the rows and columns of the algebraic statement of the problem. Inverting the problem in this way results in a dual problem. A solution to the dual problem may be found in a manner similar to that used for the primal. Once a solution is obtained, it may be converted to a solution of the primal. Solution of the dual problem normally requires less computation if

Table 15.9. INITIAL MATRIX FOR A MINIMIZATION PROBLEM

e_j			0	-M	0	-M	0	-M	0	-M	-0.07	-0.05	
e_i	Sol	b	S_1	A_1	S_2	A_2	S_3	A_3	S_4	A_4	A	B	θ
-M	A_1	0.4	-1	1	0	0	0	0	0	0	0.1	0	∞
-M	A_2	0.6	0	0	-1	1	0	0	0	0	0	0.1	6
-M	A_3	2.0	0	0	0	0	-1	1	0	0	0.1	0.2	10
-M	A_4	1.8	0	0	0	0	0	0	-1	1	0.2	0.1	18
E_j		-4.8M	M	-M	M	-M	M	-M	M	-M	-0.4M	-0.4M	
$e_j - E_j$			-M	0	-M	0	-M	0	-M	0	-0.07+0.4M	-0.05+0.4M	

Table 15.10. FIRST ITERATION FOR A MINIMIZATION PROBLEM

e_j			0	-M	0	-M	0	-M	0	-M	-0.07	-0.05	
e_i	Sol	b	S_1	A_1	S_2	A_2	S_3	A_3	S_4	A_4	A	B	θ
-M	A_1	0.4	-1	1	0	0	0	0	0	0	0.1	0	∞
-0.05	B	6	0	0	-10	10	0	0	0	0	0	1	-0.6
-M	A_3	0.8	0	0	2	-2	-1	1	0	0	0.1	0	0.4
-M	A_4	1.2	0	0	1	-1	0	0	-1	1	0.2	0	1.2
E_j		-0.3-2.4M	M	-M	0.5-3M	-0.5+3M	M	-M	M	-M	-0.4M	-0.05	
$e_j - E_j$			-M	0	-0.5+3M	0.5-4M	-M	0	-M	0	-0.07+0.4M	0	

Table 15.11. SECOND ITERATION FOR A MINIMIZATION PROBLEM

			e_j	0	$-M$	0	$-M$	0	$-M$	0	$-M$	-0.07	-0.05	
e_i	Sol	b		S_1	A_1	S_2	A_2	S_3	A_3	S_4	A_4	A	B	θ
$-M$	A_1	0.4		-1	1	0	0	0	0	0	0	0.1	0	∞
-0.05	B	10		0	0	0	0	-5	5	0	0	0.5	1	-2
0	S_2	0.4		0	0	1	-1	-0.5	0.5	-1	0	0.05	0	-0.8
$-M$	A_4	0.8		0	0	0	0	0.5	-0.5	-1	1	0.15	0	1.6
E_j		$-0.5 - 1.2M$		M	$-M$	0	0	$0.25 - 0.5M$	$-0.25 + 0.5M$	M	$-M$	$-0.025 - 0.25M$	-0.05	
$e_j - E_j$				$-M$	0	0	$-M$	$-0.25 + 0.5M$	$0.25 - 1.5M$	$-M$	0	$-0.045 + 0.25M$		

(r = row indicator, k = column indicator)

Table 15.12. THIRD ITERATION FOR A MINIMIZATION PROBLEM

			e_j	0	$-M$	0	$-M$	0	$-M$	0	$-M$	-0.07	-0.05	
e_i	Sol	b		S_1	A_1	S_2	A_2	S_3	A_3	S_4	A_4	A	B	θ
$-M$	A_1	0.4		-1	1	0	0	0	0	0	0	0.1	0	4
-0.05	B	18		0	0	0	0	0	0	-10	10	2.0	1	9
0	S_2	1.2		0	0	1	-1	0	0	-1	1	0.2	0	6
0	S_3	1.6		0	0	0	0	1	-1	-2	2	0.3	0	5.33
E_j		$-0.9 - 0.4M$		M	$-M$	0	0	0	0	0.5	-0.5	$-0.1M - 0.1$	-0.05	
$e_j - E_j$				$-M$	0	0	$-M$	0	$-M$	-0.5	$M + 0.5$	$+0.03 + 0.1M$	0	

(r = row indicator, k = column indicator)

Table 15.13. FOURTH ITERATION FOR A MINIMIZATION PROBLEM

e_i	Sol	b	S_1 0	A_1 $-M$	S_2 0	A_2 $-M$	S_3 0	A_3 $-M$	S_4 0	A_4 $-M$	A -0.07	B -0.05	θ
-0.07	A	4	-10	10	0	0	0	0	0	0	1	0	-0.4
-0.05	B	10	20	-20	0	0	0	0	-10	10	0	1	0.5
0	S_2	0.4	2	-2	1	-1	0	0	-1	1	0	0	0.2
0	S_3	0.4	3	-3	0	0	1	-1	-2	2	0	0	0.133
E_j		-0.78	-0.3	0.3	0	0	0	0	0.5	-0.5	-0.07	-0.05	
$e_j - E_j$			0.3	$-0.3 - M$	0	$-M$	0	$-M$	-0.5	$0.5 - M$	0	0	

Table 15.14. FIFTH ITERATION FOR A MINIMIZATION PROBLEM

e_i	Sol	b	S_1 0	A_1 $-M$	S_2 0	A_2 $-M$	S_3 0	A_3 $-M$	S_4 0	A_4 $-M$	A -0.07	B -0.05	θ
-0.07	A	5.33	0	0	0	0	3.30	-3.30	-6.70	6.70	1	0	
-0.05	B	7.34	0	0	0	0	-6.60	6.60	3.40	-3.40	0	1	
0	S_2	0.134	0	0	1	-1	-0.66	0.66	0.34	-0.34	0	0	
0	S_1	0.133	1	-1	0	0	0.33	-0.33	-0.67	0.67	0	0	
E_j		-0.74	0	0	0	0	0.099	-0.099	-0.299	0.299	-0.07	-0.05	
$e_j - E_j$			0	$-M$	0	$-M$	-0.099	$0.099 - M$	0.299	$-0.299 - M$	0	0	

the primal problem contains a large number of rows and a small number of columns; hence, it offers an advantage in many applications.

Consider the following algebraic statement of the general linear programming problem, called the *primal*. Minimize

$$e_1 x_1 + e_2 x_2 + \cdots + e_n x_n$$

subject to the constraints

$$a_{11} x_1 + a_{12} x_2 + \cdots + a_{1n} x_n \geq b_1$$
$$a_{21} x_1 + a_{22} x_2 + \cdots + a_{2n} x_n \geq b_2$$
$$\cdots \qquad\qquad \cdots$$
$$a_{m1} x_1 + a_{m2} x_2 + \cdots + a_{mn} x_n \geq b_m.$$

The algebraic statement of the dual problem may be presented by transposing rows and columns, the vector of constants b_i and the effectiveness function, reversing the inequalities, and maximizing instead of minimizing. The use of dual variables $y_1, y_2, \ldots, y_m$ with $y_j \geq 0$ results in the dual. Maximize

$$b_1 y_1 + b_2 y_2 + \cdots + b_m y_m$$

subject to the constraints

$$a_{11} y_1 + a_{21} y_2 + \cdots + a_{m1} y_m \leq e_1$$
$$a_{12} y_1 + a_{22} y_2 + \cdots + a_{m2} y_m \leq e_2$$
$$\cdots \qquad\qquad \cdots$$
$$a_{1n} y_1 + a_{2n} y_2 + \cdots + a_{mn} y_m \leq e_n.$$

If the inequalities of the primal were not of the greater than or equal to type, algebraic manipulation would have to be used to put them in this form.

As an example of the application of the dual, consider the feed-mixing problem presented previously. The original algebraic statement of this problem can be transformed to the dual. Maximize

$$0.4 y_1 + 0.6 y_2 + 2.0 y_3 + 1.8 y_4$$

subject to the constraints

$$0.1 y_1 + 0.0 y_2 + 0.1 y_3 + 0.2 y_4 \leq 0.07$$
$$0.0 y_1 + 0.1 y_2 + 0.2 y_3 + 0.1 y_4 \leq 0.05.$$

Adding slack variables results in the initial matrix of Table 15.15. The simplex method may now be applied as was outlined previously. This results in Table 15.16 and Table 15.17.

Values for the activity variables of the primal appear in the columns of slack variables in the dual with negative signs. These are indicated in Table 15.17. Finally, the value for the effectiveness function is in the same location in both the primal and dual, but with opposite sign. Table 15.14 should be compared with Table 15.17.

Table 15.15. DUAL MATRIX FOR PRIMAL OF TABLE 15.9

e_j			0	0	0.4	0.6	2.0	1.8	
e_i	Sol	b	S_1	S_2	y_1	y_2	y_3	y_4	θ
0	S_1	0.07	1	0	0.1	0.0	0.1	0.2	0.70
0	S_2	0.05	0	1	0.0	0.1	0.2	0.1	0.25
	E_j	0	0	0	0	0	0	0	
	$e_j - E_j$		0	0	0.4	0.6	2.0	1.8	

r

k

Table 15.16. FIRST ITERATION FOR DUAL PROBLEM

e_j			0	0	0.4	0.6	2.0	1.8	
e_i	Sol	b	S_1	S_2	y_1	y_2	y_3	y_4	θ
0	S_1	0.045	1	−0.5	0.1	−0.05	0	0.15	0.30
2.0	y_3	0.250	0	5	0	0.5	1	0.50	0.50
	E_j	0.50	0	10	0	1	2.0	1.0	
	$e_j - E_j$		0	−10	0.4	−0.4	0	0.81	

r

k

Table 15.17. FINAL MATRIX FOR DUAL PROBLEM

e_j			0	0	0.4	0.6	2.0	1.8	
e_i	Sol	b	S_1	S_2	y_1	y_2	y_3	y_4	θ
1.8	y_4	0.3	6.6667	−3.3334	0.6667	−0.3334	0	1	
2.0	y_3	0.1	−3.3350	6.6667	−0.3334	0.6667	1	0	
	E_j	0.74	5.333	7.333	0.5468	0.7333	2.0	1.8	
	$e_j - E_j$		−5.333	−7.333	−0.1468	−0.1333	0	0	

Degeneracy in the simplex method. Degeneracy becomes evident in the simplex method at the time that the outgoing variable is being selected. In step 3 of the iterative process, the minimum positive value of θ_i determines the outgoing variable. If two or more values of θ_i are minimal, the problem is degenerate. An arbitrary choice of one of the tied variables may result in more iterations than some other choice. More serious, however, is the condition of cycling which might occur because of a poor choice from among the tied variables.

Although cycling seldom occurs in practical problems, it can be prevented by applying the following procedure:

(1) Divide each element in the tied rows by the positive coefficients of the kth column progressing from left to right.

(2) Compare the resulting ratios from left to right.

(3) The row which first contains the smallest algebraic ratio is designated r.

As an example of the preceding procedure, consider the degenerate problem of Table 15.18. A dilemma exists regarding the choice of row 1 or row 2

Table 15.18. A DEGENERATE SIMPLEX PROBLEM

e_j			0	0	0	40	60	80	
e_i	Sol	b	S_1	S_2	S_3	A	B	C	θ
0	S_1	0	1	0	0	-2	0	4	0
0	S_2	0	0	1	0	3	0	6	0
60	B	60	0	0	1	2	1	1	60
E_j		360	0	0	0	120	60	60	
$e_j - E_j$			0	0	0	-80	0	20	

k

as the outgoing variable. The first ratio for row 1 is 1/4. Likewise, the first ratio for row 2 is 0/6. Since the second row yields the smallest ratio, it is designated r and the simplex procedure is continued.

Treating equality constraints. Some problems solvable by the simplex method of linear programming require that a given resource be fully utilized. For example, a production manager might specify that the entire capacity of the assembly department be utilized in the interest of stabilizing manpower. In such cases, the algebraic statement of the problem will contain an equality constraint. This is unlike the foregoing problems which utilized only inequalities.

As an example of a situation in which an equality constraint is needed, consider the case of a manufacturer who has two manufacturing resources, machine hours and labor hours. In each working day, the manager has 180 machine hours and 240 labor hours to spend on three products, A, B, and C. Product A requires 4 machine hours and 3 labor hours per unit, product B requires 4 machine hours and 5 labor hours per unit, and product C requires 2 machine hours and 6 labor hours per unit. The profit per unit of product A is $12, per unit of product B is $8, and per unit of product C is $10.

The production manager wishes to maximize profit subject to the limitation on machine time and labor hours. He requires, however, that all labor hours be fully utilized so that his manpower level will remain constant. Therefore, the algebraic statement of this problem requires the maximization of

$$TP = \$12A + \$8B + \$10C$$

subject to

$$3A + 5B + 6C = 240$$

$$4A + 4B + 2C \leq 180$$

$$A \geq 0, B \geq 0 \quad \text{and} \quad C \geq 0.$$

The initial simplex matrix for this problem is exhibited in Table 15.19. Note that an artificial variable is employed to yield an initial feasible solution.

Table 15.19. INITIAL SIMPLEX MATRIX FOR EQUALITY CONSTRAINT

e_j			$-M$	0	12	8	10	
e_i	Sol	b	A_1	S_1	A	B	C	0
$-M$	A_1	240	1	0	3	5	6	
0	S_1	180	0	1	4	4	2	
	E_j							
	$e_j - E_j$							

Although this is a maximization problem, the effectiveness coefficient associated with the artificial variable is $-M$. This is required since artificial variables are used only to obtain an initial feasible solution and must be forced out of solution as the computations proceed.

The simplex method may be applied to Table 15.19 to find a maximum profit program. Total profit, however, will be less with the equality constraint than it would be without such a constraint. The production manager will incur a penalty for his desire to utilize the available labor hours fully.

PROBLEMS

1. Solve graphically for the values of x and y that maximize the functions

$$Z = 2.2x + 3.8y$$

subject to the constraints

$$2.4x + 3.2y \leq 140$$

$$0.0x + 2.6y \leq 80$$

$$4.1x + 0.0y \leq 120$$

$$x \geq 0 \quad \text{and} \quad y \geq 0.$$

2. Solve graphically for the values of A and B that maximize total profit expressed as

$$TP = \$0.28A + \$0.36B$$

subject to the constraints

$$A \leq 42$$
$$B \leq 30$$
$$A + B \leq 62$$
$$A \geq 0 \quad \text{and} \quad B \geq 0.$$

3. A small machine shop has capability in turning, milling, drilling, and welding. The machine capacity is 16 hours per day in turning, 16 hours per day in milling, 8 hours per day in drilling, and 8 hours per day in welding. Two products, designated A and B, are under consideration. Each will yield a net profit of $0.25 per unit and will require the following amount of machine time:

	Product A	Product B
turning	0.064	0.106
milling	0.106	0.053
drilling	0.000	0.080

Solve graphically for the number of units of each product that should be scheduled to maximize profit.

4. Solve graphically for the values of x, y, and z that maximize the function

$$Z = 5.1x + 7.6y + 10.0z$$

subject to the constraints

$$5.0x + 10.2y + 4.2z \leq 2,200$$
$$0.8x + 1.2y + 2.0z \leq 450$$
$$10.5x + 4.8y + 1.9z \leq 2,600$$
$$x \geq 0, y \geq 0 \quad \text{and} \quad z \geq 0.$$

5. Solve graphically for the values of x and y that minimize the function

$$Z = 8x + 5y$$

subject to the constraints

$$22x + 12y \geq 220$$
$$8x + 0y \geq 40$$
$$0x + 6y \geq 24$$
$$x \geq 0 \quad \text{and} \quad y \geq 0.$$

6. Use the simplex method to find the values of x and y that maximize the function given in Problem 1.

7. Use the simplex method to find the maximum profit production program for the situation given in Problem 3.

8. Use the simplex method to find the values of x, y, and z that maximize the function given in Problem 4.

9. Use the simplex method to find the values of x and y that minimize the function given in Problem 5.

10. Minimize the function given in Problem 5 by formulating the dual problem.

11. Use the simplex method to find the values for a, b, c, d, and e that maximize total profit expressed as

$$TP = 0.90a + 0.40b + 0.50c + 0.30d + 0.10e$$

subject to the constraints

$$0.50a + 0.50b + 0.10c + 0.20d + 0.10e = 1.4$$
$$0.50a + 0.10b + 0.40c + 0.20d + 0.30e = 1.5$$
$$0.30a + 0.60b + 0.20c + 0.00d + 0.00e > 0.6$$
$$a \geq 0, b \geq 0, c \geq 0, d \geq 0, \quad \text{and} \quad e \geq 0.$$

12. A refinery produces three grades of gasoline; premium, regular, and economy. Each grade requires straight gasoline, octane, and additives which are available in the amount of 3,200,000 2,400,000, and 1,100,000 gal per week, respectively. A gallon of premium requires 0.22 gal of straight gasoline, 0.50 gal of octane, and 0.28 gal of additives. One gal of regular requires 0.55 gal of straight gasoline, 0.32 gal of octane, and 0.13 gal of additives. A gallon of economy requires 0.72 gal of straight gasoline, 0.20 gal of octane, and 0.08 gal of additives. A profit of $0.048, $0.040, and $0.029 per gallon is received for premium, regular, and economy, respectively. How many gallons of each grade of gasoline should be produced each week to maximize profit?

13. Sir Francis Drake, operating under a privateer's commission by Queen Elizabeth of England captured and destroyed the town of Porto Bello on the Isthmus of Panama in 1572. As a result of this victory, he assumed control of 62,000 lb of silver ornaments, pottery, and other filigree, 11,000 lb of gold pottery, trinkets, and other ornaments and 21,000 lb of precious jewelry, gems, and pearls. His only cargo ship has three holds, forward, center, and aft, with the following capacity limits.

	Pounds	Cubic Feet
Forward	19,800	1,100
Center	30,000	1,340
Aft	15,200	480

The silver filigree, with its necessary packing, will require 0.6 cu ft of cargo space per pound. The gold pottery will require 0.52 cu ft per pound and the precious jewelry will require 0.24 cu ft of cargo space per pound. The weight in each hold must be proportional to the capacity in pounds so that the trim of the ship is preserved. The value of the silver filigree is 24 shillings per ounce, the value of the gold pottery is 32 shillings per ounce, and the value of the precious jewelry is 19 shillings per ounce. How much of each product should be loaded, and how should it be distributed among the holds of the ship, so as to maximize the value of the haul to the English Crown?

14. A manufacturer has three engine lathes and two profile mills available for machining four products. The unit machining times in hours per unit, the capacities of each machine in hours per week, and the profit per unit are summarized below.

Machine	Product A	Product B	Product C	Product D	Capacity
lathe 1	0.6	—	—	0.6	30
lathe 2	0.4	0.2	0.8	0.4	40
lathe 3	0.3	0.2	—	—	26
mill 1	—	0.6	0.5	0.5	34
mill 2	—	0.5	—	0.4	40
Profit	$0.20	$0.15	$0.30	$0.40	

Each product needs processing on only one lathe and/or one mill. The unit times given apply if the designated choice is made. Determine the maximum profit production program.

15. Consider the primal requiring the maximization of

$$x_1 + x_2$$

subject to the constraints

$$2x_1 + 1x_2 \geq 8$$
$$3x_1 + 8x_2 \geq 24$$
$$x_1 \geq 0 \quad \text{and} \quad x_2 \geq 0.$$

Solve the primal and the dual graphically and verify that optimum effectiveness for the primal is equal to optimum effectiveness for the dual.

16. Apply the simplex algorithm to the initial matrix for equality constraint of Table 15.19. What is the maximum profit?

17. Change the equality constraint in the problem given by Table 15.19 to a constraint of the less than or equal type. Solve by the simplex method and compare the maximum profit with that of Problem 16.

sixteen

SOME APPLICATIONS
OF DYNAMIC PROGRAMMING

*Dynamic programming is concerned with decision situations involving
effectiveness functions of many variables which may be
subject to constraints. Rather than approach these
situations in the usual manner, we analyze a sequence of simpler problems,
expanding the scope of analysis until the original problem is solved.
As a result, problems exhibiting a large number of variables are reduced to a
sequence of problems with only a single variable.
The process is characterized by the determination of one variable leaving a
similar problem with one less variable.*

*Differential calculus is not always applicable as a
technique of optimization. This is especially true when the
effectiveness function has local maximums or minimums or if it is discontinuous.
Maximums or minimums occurring on a boundary may be bypassed and points
of inflection will cause difficulty in functions of several variables.
Numerical enumeration is successful in these instances only when the amount of
computation required is reasonable. This chapter presents selected
applications of dynamic programming that overcome these difficulties.
The first group will illustrate static multi-activity processes in which a
sequence of decisions is artificially utilized in the computational process.
The second group presents true dynamic processes in which
a sequence of decisions spanning several
time periods must be made.*

421

16.1. THE CONCEPT OF DYNAMIC PROGRAMMING

Dynamic programming owes much of its development to Richard Bellman and his associates at the RAND Corporation.[1] The computational technique is based on the principle of optimality which states: *An optimal policy has the property that, whatever the initial state and initial decision are, the remaining decisions must constitute an optimal policy with regard to the state resulting from the first decision.* The discussion in this section and the examples of subsequent sections are based on this principle.

The dynamic programming model. A general dynamic programming model may be developed quite easily from the principle of optimality for single-dimensional processes. The programming situation involves a certain quantity of an economic resource, such as machines, space, money, or men, which can be allocated to a number of different activities. A conflict arises from the numerous ways in which the allocation can be made. A certain return is derived from the allocation of all or part of the resource to a given activity. The magnitude of the return depends jointly upon the specific activity and the quantity of the resource allocated. It is assumed that the returns from different activities can be measured in a common unit, that the return from any activity is independent of the allocations to the other activities, and that the total return is the sum of the individual returns. The objective is to allocate the available resource among the various activities so as to maximize the total return.

Let the number of activities be designated by N, enumerated in fixed order, $1, 2, \ldots, N$. Associated with each activity is a return function which gives the dependence of the return from the activity upon the quantity of the resource allocated. The quantity of the resource allocated to the ith activity may be designated x_i and $g_i(x_i)$ denotes the return function. Since it was assumed that the activities are independent and that the returns from all activities are additive, the total return may be expressed as

$$R(x_1, x_2, \ldots, x_N) = g_1(x_1) + g_2(x_2) + \cdots + g_N(x_N). \qquad (16.1)$$

The limited quantity of the resource, Q, leads to the constraint

$$Q = x_1 + x_2 + \cdots + x_N; \qquad x_i \geq 0.$$

The objective is to maximize the total return over all x_i, subject to the above constraint.

The problem of maximizing the total return from the allocation process is viewed as one member of a family of allocation processes. The quantity of

---

[1] A complete treatment of the subject may be found in R. Bellman, *Dynamic Programming* (Princeton, N.J.: Princeton University Press, 1957).

the resource, Q, and the number of activities, N, will not be assumed to be fixed, but may take on any value subject to the restriction that N be an integer. It is artifically required that the allocations be made one at a time; that is, a quantity of the resource is allocated to the Nth activity, then to the $(N-1)$th activity, and so on.

Since the maximization of R depends upon Q and N, the dependence must be explicitly stated by a sequence of functions

$$f_N(Q) = \max_{x_i} \{R(x_1, x_2, \ldots, x_N)\}. \qquad (16.2)$$

The function $f_N(Q)$ represents the maximum return from the allocation of the resource Q to the N activities. If it is assumed that $g_i(0) = 0$ for each activity, it is evident that

$$f_N(0) = 0, \qquad N = 1, 2, \ldots, \text{ and so forth}$$

and that

$$f_1(Q) = g_1(Q). \qquad (16.3)$$

These two statements express the return to be expected from the Nth activity if no resources are allocated and the return to be expected from the first activity if all the resources are allocated to it.

A functional relation connecting $f_N(Q)$ and $f_{N-1}(Q)$ for arbitrary values of N and Q may be developed by the following procedure. If x_N, $0 \leq x_N \leq Q$, is the allocation of the resource to the Nth activity, then, regardless of the value of x_N, a quantity of resource $Q - x_N$ will remain. The return from the $N-1$ activities may be expressed as $f_{N-1}(Q - x_N)$. Therefore, the total return from the N activity process may be expressed as

$$g_N(x_N) + f_{N-1}(Q - x_N).$$

An optimal choice of x_N would be that choice which maximizes the foregoing function. Thus, the fundamental dynamic programming model may be written as

$$f_N(Q) = \max_{0 \leq x_N \leq Q} \{g_N(x_N) + f_{N-1}(Q - x_N)\}, \qquad N = 2, 3, \ldots, \text{ and so forth} \qquad (16.4)$$

where $f_1(Q)$ is determined from Equation (16.3). This model is based on the concept given by the principle of optimality.

The computational procedure. Equation (16.4) provides a method for obtaining the sequence $f_N(Q)$ once $f_1(Q)$ is known. Since $f_1(Q)$ determines $f_2(Q)$, it is also true that $f_2(Q)$ leads to an evaluation of $f_3(Q)$. This recursive relationship progresses in this manner until $f_{N-1}(Q)$ determines $f_N(Q)$ at which time the process stops.

As an example of this procedure, consider the network of Figure 16.1.

The maximum path through the network is desired. There are three possible starting points (A, B, and C), and three possible ending points (a, b, and c). The problem might be solved by identifying all possible paths and calculating the value of each. It is evident, however, that this method might result in the omission of a path. In addition, this process requires much calculation.

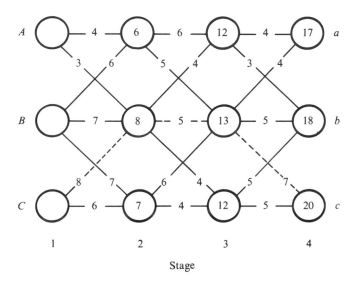

Figure 16.1 A network illustration of dynamic programming.

By utilizing the concept of dynamic programming, the problem is viewed as a stagewise process. The maximum path from stage 1 to stage 2 is entered for each terminal point of stage 2. This occurs because whatever the starting point chosen, the path to the terminal point must be a maximum for an optimal two-stage policy to exist. Thus, the optimal two-stage policy is easily identified with little calculation. The optimal three-stage policy is found by again calculating the maximum of each terminal point from a knowledge of the results of the optimal two-stage policies. Continuing to the fourth stage with the same philosophy results in an optimal four-stage policy. This maximum path will have a value of 20 and is indicated by the broken line.

Consider the resource allocation situation next. The entire set of values $f_N(Q)$ in the range 0 to Q may be found by assuming a finite grid of points. Each element of the sequence $f_N(Q)$ may be evaluated and tabulated at each of these grid points. Maximization of Equation (16.4) may be performed when $N = 1$ since $f_1(Q) = g_1(Q)$. A set of values $f_1(Q)$ may be computed and tabulated. Equation (16.4) may then be used to compute $f_2(Q)$ for $N = 2$; that is,

$$f_2(Q) = \max_{0 \leq x_2 \leq Q} \{g_2(x_2) + f_1(Q - x_2)\}.$$

The maximization process begins by evaluating $g_2(0) + f_1(Q)$ and $g_2(\Delta) + f_1(Q - \Delta)$. The larger of these values is retained and compared with the values $g_2(2\Delta) + f_1(Q - 2\Delta)$. As before, the larger of these values is retained and compared with $g_2(3\Delta) + f_1(Q - 3\Delta)$. This process is continued until all values of Δ are considered. The result is a table of values for $f_2(Q)$ at the Q values of $0, \Delta, 2\Delta, \ldots$, and so forth, as given by Table 16.1. For any given

Table 16.1. TABULAR REPRESENTATION OF COMPUTATIONAL SCHEME

Q	x_1	$f_1(Q)$	x_2	$f_2(Q)$	$\cdots$
0					
Δ					
2Δ					
.					
.					
.					

value of Q, subject to the grid established, the table gives the corresponding allocation, x_2, for the second activity, $N = 2$, since only a two-stage process was considered. Once the allocation x_2 to the second activity is determined, the allocation of the remaining resources, $Q - x_2$, to the first activity may be determined. The computational procedure can be extended for N stages, giving an expanded table and a means for determining all allocations.

The primary argument in favor of the dynamic programming algorithm its avoiding the difficulties associated with the classical variational approach of the calculus. These difficulties can, however, also be avoided by direct enumeration of all cases. In certain instances, direct enumeration is not only feasible but desirable. In others, it must be ruled out, because of the magnitude of the number of cases that must be considered. When this is the case, the dynamic programming algorithm which is based on the functional equation technique may be fruitfully employed.

Dynamic programming provides a search process that is far more efficient than the direct enumeration process and thereby provides a feasible approach to many multistage decision problems. The principle of optimality is the key to the success of dynamic programming. Having chosen some initial x_N it is not necessary to examine all policies involving the particular choice of x_N. Only those policies which are optimal for an $N - 1$ stage process with available resources $Q - x_N$ must be examined. Thus, the calculations required are not multiplicative, but are additive as the number of stages in the process increases.

16.2. A CAPITAL INVESTMENT PROBLEM

As a simple application of the concept developed in the previous section consider the following situation: A conflict arises from the numerous ways in which a fixed amount of capital can be allocated to a number of activities. A certain return is derived as a result of allocating all or part of the capital to a given activity. The total return depends upon the manner in which the allocation is made. Therefore, the objective is to find that allocation which maximizes the total return.

Description of the problem. Suppose that eight units of capital are available and that three different activities are under consideration. The return functions for each venture are given in Table 16.2, with each return

Table 16.2. RETURN FUNCTIONS FOR CAPITAL INVESTMENT

Q	$g_1(Q)$	$g_2(Q)$	$g_3(Q)$
0	0	0	0
1	5	5	4
2	15	15	26
3	40	40	40
4	80	60	45
5	90	70	50
6	95	73	51
7	98	74	52
8	100	75	53

being measured in a common unit. The return from each activity is independent of the allocations to the other activities. In addition, the total return is the sum of the individual returns. Each activity exhibits a return function that increases for a portion of its range and then levels off. This is owing to the law of diminishing returns and is typical of many activities.

A finite grid of points is established for this problem by the discrete nature of the return functions. Direct enumeration of all ways in which the eight units of capital can be allocated to the three activities would be possible. The dynamic programming model given by Equation (16.4) may, however, be used with a saving in computational effort.

The computational procedure. The return expected from the first activity if all the available capital is allocated to it is determined from Equation (16.3) as

$$f_1(0) = g_1(0) = \quad 0$$
$$f_1(1) = g_1(1) = \quad 5$$
$$f_1(2) = g_1(2) = \quad 15$$
$$f_1(3) = g_1(3) = \quad 40$$
$$f_1(4) = g_1(4) = \quad 80$$
$$f_1(5) = g_1(5) = \quad 90$$
$$f_1(6) = g_1(6) = \quad 95$$
$$f_1(7) = g_1(7) = \quad 98$$
$$f_1(8) = g_1(8) = 100$$

This completes the computation of $f_1(Q)$. Each value is entered in the first stage of Table 16.3.

Table 16.3. TABULAR SOLUTION FOR A CAPITAL INVESTMENT PROBLEM

Q	x_1	$f_1(Q)$	x_2	$f_2(Q)$	x_3	$f_3(Q)$
0	0	0	0	0	0	0
1	1	5	1	5	0	5
2	2	15	2	15	2	26
3	3	40	3	40	3	40
4	4*	80	0	80	0	80
5	5	90	0	90	0	90
6	6	95	2	95	2	106
7	7	98	3	120	3	120
8	8	100	4*	140	0*	140

From the results of $f_1(Q)$, $f_2(Q)$ may be computed by use of Equation (16.4). It is evident that when $Q = 0$, $f_2(Q) = 0$. When $Q = 1$,

$$f_2(1) = \max_{0 \leq x_2 \leq 1} \{g_2(x_2) + f_1(1 - x_2)\}.$$

For values of x_2 ranging from 0 to 1, this gives

$$f_2(1) = \max \begin{cases} g_2(0) + f_1(1) = 5 \\ g_2(1) + f_1(0) = 5 \end{cases}.$$

When $Q = 2$,

$$f_2(2) = \max_{0 \leq x_2 \leq 2} \{g_2(x_2) + f_1(2 - x_2)\}.$$

For values of x_2 ranging from 0 to 2, this gives

$$f_2(2) = \max \begin{cases} g_2(0) + f_1(2) = 15 \\ g_2(1) + f_1(1) = 10 \\ g_2(2) + f_1(0) = 15 \end{cases}.$$

When $Q = 3$,

$$f_2(3) = \max_{0 \le x_2 \le 3} \{g_2(x_2) + f_1(3 - x_2)\}.$$

For values of x_2 ranging from 0 to 3, this gives

$$f_2(3) = \max \begin{pmatrix} g_2(0) + f_1(3) = 40 \\ g_2(1) + f_1(2) = 20 \\ g_2(2) + f_1(1) = 20 \\ g_2(3) + f_1(0) = 40 \end{pmatrix}.$$

This process is continued until $f_2(8)$ is evaluated. The maximum value of $f_2(Q)$ is identified for each value of Q and entered in the second stage of Table 16.3 together with its associated value of x_2. An arbitrary choice may be made when a tie is involved.

The third stage is considered next. Using the results of $f_2(Q), f_3(Q)$ may be computed by use of Equation (16.4). As before, when $Q = 0, f_3(Q) = 0$. When $Q = 1$,

$$f_3(1) = \max_{0 \le x_3 \le 1} \{g_3(x_3) + f_2(1 - x_3)\}.$$

For values of x_3 ranging from 0 to 1, this gives

$$f_3(1) = \max \begin{pmatrix} g_3(0) + f_2(1) = 5 \\ g_3(1) + f_2(0) = 4 \end{pmatrix}.$$

When $Q = 2$,

$$f_3(2) = \max_{0 \le x_3 \le 2} \{g_3(x_3) + f_2(2 - x_3)\}.$$

For values of x_3 ranging from 0 to 2, this gives

$$f_3(2) = \max \begin{pmatrix} g_3(0) + f_2(2) = 15 \\ g_3(1) + f_2(1) = 9 \\ g_3(2) + f_2(0) = 26 \end{pmatrix}.$$

When $Q = 3$,

$$f_3(3) = \max_{0 \le x_3 \le 3} \{g_3(x_3) + f_2(3 - x_3)\}.$$

For values of x_3 ranging from 0 to 3, this gives

$$f_3(3) = \max \begin{pmatrix} g_3(0) + f_2(3) = 40 \\ g_3(1) + f_2(2) = 19 \\ g_3(2) + f_2(1) = 31 \\ g_3(3) + f_2(0) = 40 \end{pmatrix}.$$

Again, this process is continued until $f_3(8)$ is evaluated. The maximum value of $f_3(Q)$ is identified for each value of Q and entered in the third stage of Table 16.3 together with its associated value of x_3.

Table 16.3 may now be used to find the maximum return allocation of capital. This maximum is found in the third stage of the table to be 140 units. The allocation of capital associated with this return may be found by noting that $x_3 = 0$ at $f_3(Q) = 140$. Therefore, 8 units of capital remain for the two-stage process giving a value for x_2 of 4 units. This leaves 4 units for the first stage; $x_1 = 4$. Each allocation is indicated with an asterisk in Table 16.3.

Note that Table 16.3 can be used to find the maximum return investment policy for investments ranging from 1 to 8 units of capital. It may also be used to find the optimal policy for a reduced number of activities. For example, if 6 units of capital are to be invested in activity 1 and 2, the solution would be found by noting that $x_2 = 2$ at $f_2(Q) = 95$. This means that 4 units would remain for the first activity; $x_1 = 4$. Thus, the maximization of R depends on Q and N, as was expressed in Equation (16.2).

16.3. A SHIPPING PROBLEM

A given number of items, each with a different weight and value, are to make up a shipment the total weight of which must not exceed a certain maximum. The objective is to select the number of each item to include in the shipment so that its value will be a maximum. Problems, such as this, arise in shipping operations where the value of the shipment may be measured in terms of its worth to the receiver or where its value is a function of the shipping revenue. This latter case will be considered in the example of this section.

Description of the problem. Suppose that four items with different weights and values are to form a shipment with a total weight of not more than 9 tons. Table 16.4 gives the weight and net profit to be derived from

Table 16.4. WEIGHTS AND VALUES OF ITEMS

Item	Weight (tons)	Net Profit
1	2	$ 50
2	4	120
3	5	170
4	3	80

each item. In this problem, the weight of the shipment is a restriction and constitutes a resource to be distributed or allocated to the four items. Thus, the concept outlined previously is applicable.

The first step in the solution is to determine the return functions for each individual item. This is accomplished by considering different weights to be

Table 16.5. RETURN FUNCTIONS FOR SHIPPING PROBLEMS

Q	$g_1(Q)$	$g_2(Q)$	$g_3(Q)$	$g_4(Q)$
0	0	0	0	0
1	0	0	0	0
2	50	0	0	0
3	50	0	0	80
4	100	120	0	80
5	100	120	170	80
6	150	120	170	160
7	150	120	170	160
8	200	240	170	160
9	200	240	170	240

allocated to each item and by identifying the whole number of items than can be accommodated within these weights. By reference to Table 16.4, the return functions of Table 16.5 are developed. Each function gives the return to be expected from allocating designated amounts of the scarce resource (shipping weight) to each activity (item).

Performing the calculations. First, the return to be expected from the first item if all the available weight is allocated to it must be determined from Equation (16.3) as

$$f_1(0) = g_1(0) = 0$$
$$f_1(1) = g_1(1) = 0$$
$$f_1(2) = g_1(2) = 50$$
$$f_1(3) = g_1(3) = 50$$
$$f_1(4) = g_1(4) = 100$$
$$f_1(5) = g_1(5) = 100$$
$$f_1(6) = g_1(6) = 150$$
$$f_1(7) = g_1(7) = 150$$
$$f_1(8) = g_1(8) = 200$$
$$f_1(9) = g_1(9) = 200$$

This completes the computation of $f_1(Q)$. Each value is entered in the first stage of Table 16.6.

From the results of $f_1(Q)$, $f_2(Q)$ may be computed by use of Equation (16.4). When $Q = 0$, $f_2(0) = 0$. When $Q = 1$,

$$f_2(1) = \max_{0 \le x_2 \le 1} \{g_2(x_2) + f_1(1 - x_2)\}.$$

For values of x_2 ranging from 0 to 1, this gives

$$f_2(1) = \max \begin{cases} g_2(0) + f_1(1) = 0 \\ g_2(1) + f_1(0) = 0 \end{cases}.$$

When $Q = 2$,

$$f_2(2) = \max_{0 \le x_2 \le 2} \{g_2(x_2) + f_1(2 - x_2)\}.$$

Table 16.6. TABULAR SOLUTION FOR A SHIPPING PROBLEM

Q	x_1	$f_1(Q)$	x_2	$f_2(Q)$	x_3	$f_3(Q)$	x_4	$f_4(Q)$
0	0*	0	0	0	0	0	0	0
1	1	0	0	0	0	0	0	0
2	2	50	0	50	0	50	0	50
3	3	50	1	50	1	50	3	80
4	4	100	4*	120	0	120	0	120
5	5	100	5	120	5	170	0	170
6	6	150	4	170	6	170	1	170
7	7	150	5	170	5	220	0	220
8	8	200	8	240	0	240	3	250
9	9	200	9	240	5*	290	0*	290

For values of x_2 ranging from 0 to 2, this gives

$$f_2(2) = \max \begin{cases} g_2(0) + f_1(2) = 50 \\ g_2(1) + f_1(1) = 0 \\ g_2(2) + f_1(0) = 0 \end{cases}.$$

When $Q = 3$,

$$f_2(3) = \max_{0 \le x_2 \le 3} \{g_2(x_2) + f_1(3 - x_2)\}.$$

For values of x_2 ranging from 0 to 3, this gives

$$f_2(3) = \max \begin{cases} g_2(0) + f_1(3) = 50 \\ g_2(1) + f_1(2) = 50 \\ g_2(2) + f_1(1) = 0 \\ g_2(3) + f_1(0) = 0 \end{cases}.$$

This process is continued until $f_2(9)$ is evaluated. The maximum value of $f_2(Q)$ are identified for each value of Q and entered in the second stage of Table 16.4 together with their associated values of x_2.

The third stage is considered next. Using the results of $f_2(Q), f_3(Q)$ may be computed by use of Equation (16.4). As before, when $Q = 0, f_3(Q) = 0$. When $Q = 1$,

$$f_3(1) = \max_{0 \le x_3 \le 1} \{g_3(x_3) + f_2(1 - x_3)\}.$$

For values of x_3 ranging from 0 to 1, this gives

$$f_3(1) = \max \begin{Bmatrix} g_3(0) + f_2(1) = 0 \\ g_3(1) + f_2(0) = 0 \end{Bmatrix}.$$

When $Q = 2$,

$$f_3(2) = \max_{0 \le x_3 \le 2} \{g_3(x_3) + f_2(2 - x_3)\}.$$

For values of x_3 ranging from 0 to 2, this gives

$$f_3(2) = \max \begin{Bmatrix} g_3(0) + f_2(2) = 50 \\ g_3(1) + f_2(1) = 0 \\ g_3(2) + f_2(0) = 0 \end{Bmatrix}.$$

When $Q = 3$,

$$f_3(3) = \max_{0 \le x_3 \le 3} \{g_3(x_3) + f_2(3 - x_3)\}.$$

For values of x_3 ranging from 0 to 3, this gives

$$f_3(3) = \max \begin{Bmatrix} g_3(0) + f_2(3) = 50 \\ g_3(1) + f_2(2) = 50 \\ g_3(2) + f_2(1) = 0 \\ g_3(3) + f_2(0) = 0 \end{Bmatrix}.$$

Again, this process is continued until $f_3(9)$ is evaluated. The maximum values of $f_3(Q)$ are identified for each value of Q and entered in the third stage of Table 16.6 together with their associated values of x_3.

By continuing this pattern for the fourth stage, Table 16.6 is completed. The maximum profit is found in stage 4 to be $290. The number of tons to be allocated to item 4 is found by noting that $x_4 = 0$ at $f_4(Q) = \$290$. Since 9 tons are still available, x_3 will be 5. This leaves 4 tons for item 2 and none for item 1. Thus, the shipment resulting in a maximum profit would contain one each of items 2 and 3.

16.4. A PROCUREMENT PROBLEM

The problems considered in the previous sections were static allocation processes viewed dynamically. This was necessary to make them multistage in nature so that the dynamic programming model would apply. In this section, a procurement problem which spans several time periods and which requires a sequence of decisions will be presented. Also, the objective will be to minimize an effectiveness function, whereas the previous applications involved maximization. The problem requires a decision at the beginning of each period regarding the amount to procure to meet demand. The demand over a planning horizon is specified, the cost of procurement is known, and the cost of holding stock is specified. The objective is to minimize total cost over the planning horizon.

Formulation of the problem. The problem under consideration is based on the following assumptions:

(1) Procurement lead time is zero.

(2) Procurement action can be initiated only at the beginning of a period.

(3) There is no stock on hand at the beginning of the first or at the end of the last period.

(4) Demand occurs at the beginning of the period.

(5) No shortages are allowed.

Demand for the item is to span a five-period planning horizon with a requirement schedule of 10, 20, 30, 30, and 20 units. Procurement quantities must be in increments of 10 units with a maximum quantity of 60 units. Procurement cost is $20 per procurement. Holding cost for the period is based on the stock level at the end of the period and is $0.10 per unit per period. The maximum stock level is 40 units.

Let I_i be the stock level during period i, Q_i be the quantity procured at the beginning of the period, and D_i be the demand at the beginning of the period. Also, let $(PC)_i$ be the procurement cost for the period and $(IIC)_i$ be the holding cost for the period. The objective is to minimize total system cost over the N period planning horizon. This may be expressed as

$$TC - \sum_{i}^{N} [(PC)_i + (IIC)_i]. \tag{16.5}$$

A decision to procure a quantity Q_i at the beginning of the ith period will bring the stock level up to I_i in the period. This requires that

$$I_{i-1} = I_i + D_i - Q_i. \tag{16.6}$$

Since the stock level cannot exceed 40 units, or be less than zero units

$$0 \leq I_{i-1} \leq 40.$$

Substituting Equation (16.6) for I_{i-1} gives

$$0 \leq I_i + D_i - Q_i \leq 40.$$

Solving for Q_i gives

$$I_i + D_i \geq Q_i \geq I_i + D_i - 40. \tag{16.7}$$

The principle of optimality yields the following functional equation which may be used to find a vector of procurement quantities which minimize total

This completes the computation of $f_2(I_2)$. The minimum value of $f_2(I_2)$ is identified for each value of I_2 and entered in the second stage of Table 16.7 together with its associated value of Q_2. The third, fourth, and fifth stages are calculated in the same manner, and the minimum results are used to complete Table 16.7. The required sequence of procurement quantities resulting in a minimum cost can now be found. First, the total system cost for the planning horizon is seen to be $64 from the table. This has an associated Q_5 of 0 units. From Equation (16.6), the value of I_4 is found to be $0 + 20 - 0 = 20$. Reference to Table 16.7 indicates that Q_4 should be 50 units. Again applying Equation (16.6) gives a value for I_3 of $20 + 30 - 50 = 0$. This gives a value for Q_3 of 30 units in Table 16.7. Continuing the foregoing analysis gives a value of $Q_2 = 0$ and a value of $Q_1 = 30$. The vector of procurement quantities previously identified is designated by asterisks in Table 16.7.

16.5. A REPLACEMENT PROBLEM

This section presents another application of dynamic programming that actually spans several time periods. Because of deterioration and the passage of time, the net revenue earned by a piece of equipment becomes less and less. A series of decisions of whether to keep an existing asset or purchase a replacement must be made. From a set of future revenue and cost predictions for the existing machine and subsequent replacements, it is possible to derive a sequence of replacement decisions that maximize total profit. Although this problem does not follow the resource allocation format presented earlier, the functional equation approach is applicable.

Definitions and problem formulation. The following terminology will be used in formulating the machine replacement problem.

(1) Existing machine, M_e: a machine in possession at the time of decision
(2) Replacement machine, M_r: a machine offered as a replacement at the time of decision
(3) Replacement cost, C_{er}: the cost of replacing an existing machine by a new machine calculated as the difference between the cost of purchasing and installing a new machine and the depreciated value of the existing machine
(4) Net revenue, R: the net revenue derived from the use of a machine after making allowances for maintenance and operating costs

In addition to the preceding definitions and notation, it is assumed that a decision is made only at the beginning of the year and that the decision will be either to keep the existing machine, designated K, or to purchase a new machine, designated P.

If the planning horizon consists of N years, the decision sequence is an N-stage process. The state of the process may be described by the existing and the replacement machine at the time of decision. At the beginning of the ith year, the state of the process is described as $(M_e)_i$, $(M_r)_i$. Let the net revenue from machine M_e for the ith year be designated $(R_e)_i$. Similarly, let the net revenue from the replacement machine be designated $(R_r)_i$ for the ith year. If the decision is to keep the existing machine in the ith year, D_i, the gain will be zero. If the decision is to purchase a new machine, the gain will be

$$g(D_i) = \sum_{i}^{N} (R_r)_i - (C_{er})_i - \sum_{i}^{N} (R_e)_i. \tag{16.9}$$

The principle of optimality and Equation (16.9) yields the following functional equation which may be used to make the replacement decision:

$$f_N[(M_e)_N, (M_r)_N] = \max \left\{ \sum_{0}^{N} (R_r)_i - (C_{er})_N - \sum_{}^{N} (R_e)_i \right\} + f_{N-1}[(M_e)_{N-1}, (M_r)_{N-1}]. \tag{16.10}$$

Table 16.8. NET REVENUES FOR MACHINE REPLACEMENT

Year of Decision	Year of Manufacture of Machine				
	1	2	3	4	5
1	10				
2	9	14			
3	8	12	13		
4	7	11	13	14	
5	6	9	12	13	17
Totals	40	46	40	27	17

Equation (16.10) takes the form of the maximum of the expected revenue from the present stage plus the decision from the previous stage. The maximum of the expected revenue from the present stage being derived from the revenue of the replacement minus the cost of replacement minus the expected revenues from the existing machine.

As an example of the application of Equation (16.10), assume that the net revenues to be derived from a machine are a function of the year of replacement and the year of manufacture as given in Table 16.8. Also assume that the replacement cost is a function of the year of decision and the year of manufacture as given in Table 16.9. The objective is to determine a series of decisions, one for each year, that specifies whether the existing machine should be kept or the replacement should be purchased.

Table 16.9. REPLACEMENT COST FOR MACHINE REPLACEMENT

Year of Replacement	Existing Machine Manufactured in Year				
	1	2	3	4	5
1	0				
2	5	0			
3	8	4	0		
4	12	5	3	0	
5	14	8	5	2	0

The solution procedure. The solution to a machine replacement problem formulated in this manner is facilitated by the use of a solution matrix of the form given in Table 16.10. Each entry in each column is the sum of the net revenues given in Table 16.8 from the year of decision to the end of the planning horizon. Thus, if i is the year of decision, then the values in Table 16.10 are the summations given in Equation (16.9). Decisions for each year, given in the last column of Table 16.10, are based on the data of this table and the replacement costs given in Table 16.9.

Table 16.10. SOLUTION MATRIX FOR MACHINE REPLACEMENT

Year of Decision	1	2	3	4	5	D_i
1	40*					P
2	30	46*				P
3	21	32	40*			P
4	13	20	25*	27		K
5	6	9	12*	13	17	K

The solution procedure utilizes Equation (16.10). For each year of decision, the cumulative revenue from the existing machine plus the cost of replacement is subtracted from the cumulative revenue from a new machine manufactured in that year. If the result is less than zero, the decision is to keep the existing machine and the total return is carried over from the previous year. If the result is greater than zero, the decision is to purchase. The value obtained is added to the previous total return giving a new total up to the year considered.

At the beginning of the first year, there is no existing machine. Therefore, the decision is to purchase. The net return from this decision is found from Equation (16.10) as

$$f_1[(M_e)_1, (M_r)_1] = \max \left\{ \sum_{i=1}^{5} (R_r)_i - \underset{0}{(C_{er})_1} - \sum_{i=1}^{5} (R_e)_i \right\} + f_0[(M_e)_0, (M_r)_0]$$

$$= \max \left\{ \underset{0}{40 - 0 - 0} \right\} + 0 = 40.$$

At the beginning of the second year, the existing machine was manufactured in year 1 and the replacement was manufactured in year 2. Equation (16.10) gives

$$f_2[(M_e)_1, (M_r)_2] = \max \left\{ \sum_{i=2}^{5} (R_r)_i - (C_{er})_2 - \sum_{i=2}^{5} (R_e)_i \atop 0 \right\} + f_1[(M_e)_1, (M_r)_1]$$

$$= \max \left\{ 46 - 5 - 30 \atop 0 \right\} + 40 = 51.$$

Since $46 - 5 - 30 > 0$, the decision is to purchase and the net return for the two-stage process is 51.

At the beginning of the third year, the existing machine was manufactured in year 2 and the replacement machine in year 3. Equation (16.10) gives

$$f_3[(M_e)_2, (M_r)_3] = \max \left\{ \sum_{i=3}^{5} (R_r)_i - (C_{er})_3 - \sum_{i=3}^{5} (R_e)_i \atop 0 \right\} + f_2[(M_e)_2, (M_r)_2]$$

$$= \max \left\{ 40 - 4 - 32 \atop 0 \right\} + 51 = 55.$$

Since $40 - 4 - 32 > 0$, the decision is to purchase and the net return for the three-stage process is 55.

At the beginning of the fourth year, the existing machine was manufactured in year 3 and the replacement was manufactured in year 4. Equation (16.10) gives

$$f_4[(M_e)_3, (M_r)_4] = \max \left\{ \sum_{i=4}^{5} (R_r)_i - (C_{er})_4 - \sum_{i=4}^{5} (R_e)_i \atop 0 \right\} + f_3[(M_e)_3, (M_r)_3]$$

$$= \max \left\{ 27 - 3 - 25 \atop 0 \right\} + 55 = 55.$$

Since $27 - 3 - 25 < 0$, the decision is to keep the existing machine. The net return for the four-stage process is 55.

At the beginning of the fifth year, the existing machine was manufactured in year 3 and its replacement was manufactured in year 5. Equation (16.10) gives

$$f_5[(M_e)_4, (M_r)_5] = \max \left\{ \sum_{i=5}^{5} (R_r)_i - (C_{er})_5 - \sum_{i=5}^{5} (R_e)_i \atop 0 \right\} + f_4[(M_e)_4, (M_r)_4]$$

$$= \max \left\{ 17 - 5 - 12 \atop 0 \right\} + 55 = 55.$$

Since $17 - 5 - 12 = 0$, the decision is to either keep or purchase. The net return will be 55 for the five-stage process.

Table 16.10 indicates that the sequence of decisions for this five-year planning horizon should be P, P, P, K, K. The total return to be expected is 55. Only the alternate optimum solution of P, P, P, K, P will yield a return as great as this. All other decision sequences will yield less return for the planning horizon considered.

PROBLEMS

1. Use the concept of dynamic programming to find the maximum path through the given network. What is the maximum path to stage 4?

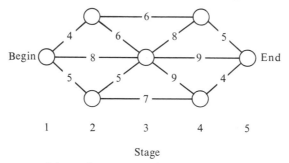

2. Use the concept of dynamic programming to find the minimum path through the given network. What is the minimum path to stage 3?

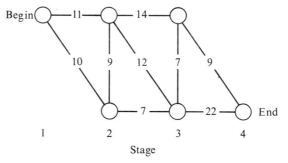

3. Seven units of capital can be invested in three activities with the return from each activity given in the accompanying table. Find the allocation of capital to each activity that will maximize the total return. What will be the total return if the available capital is reduced by one unit?

Q	$g_1(Q)$	$g_2(Q)$	$g_3(Q)$
0	0	0	0
1	2	3	2
2	4	5	3
3	6	7	4
4	7	9	5
5	8	10	5
6	9	11	5
7	9	12	5

4. The profit associated with each of four activities as a function of the man-hours allocated to each is given in the accompanying table. If eight man-hours are available each day, how should the allocation of time be made so that the profit per day is maximized?

H	$g_1(H)$	$g_2(H)$	$g_3(H)$	$g_4(H)$
0	0	0	0	0
1	1	2	3	2
2	3	5	7	5
3	6	8	10	8
4	9	11	12	10
5	12	13	13	10
6	14	15	13	12
7	15	16	13	13
8	16	17	13	14

5. The athletic director of Fun State University has 16 athletic scholarships available to allocate to the minor sports of tennis, golf, and volley ball. During the coming season, Fun State will play 10 games of tennis, 10 of golf, and 10 of volley ball. Being quite concerned with the reputation of his institution as an academic power house, the athletic director wishes to be sure that the total number of games won in these minor sports is maximized. He estimates that the number of games won as a function of the allocation of scholarships will be as given in the accompanying table. How should the available scholarships be allocated so as to maximize the esteem of Fun State in minor sports?

	Tennis	Golf	Volley Ball
Q	$g_1(Q)$	$g_2(Q)$	$g_3(Q)$
0	2	3	1
1	2	3	2
2	3	3	3
3	3	4	3
4	3	4	4
5	4	4	4
6	4	5	4
7	4	5	4
8	4	5	4
9	5	5	4
10	5	6	5
11	5	6	5
12	6	6	6
13	7	7	6
14	8	7	6
15	8	8	6
16	9	8	7

6. Find the number of each of three items to include in a package so that the value of the package will be a maximum. The total weight of the package must not exceed 11 lb.

Item	Weight (lb)	Value
1	3	$6
2	2	4
3	4	7

7. Find the number of each of four items to include in a package so that the cost of the package will be a minimum. The weight of the package is not to exceed 9 oz.

Item	Weight (oz)	Cost
1	2	$0.20
2	3	0.40
3	5	1.00
4	4	0.50

8. A railroad wishes to load a certain group of box cars with a selection of certain bulky items that will result in a maximum revenue per car. The capacity of a box car is 1,900 cu ft and the items to be shipped are described in the accompanying table. How many of each item should be included in each car?

Item	Volume (cu ft)	Revenue
1	100	$13
2	100	12
3	200	27

9. The demand for a certain item in each of the next five periods is 100, 200, 300, 300, and 200 units. The procurement cost is $12 per procurement, and it costs $0.02 per unit per period to hold stock in storage. The procurement quantities must be in increments of 100 units, with a maximum procurement quantity of 600 units. The maximum stock level is 400 units. If the assumptions of Section 16.4 are applicable, what is the maximum profit procurement schedule.

10. Net revenue and replacement costs of four machines for four successive years follow. Find the sequence of decisions regarding replacement that will result in a maximum profit for the four-year period if the assumptions of Section 16.5 are applicable.

	Revenue					Replacement Cost			
	1	2	3	4		1	2	3	4
1	8				1	0			
2	7	10			2	4	0		
3	6	8	12		3	7	3	0	
4	5	6	10	14	4	9	5	2	0

APPENDICES

STATISTICAL TABLES

Table A.1. Cumulative Poisson Probabilities

Cumulative probabilities $\times$ 1,000 for the Poisson distribution are given for μ up to 24. The tabular values were computed from $\sum (\mu^x e^{-\mu}/x!)$.

Table A.2. Random Rectangular Variates

Random variates from the rectangular distribution, $f(x) = 1/10$, are presented. (*These tables reproduced with permission from the RAND Corporation, A Million Random Digits with 100,000 Normal Deviates. Glencoe, Ill.: The Free Press, 1955, pp. 130–31.*)

Table A.3. Cumulative Normal Probabilities

Cumulative probabilities are given from $-\infty$ to $Z = (x - \mu)/\sigma$ for the standard normal distribution. (*Tabular values adapted with permission from E. L. Grant, Statistical Quality Control, 3rd ed. New York: McGraw-Hill Book Company, Inc., 1964.*)

Table A.1. CUMULATIVE POISSON PROBABILITIES × 1,000

μ \ x	0	1	2	3	4	5	6	7	8	9	10	11	12	13	14
0.1	905	995	1,000												
0.2	819	982	999	1,000											
0.3	741	963	996	1,000											
0.4	670	938	992	999	1,000										
0.5	607	910	986	998	1,000										
0.6	549	878	977	997	1,000										
0.7	497	844	966	994	999	1,000									
0.8	449	809	953	991	999	1,000									
0.9	407	772	937	987	998	1,000									
1.0	368	736	920	981	996	999	1,000								
1.1	333	699	900	974	995	999	1,000								
1.2	301	663	879	966	992	998	1,000								
1.3	273	627	857	957	989	998	1,000								
1.4	247	592	833	946	986	997	999	1,000							
1.5	223	558	809	934	981	996	999	1,000							
1.6	202	525	783	921	976	994	999	1,000							
1.7	183	493	757	907	970	992	998	1,000							
1.8	165	463	731	891	964	990	997	999	1,000						
1.9	150	434	704	875	956	987	997	999	1,000						
2.0	135	406	677	857	947	983	995	999	1,000						
2.2	111	355	623	819	928	975	993	998	1,000						
2.4	091	308	570	779	904	964	988	997	999	1,000					
2.6	074	267	518	736	877	951	983	995	999	1,000					

Table A.1. CUMULATIVE POISSON PROBABILITIES $\times$ 1,000 (Continued)

μ \ x	0	1	2	3	4	5	6	7	8	9	10	11	12	13	14
2.8	061	231	469	692	848	935	976	992	998	999	1,000				
3.0	050	199	423	647	815	916	966	988	996	999	1,000				
3.2	041	171	380	603	781	895	955	983	994	998	1,000				
3.4	033	147	340	558	744	871	942	977	992	997	999	1,000			
3.6	027	126	303	515	706	844	927	969	988	996	999	1,000			
3.8	022	107	269	473	668	816	909	960	984	994	998	999	1,000		
4.0	018	092	238	433	629	785	889	949	979	992	997	999	1,000		
4.2	015	078	210	395	590	753	867	936	972	989	996	999	1,000		
4.4	012	066	185	359	551	720	844	921	964	985	994	998	999	1,000	
4.6	010	056	163	326	513	686	818	905	955	980	992	997	999	1,000	
4.8	008	048	143	294	476	651	791	887	944	975	990	996	999	1,000	
5	007	040	125	265	440	616	762	867	932	968	986	995	998	999	1,000
6	002	017	062	151	285	446	606	744	847	916	957	980	991	996	1,000
7	001	007	030	082	173	301	450	599	729	830	901	947	973	987	994
8	000	003	014	042	100	191	313	453	593	717	816	888	936	966	983
9	000	001	006	021	055	116	207	324	456	587	706	803	876	926	959
10	000	000	003	010	029	067	130	220	333	458	583	697	792	864	917
11		000	001	005	015	038	079	143	232	341	460	579	689	781	854
12		000	001	002	008	020	046	090	155	242	347	462	576	682	772
13			000	001	004	011	026	054	100	166	252	353	463	573	675
14				000	002	006	014	032	062	109	176	260	358	464	570
15				000	001	003	008	018	037	070	118	185	268	363	466

Table A.1. CUMULATIVE POISSON PROBABILITIES × 1,000 (*Continued*)

μ \ x	15	16	17	18	19	20	21	22	23	24	25	26	27	28	29
7	998	999	1,000												
8	992	996	998	999	1,000										
9	978	989	995	998	999	1,000									
10	951	973	986	993	997	998	999								
11	907	944	968	982	991	995	998	999	1,000						
12	844	899	937	963	979	988	994	997	999	999	1,000				
13	764	835	890	930	957	975	986	992	996	998	999	1,000			
14	669	756	827	883	923	952	971	983	991	995	997	999	999	1,000	
15	568	664	749	819	875	917	947	967	981	989	994	997	998	999	1,000

μ \ x	0	1	2	3	4	5	6	7	8	9	10	11	12	13	14
16					000	001	004	010	022	043	077	127	193	275	368
17					000	001	002	005	013	026	049	085	135	201	281
18						000	001	003	007	015	030	055	092	143	208
19						000	001	002	004	009	018	035	061	098	150
20							000	001	002	005	011	021	039	066	105
21								000	001	003	006	013	025	043	072
22								000	001	002	004	008	015	028	048
23									000	001	002	004	009	017	031
24									000	001	003	005	011	020

Table A.1. CUMULATIVE POISSON PROBABILITIES × 1,000 (Continued)

x \ μ	15	16	17	18	19	20	21	22	23	24	25	26	27	28	29
16	467	566	659	742	812	868	911	942	963	978	987	993	996	998	999
17	371	468	564	655	736	805	861	905	937	959	975	985	991	995	997
18	287	375	469	562	651	731	799	855	899	932	955	972	983	990	994
19	215	292	378	469	561	647	725	793	849	893	927	951	969	980	988
20	157	221	297	381	470	559	644	721	787	843	888	922	948	966	978
21	111	163	227	302	384	471	558	640	716	782	838	883	917	944	963
22	077	117	169	232	306	387	472	556	637	712	777	832	877	913	940
23	052	082	123	175	238	310	389	472	555	635	708	772	827	873	908
24	034	056	087	128	180	243	314	392	473	554	632	704	768	823	868

x \ μ	30	31	32	33	34	35	36	37	38	39	40	41	42	43	44
16	999	1,000													
17	999	999	1,000												
18	997	998	999	1,000											
19	993	996	998	999	999	1,000									
20	987	992	995	997	998	999	1,000								
21	976	985	991	994	997	998	999	999	1,000						
22	959	973	983	989	994	996	998	999	999	1,000					
23	936	956	971	981	988	993	996	997	999	999	1,000				
24	904	932	953	969	979	987	992	995	997	998	999	999	1,000		

449

Table A.2. RANDOM RECTANGULAR VARIATES

14541	36678	54343	94932	25238	84928	30668	34992	69955	06633
88626	98899	01337	48085	83315	33563	78656	99440	55584	54178
31466	87268	62975	19310	28192	06654	06720	64938	67111	55091
52738	52893	51373	43430	95885	93795	20129	54847	68674	21040
17444	35560	35348	75467	26026	89118	51810	06389	02391	96061
62596	56854	76099	38469	26285	86175	65468	32354	02675	24070
38338	83917	50232	29164	07461	25385	84838	07405	38303	55635
29163	61006	98106	47538	99122	36242	90365	15581	89597	03327
59049	95306	31227	75288	10122	92687	99971	97105	37597	91673
67447	52922	58657	67601	96148	97263	39110	95111	04682	64873
57082	55108	26992	19196	08044	57300	75095	84330	92314	11370
00179	04358	95645	91751	56618	73782	38575	17401	38686	98435
65420	87257	44374	54312	94692	81776	24422	99198	51432	63943
52450	75445	40002	69727	29775	32572	79980	67902	97260	21050
82767	26273	02192	88536	08191	91750	46993	02245	38659	28026
17066	64286	35972	32550	82167	53177	32396	34014	20993	03031
86168	32643	23668	92038	03096	51029	09693	45454	89854	70103
33632	69631	70537	06464	83543	48297	67693	63137	62675	56572
77915	56481	43065	24231	43011	40505	90386	13870	84603	73101
90000	92887	92668	93521	44072	01785	27003	01851	40232	25842
55809	70237	10368	58664	39521	11137	20461	53081	07150	11832
50948	64026	03350	03153	75913	72651	28651	94299	67706	92507
27138	59012	27872	90522	69791	85482	80337	12252	83388	48909
03534	58643	75913	63557	25527	47131	72295	55801	44847	48019
48895	34733	58057	00195	79496	93453	07813	66038	55245	43168
57585	23710	77321	70662	82884	80132	42281	17032	96737	93284
95913	24669	42050	92757	68677	75567	99777	49246	93049	79863
12981	37145	95773	92475	43700	85253	33214	87656	13295	09721
62349	64163	57369	65773	86217	00135	33762	72398	16343	02263
68193	37564	56257	50030	53951	84887	34590	22038	40629	29562
56203	82226	83294	60361	29924	09353	87021	08149	11167	81744
31945	23224	08211	02562	20299	85836	94714	50278	99818	62489
68726	52274	59535	80873	35423	05166	06911	25916	90728	20431
79557	25747	55585	93461	44360	18359	20493	54287	43693	88568
05764	29803	01819	51972	91641	03524	18381	65427	11394	37447
30187	66931	01972	48438	90716	21847	35114	91839	26913	68893
30858	43646	96984	80412	91973	81339	05548	49812	40775	14263
85117	38268	18921	29519	33359	80642	95362	22133	40322	37826
59422	12752	56798	31954	19859	32451	04433	62116	14899	38825
73479	91833	91122	45524	73871	77931	67822	95602	23325	37718
83648	66882	15327	89748	76685	76282	98624	71547	49089	33105
19454	91265	09051	94410	06418	34484	37929	61070	62346	79970
49327	97807	61390	08005	71795	49290	52285	82119	59348	55986
54482	51025	12382	35719	66721	84890	38106	44136	95164	92935
30487	19459	25693	09427	10967	36164	33893	07087	16141	12734
42998	68627	66295	59360	44041	76909	56321	12978	31304	97444
03668	61096	26292	79688	05625	52198	74844	69815	76591	35398
45074	91457	28311	56499	60403	13658	81838	54729	12365	24082
58444	99255	14960	02275	37925	03852	81235	91628	72136	53070
82912	91185	89612	02362	93360	20158	24796	38284	55328	96041

44553	29642	20317	69470	57789	27631	68040	73201	51302	66497
01914	36106	71351	69176	53353	57353	42430	68050	47862	61922
00768	37958	69915	17709	31629	49587	07136	42959	56207	03625
29742	67676	62608	54215	97167	07008	77130	15806	53081	14297
07721	20143	56131	56112	23451	48773	38121	74419	11696	42614
99158	07133	04325	43936	83619	77182	55459	28808	38034	01054
97168	13859	78155	55361	04871	78433	58538	78437	14058	79510
07508	63835	83056	74942	70117	91928	10383	93793	31015	60839
68400	66460	67212	28690	66913	90798	71714	07698	31581	31086
88512	62908	65455	64015	00821	23970	58118	93174	02201	16771
94549	31145	62897	91582	94064	14687	47570	83714	45928	32685
02307	86181	44897	60884	68072	77693	83413	61680	55872	12111
28922	89390	66771	39185	04266	55216	91537	36500	48154	04517
73898	85742	97914	74170	10383	16366	37404	73282	20524	85004
66220	81596	18533	84825	43509	16009	00830	13177	54961	31140
64452	91627	21897	31830	62051	00760	43702	22305	79009	15065
26748	19441	87908	06086	62879	99865	50739	98540	54002	98337
61328	52330	17850	53204	29955	48425	84694	11280	70661	27303
89134	85791	73207	93578	62563	37205	97667	61453	01067	31982
91365	23327	81658	56441	01480	09677	86053	11505	30898	82143
54576	02572	60501	98257	40475	81401	31624	27951	60172	21382
39870	60476	02934	39857	06430	59325	84345	62302	98616	13452
82288	29758	35692	21268	35101	77554	35201	22795	84532	29927
57404	93848	87288	30246	34990	50575	49485	60474	17377	46550
22043	17104	49653	79082	45099	24889	04829	49097	58065	23492
61981	00340	43594	22386	41782	94104	08867	68590	61716	36120
96056	16227	74598	28155	23304	66923	07918	15303	44988	79076
64013	74715	31525	62676	75435	93055	37086	52737	89455	83016
59515	37354	55422	79471	23150	79170	74043	49340	61320	50390
38534	33169	40448	21683	82153	23411	53057	26069	86906	49708
41422	50502	40570	59748	59499	70322	63416	71408	06429	70123
38633	80107	10241	30880	13914	09228	68929	06438	17749	81149
48214	75994	31689	25257	28641	14854	72571	78189	35508	26381
54799	37862	06714	55885	07481	16966	04797	57846	69080	49631
25848	27142	63477	33416	60961	19781	65457	23981	90348	24499
27576	47298	47163	69614	29372	24859	62090	81667	50635	08295
52970	93916	81350	81057	16962	56039	27739	59574	79617	45698
69516	87573	13313	69388	32020	66294	99126	50474	04258	03084
94504	41733	55936	77595	55959	90727	61367	83645	80997	62103
67935	14568	27992	09784	81917	79303	08616	83509	64932	34764
63345	09579	40232	51061	09455	36491	04810	06040	78959	41435
87119	21605	86917	97715	91250	79587	80967	39872	52512	78444
02612	97319	10487	68923	58607	38261	67119	36351	48521	69965
69860	16526	41420	01514	46902	03399	12286	52467	80387	10561
27669	67730	53932	38578	25746	00025	98917	18790	51091	24920
59705	91472	01302	33123	35274	88433	55491	27609	02824	05245
36508	74042	44014	36243	12724	06092	23742	90436	33419	12301
13612	24554	73326	61445	77198	43360	62006	31038	54756	88137
82893	11961	19656	71181	63201	44946	14169	72755	47883	24119
97914	61228	42903	71187	54964	14945	20809	33937	13257	66387

Table A.3. CUMULATIVE NORMAL PROBABILITIES

Z	0.09	0.08	0.07	0.06	0.05	0.04	0.03	0.02	0.01	0.00
−3.5	0.00017	0.00017	0.00018	0.00019	0.00019	0.00020	0.00021	0.00022	0.00022	0.00023
−3.4	0.00024	0.00025	0.00026	0.00027	0.00028	0.00029	0.00030	0.00031	0.00033	0.00034
−3.3	0.00035	0.00036	0.00038	0.00039	0.00040	0.00042	0.00043	0.00045	0.00047	0.00048
−3.2	0.00050	0.00052	0.00054	0.00056	0.00058	0.00060	0.00062	0.00064	0.00066	0.00069
−3.1	0.00071	0.00074	0.00076	0.00079	0.00082	0.00085	0.00087	0.00090	0.00094	0.00097
−3.0	0.00100	0.00104	0.00107	0.00111	0.00114	0.00118	0.00122	0.00126	0.00131	0.00135
−2.9	0.0014	0.0014	0.0015	0.0015	0.0016	0.0016	0.0017	0.0017	0.0018	0.0019
−2.8	0.0019	0.0020	0.0021	0.0021	0.0022	0.0023	0.0023	0.0024	0.0025	0.0026
−2.7	0.0026	0.0027	0.0028	0.0029	0.0030	0.0031	0.0032	0.0033	0.0034	0.0035
−2.6	0.0036	0.0037	0.0038	0.0039	0.0040	0.0041	0.0043	0.0044	0.0045	0.0047
−2.5	0.0048	0.0049	0.0051	0.0052	0.0054	0.0055	0.0057	0.0059	0.0060	0.0062
−2.4	0.0064	0.0066	0.0068	0.0069	0.0071	0.0073	0.0075	0.0078	0.0080	0.0082
−2.3	0.0084	0.0087	0.0089	0.0091	0.0094	0.0096	0.0099	0.0102	0.0104	0.0107
−2.2	0.0110	0.0113	0.0116	0.0119	0.0122	0.0125	0.0129	0.0132	0.0136	0.0139
−2.1	0.0143	0.0146	0.0150	0.0154	0.0158	0.0162	0.0166	0.0170	0.0174	0.0179
−2.0	0.0183	0.0188	0.0192	0.0197	0.0202	0.0207	0.0212	0.0217	0.0222	0.0228
−1.9	0.0233	0.0239	0.0244	0.0250	0.0256	0.0262	0.0268	0.0274	0.0281	0.0287
−1.8	0.0294	0.0301	0.0307	0.0314	0.0322	0.0329	0.0336	0.0344	0.0351	0.0359
−1.7	0.0367	0.0375	0.0384	0.0392	0.0401	0.0409	0.0418	0.0427	0.0436	0.0446
−1.6	0.0455	0.0465	0.0475	0.0485	0.0495	0.0505	0.0516	0.0526	0.0537	0.0548
−1.5	0.0559	0.0571	0.0582	0.0594	0.0606	0.0618	0.0630	0.0643	0.0655	0.0668
−1.4	0.0681	0.0694	0.0708	0.0721	0.0735	0.0749	0.0764	0.0778	0.0793	0.0808
−1.3	0.0823	0.0838	0.0853	0.0869	0.0885	0.0901	0.0918	0.0934	0.0951	0.0968
−1.2	0.0985	0.1003	0.1020	0.1038	0.1057	0.1075	0.1093	0.1112	0.1131	0.1151
−1.1	0.1170	0.1190	0.1210	0.1230	0.1251	0.1271	0.1292	0.1314	0.1335	0.1357
−1.0	0.1379	0.1401	0.1423	0.1446	0.1469	0.1492	0.1515	0.1539	0.1562	0.1587
−0.9	0.1611	0.1635	0.1660	0.1685	0.1711	0.1736	0.1762	0.1788	0.1814	0.1841
−0.8	0.1867	0.1894	0.1922	0.1949	0.1977	0.2005	0.2033	0.2061	0.2090	0.2119
−0.7	0.2148	0.2177	0.2207	0.2236	0.2266	0.2297	0.2327	0.2358	0.2389	0.2420
−0.6	0.2451	0.2483	0.2514	0.2546	0.2578	0.2611	0.2643	0.2676	0.2709	0.2743
−0.5	0.2776	0.2810	0.2843	0.2877	0.2912	0.2946	0.2981	0.3015	0.3050	0.3085
−0.4	0.3121	0.3156	0.3192	0.3228	0.3264	0.3300	0.3336	0.3372	0.3409	0.3446
−0.3	0.3483	0.3520	0.3557	0.3594	0.3632	0.3669	0.3707	0.3745	0.3783	0.3821
−0.2	0.3859	0.3897	0.3936	0.3974	0.4013	0.4052	0.4090	0.4129	0.4168	0.4207
−0.1	0.4247	0.4286	0.4325	0.4364	0.4404	0.4443	0.4483	0.4522	0.4562	0.4602
−0.0	0.4641	0.4681	0.4721	0.4761	0.4801	0.4840	0.4880	0.4920	0.4960	0.5000

Table A.3. CUMULATIVE NORMAL PROBABILITIES (*Continued*)

Z	0.00	0.01	0.02	0.03	0.04	0.05	0.06	0.07	0.08	0.09
+0.0	0.5000	0.5040	0.5080	0.5120	0.5160	0.5199	0.5239	0.5279	0.5319	0.5359
+0.1	0.5398	0.5438	0.5478	0.5517	0.5557	0.5596	0.5636	0.5675	0.5714	0.5753
+0.2	0.5793	0.5832	0.5871	0.5910	0.5948	0.5987	0.6026	0.6064	0.6103	0.6141
+0.3	0.6179	0.6217	0.6255	0.6293	0.6331	0.6368	0.6406	0.6443	0.6480	0.6517
+0.4	0.6554	0.6591	0.6628	0.6664	0.6700	0.6736	0.6772	0.6808	0.6844	0.6879
+0.5	0.6915	0.6950	0.6985	0.7019	0.7054	0.7088	0.7123	0.7157	0.7190	0.7224
+0.6	0.7257	0.7291	0.7324	0.7357	0.7389	0.7422	0.7454	0.7486	0.7517	0.7549
+0.7	0.7580	0.7611	0.7642	0.7673	0.7704	0.7734	0.7764	0.7794	0.7823	0.7852
+0.8	0.7881	0.7910	0.7939	0.7967	0.7995	0.8023	0.8051	0.8079	0.8106	0.8133
+0.9	0.8159	0.8186	0.8212	0.8238	0.8264	0.8289	0.8315	0.8340	0.8365	0.8389
+1.0	0.8413	0.8438	0.8461	0.8485	0.8508	0.8531	0.8554	0.8577	0.8599	0.8621
+1.1	0.8643	0.8665	0.8686	0.8708	0.8729	0.8749	0.8770	0.8790	0.8810	0.8830
+1.2	0.8849	0.8869	0.8888	0.8907	0.8925	0.8944	0.8962	0.8980	0.8997	0.9015
+1.3	0.9032	0.9049	0.9066	0.9082	0.9099	0.9115	0.9131	0.9147	0.9162	0.9177
+1.4	0.9192	0.9207	0.9222	0.9236	0.9251	0.9265	0.9279	0.9292	0.9306	0.9319
+1.5	0.9332	0.9345	0.9357	0.9370	0.9382	0.9394	0.9406	0.9418	0.9429	0.9441
+1.6	0.9452	0.9463	0.9474	0.9484	0.9495	0.9505	0.9515	0.9525	0.9535	0.9545
+1.7	0.9554	0.9564	0.9573	0.9582	0.9591	0.9599	0.9608	0.9616	0.9625	0.9633
+1.8	0.9641	0.9649	0.9656	0.9664	0.9671	0.9678	0.9686	0.9693	0.9699	0.9706
+1.9	0.9713	0.9719	0.9726	0.9732	0.9738	0.9744	0.9750	0.9756	0.9761	0.9767
+2.0	0.9773	0.9778	0.9783	0.9788	0.9793	0.9798	0.9803	0.9808	0.9812	0.9817
+2.1	0.9821	0.9826	0.9830	0.9834	0.9838	0.9842	0.9846	0.9850	0.9854	0.9857
+2.2	0.9861	0.9864	0.9868	0.9871	0.9875	0.9878	0.9881	0.9884	0.9887	0.9890
+2.3	0.9893	0.9896	0.9898	0.9901	0.9904	0.9906	0.9909	0.9911	0.9913	0.9916
+2.4	0.9918	0.9920	0.9922	0.9925	0.9927	0.9929	0.9931	0.9932	0.9934	0.9936
+2.5	0.9938	0.9940	0.9941	0.9943	0.9945	0.9946	0.9948	0.9949	0.9951	0.9952
+2.6	0.9953	0.9955	0.9956	0.9957	0.9959	0.9960	0.9961	0.9962	0.9963	0.9964
+2.7	0.9965	0.9966	0.9967	0.9968	0.9969	0.9970	0.9971	0.9972	0.9973	0.9974
+2.8	0.9974	0.9975	0.9976	0.9977	0.9977	0.9978	0.9979	0.9979	0.9980	0.9981
+2.9	0.9981	0.9982	0.9983	0.9983	0.9984	0.9984	0.9985	0.9985	0.9986	0.9986
+3.0	0.99865	0.99869	0.99874	0.99878	0.99882	0.99886	0.99889	0.99893	0.99896	0.99900
+3.1	0.99903	0.99906	0.99910	0.99913	0.99915	0.99918	0.99921	0.99924	0.99926	0.99929
+3.2	0.99931	0.99934	0.99936	0.99938	0.99940	0.99942	0.99944	0.99946	0.99948	0.99950
+3.3	0.99952	0.99953	0.99955	0.99957	0.99958	0.99960	0.99961	0.99962	0.99964	0.99965
+3.4	0.99966	0.99967	0.99969	0.99970	0.99971	0.99972	0.99973	0.99974	0.99975	0.99976
+3.5	0.99977	0.99978	0.99978	0.99979	0.99980	0.99981	0.99981	0.99982	0.99983	0.99983

PROGRESS FUNCTION TABLES

Table B.1. Manufacturing Progress Factors—Unit Values

Unit values computed from Kx^n are given for slope parameters of 70, 75, 80, 85, and 90 per cent for selected values of x up to 500.

Table B.2. Manufacturing Progress Factors—Cumulative Values

Cumulative values computed as $\sum Kx^n$ are given for slope parameters of 70, 75, 80, 85, and 90 per cent for selected values of x up to 500.

Table B.1. MANUFACTURING PROGRESS FACTORS—UNIT VALUES

Unit Number	Slope Parameter, ϕ				
	0.70	0.75	0.80	0.85	0.90
1	1.0000	1.0000	1.0000	1.0000	1.0000
2	0.7000	0.7500	0.8000	0.8500	0.9000
3	0.5682	0.6338	0.7021	0.7729	0.8462
4	0.4900	0.5625	0.6400	0.7225	0.8100
5	0.4368	0.5127	0.5956	0.6857	0.7830
6	0.3977	0.4754	0.5617	0.6570	0.7616
7	0.3674	0.4459	0.5345	0.6337	0.7439
8	0.3430	0.4219	0.5120	0.6141	0.7290
9	0.3228	0.4017	0.4929	0.5974	0.7161
10	0.3058	0.3846	0.4765	0.5828	0.7047
11	0.2912	0.3696	0.4621	0.5699	0.6945
12	0.2784	0.3565	0.4493	0.5584	0.6854
13	0.2672	0.3449	0.4379	0.5481	0.6771
14	0.2572	0.3344	0.4276	0.5386	0.6695
15	0.2482	0.3250	0.4182	0.5300	0.6626
16	0.2401	0.3164	0.4096	0.5220	0.6561
17	0.2327	0.3085	0.4017	0.5146	0.6501
18	0.2260	0.3013	0.3944	0.5078	0.6444
19	0.2198	0.2946	0.3876	0.5014	0.6392
20	0.2141	0.2884	0.3812	0.4954	0.6342
21	0.2088	0.2826	0.3753	0.4898	0.6295
22	0.2038	0.2772	0.3697	0.4845	0.6251
23	0.1992	0.2722	0.3644	0.4794	0.6209
24	0.1949	0.2674	0.3595	0.4747	0.6169
25	0.1908	0.2629	0.3548	0.4702	0.6131
26	0.1870	0.2587	0.3503	0.4658	0.6094
27	0.1834	0.2546	0.3461	0.4617	0.6059
28	0.1800	0.2508	0.3421	0.4578	0.6026
29	0.1768	0.2472	0.3382	0.4541	0.5994
30	0.1738	0.2437	0.3346	0.4505	0.5963
31	0.1708	0.2405	0.3310	0.4470	0.5933
32	0.1681	0.2373	0.3277	0.4437	0.5905
33	0.1654	0.2343	0.3244	0.4405	0.5877
34	0.1629	0.2314	0.3213	0.4375	0.5851
35	0.1605	0.2286	0.3184	0.4345	0.5825
36	0.1582	0.2260	0.3155	0.4316	0.5800
37	0.1560	0.2234	0.3127	0.4289	0.5776
38	0.1539	0.2210	0.3100	0.4262	0.5753
39	0.1518	0.2186	0.3075	0.4236	0.5730
40	0.1498	0.2163	0.3050	0.4211	0.5708
41	0.1480	0.2141	0.3026	0.4187	0.5686
42	0.1461	0.2120	0.3002	0.4163	0.5666
43	0.1444	0.2099	0.2979	0.4140	0.5645
44	0.1427	0.2079	0.2958	0.4118	0.5626
45	0.1410	0.2060	0.2936	0.4096	0.5607

Table B.1. MANUFACTURING PROGRESS FACTORS—UNIT VALUES (*Continued*)

Unit Number	Slope Parameter, ϕ				
	0.70	0.75	0.80	0.85	0.90
46	0.1394	0.2041	0.2915	0.4075	0.5588
47	0.1379	0.2023	0.2895	0.4055	0.5570
48	0.1364	0.2005	0.2876	0.4035	0.5552
49	0.1350	0.1988	0.2857	0.4015	0.5534
50	0.1336	0.1972	0.2838	0.3996	0.5517
55	0.1272	0.1895	0.2753	0.3908	0.5438
60	0.1216	0.1828	0.2676	0.3829	0.5367
65	0.1167	0.1768	0.2608	0.3758	0.5302
70	0.1124	0.1715	0.2547	0.3693	0.5242
75	0.1084	0.1666	0.2491	0.3634	0.5188
80	0.1049	0.1622	0.2440	0.3579	0.5137
85	0.1017	0.1582	0.2393	0.3529	0.5090
90	0.0987	0.1545	0.2349	0.3482	0.5046
95	0.0960	0.1511	0.2308	0.3438	0.5005
100	0.0935	0.1479	0.2271	0.3397	0.4966
105	0.0912	0.1449	0.2235	0.3358	0.4929
110	0.0890	0.1421	0.2202	0.3322	0.4894
115	0.0870	0.1395	0.2171	0.3287	0.4861
120	0.0851	0.1371	0.2141	0.3255	0.4830
125	0.0834	0.1348	0.2113	0.3224	0.4800
130	0.0817	0.1326	0.2087	0.3194	0.4772
135	0.0801	0.1306	0.2062	0.3166	0.4744
140	0.0787	0.1286	0.2038	0.3139	0.4718
145	0.0772	0.1267	0.2015	0.3113	0.4693
150	0.0759	0.1250	0.1993	0.3089	0.4669
155	0.0746	0.1233	0.1972	0.3065	0.4646
160	0.0734	0.1217	0.1952	0.3042	0.4623
165	0.0723	0.1201	0.1933	0.3021	0.4602
170	0.0712	0.1184	0.1914	0.3000	0.4581
175	0.0701	0.1172	0.1896	0.2979	0.4561
180	0.0691	0.1159	0.1879	0.2960	0.4541
185	0.0681	0.1146	0.1863	0.2941	0.4522
190	0.0672	0.1133	0.1847	0.2922	0.4504
195	0.0663	0.1121	0.1831	0.2905	0.4486
200	0.0655	0.1109	0.1817	0.2887	0.4469
225	0.0616	0.1056	0.1749	0.2809	0.4390
250	0.0584	0.1011	0.1691	0.2740	0.4320
275	0.0556	0.0972	0.1640	0.2680	0.4258
300	0.0531	0.0937	0.1594	0.2626	0.4202
325	0.0510	0.0907	0.1554	0.2577	0.4151
350	0.0491	0.0879	0.1517	0.2532	0.4105
375	0.0474	0.0854	0.1484	0.2492	0.4062
400	0.0458	0.0832	0.1453	0.2454	0.4022
450	0.0431	0.0792	0.1399	0.2387	0.3951
500	0.0409	0.0758	0.1353	0.2329	0.3888

Table C.1. 2% INTEREST FACTORS FOR ANNUAL COMPOUNDING

	Single Payment		Equal-Payment Series			
n	Compound-amount factor	Present-worth factor	Compound-amount factor	Sinking-fund factor	Present-worth factor	Capital-recovery factor
	SP *i-n* ( )	PS *i-n* ( )	SR *i-n* ( )	RS *i-n* ( )	PR *i-n* ( )	RP *i-n* ( )
1	1.020	0.98039	1.000	1.00000	0.98039	1.02000
2	1.040	0.96117	2.020	0.49505	1.94156	0.51505
3	1.061	0.94232	3.060	0.32675	2.88388	0.34675
4	1.082	0.92385	4.122	0.24262	3.80773	0.26262
5	1.104	0.90573	5.204	0.19216	4.71346	0.21216
6	1.126	0.88797	6.308	0.15853	5.60143	0.17853
7	1.149	0.87056	7.434	0.13451	6.47199	0.15451
8	1.172	0.85349	8.583	0.11651	7.32548	0.13651
9	1.195	0.83676	9.755	0.10252	8.16224	0.12252
10	1.219	0.82035	10.950	0.09133	8.98258	0.11133
11	1.243	0.80426	12.169	0.08218	9.78685	0.10218
12	1.268	0.78849	13.412	0.07456	10.57534	0.09456
13	1.294	0.77303	14.680	0.06812	11.34837	0.08812
14	1.319	0.75788	15.974	0.06260	12.10625	0.08260
15	1.346	0.74301	17.293	0.05783	12.84926	0.07783
16	1.373	0.72845	18.639	0.05365	13.57771	0.07365
17	1.400	0.71416	20.012	0.04997	14.29187	0.06997
18	1.428	0.70016	21.412	0.04670	14.99203	0.06670
19	1.457	0.68643	22.841	0.04378	15.67846	0.06378
20	1.486	0.67297	24.297	0.04116	16.35143	0.06116
21	1.516	0.65978	25.783	0.03878	17.01121	0.05878
22	1.546	0.64684	27.299	0.03663	17.65805	0.05663
23	1.577	0.63416	28.845	0.03467	18.29220	0.05467
24	1.608	0.62172	30.422	0.03287	18.91392	0.05287
25	1.641	0.60953	32.030	0.03122	19.52346	0.05122
26	1.673	0.59758	33.671	0.02970	20.12104	0.04970
27	1.707	0.58586	35.344	0.02829	20.70690	0.04829
28	1.741	0.57437	37.051	0.02699	21.28127	0.04699
29	1.776	0.56311	38.792	0.02578	21.84438	0.04578
30	1.811	0.55207	40.568	0.02465	22.39646	0.04465
35	2.000	0.50003	49.994	0.02000	24.99862	0.04000
40	2.208	0.45289	60.402	0.01656	27.35548	0.03656
45	2.438	0.41020	71.893	0.01391	29.49016	0.03391
50	2.692	0.37153	84.579	0.01182	31.42361	0.03182
55	2.972	0.33650	98.587	0.01014	33.17479	0.03014
60	3.281	0.30478	114.052	0.00877	34.76088	0.02877
70	4.000	0.25003	149.978	0.00667	37.49862	0.02667
80	4.875	0.20511	193.772	0.00516	39.74451	0.02516
90	5.943	0.16826	247.157	0.00405	41.58693	0.02405
100	7.245	0.13803	312.232	0.00320	43.09835	0.02320

Table C.2. 3% INTEREST FACTORS FOR ANNUAL COMPOUNDING

	Single Payment		Equal-Payment Series			
n	Compound-amount factor	Present-worth factor	Compound-amount factor	Sinking-fund factor	Present-worth factor	Capital-recovery factor
	SP i-n ( )	PS i-n ( )	SR i-n ( )	RS i-n ( )	PR i-n ( )	RP i-n ( )
1	1.030	0.97087	1.000	1.00000	0.97087	1.03000
2	1.061	0.94260	2.030	0.49261	1.91347	0.52261
3	1.093	0.91514	3.091	0.32353	2.82861	0.35353
4	1.126	0.88849	4.184	0.23903	3.71710	0.26903
5	1.159	0.86261	5.309	0.18835	4.57971	0.21835
6	1.194	0.83748	6.468	0.15460	5.41719	0.18460
7	1.230	0.81309	7.662	0.13051	6.23028	0.16051
8	1.267	0.78941	8.892	0.11246	7.01969	0.14246
9	1.305	0.76642	10.159	0.09843	7.78611	0.12843
10	1.344	0.74409	11.464	0.08723	8.53020	0.11723
11	1.384	0.72242	12.808	0.07808	9.25263	0.10808
12	1.426	0.70138	14.192	0.07046	9.95401	0.10046
13	1.469	0.68095	15.618	0.06403	10.63496	0.09403
14	1.513	0.66112	17.086	0.05853	11.29608	0.08853
15	1.558	0.64186	18.599	0.05377	11.93794	0.08377
16	1.605	0.62317	20.157	0.04961	12.56111	0.07961
17	1.653	0.60502	21.762	0.04595	13.16612	0.07595
18	1.702	0.58739	23.414	0.04271	13.75352	0.07271
19	1.754	0.57029	25.117	0.03981	14.32380	0.06981
20	1.806	0.55368	26.870	0.03722	14.87748	0.06722
21	1.860	0.53755	28.677	0.03487	15.41503	0.06487
22	1.916	0.52189	30.537	0.03275	15.93692	0.06275
23	1.974	0.50669	32.453	0.03081	16.44361	0.06081
24	2.033	0.49193	34.426	0.02905	16.93555	0.05905
25	2.094	0.47761	36.459	0.02743	17.41315	0.05743
26	2.157	0.46369	38.553	0.02594	17.87685	0.05594
27	2.221	0.45019	40.710	0.02456	18.32704	0.05456
28	2.288	0.43708	42.931	0.02329	18.76411	0.05329
29	2.357	0.42435	45.219	0.02211	19.18846	0.05211
30	2.427	0.41199	47.575	0.02102	19.60045	0.05102
35	2.814	0.35538	60.462	0.01654	21.48722	0.04654
40	3.262	0.30656	75.401	0.01326	23.11478	0.04326
45	3.782	0.26444	92.720	0.01079	24.51872	0.04079
50	4.384	0.22811	112.797	0.00887	25.72977	0.03887
55	5.082	0.19677	136.072	0.00735	26.77443	0.03735
60	5.892	0.16973	163.054	0.00613	27.67557	0.03613
70	7.918	0.12630	230.594	0.00434	29.12342	0.03434
80	10.641	0.09398	321.363	0.00311	30.20077	0.03311
90	14.300	0.06993	443.349	0.00226	31.00241	0.03226
100	19.219	0.05203	607.288	0.00165	31.59891	0.03165

Table C.3. 4% INTEREST FACTORS FOR ANNUAL COMPOUNDING

	Single Payment		Equal-Payment Series			
n	Compound-amount factor	Present-worth factor	Compound-amount factor	Sinking-fund factor	Present-worth factor	Capital-recovery factor
	SP i-n ( )	PS i-n ( )	SR i-n ( )	RS i-n ( )	PR i-n ( )	RP i-n ( )
1	1.040	0.96154	1.000	1.00000	0.96154	1.04000
2	1.082	0.92456	2.040	0.49020	1.88609	0.53020
3	1.125	0.88900	3.122	0.32035	2.77509	0.36035
4	1.170	0.85480	4.246	0.23549	3.62990	0.27549
5	1.217	0.82193	5.416	0.18463	4.45182	0.22463
6	1.265	0.79031	6.633	0.15076	5.24214	0.19076
7	1.316	0.75992	7.898	0.12661	6.00205	0.16661
8	1.369	0.73069	9.214	0.10853	6.73275	0.14853
9	1.423	0.70259	10.583	0.09449	7.43533	0.13449
10	1.480	0.67556	12.006	0.08329	8.11090	0.12329
11	1.539	0.64958	13.486	0.07415	8.76048	0.11415
12	1.601	0.62460	15.026	0.06655	9.38507	0.10655
13	1.665	0.60057	16.627	0.06014	9.98565	0.10014
14	1.732	0.57748	18.292	0.05467	10.56312	0.09467
15	1.801	0.55526	20.024	0.04994	11.11839	0.08994
16	1.873	0.53391	21.825	0.04582	11.65230	0.08582
17	1.948	0.51337	23.698	0.04220	12.16567	0.08220
18	2.026	0.49363	25.645	0.03899	12.65930	0.07899
19	2.107	0.47464	27.671	0.03614	13.13394	0.07614
20	2.191	0.45639	29.778	0.03358	13.59033	0.07358
21	2.279	0.43883	31.969	0.03128	14.02916	0.07128
22	2.370	0.42196	34.248	0.02920	14.45112	0.06920
23	2.465	0.40573	36.618	0.02731	14.85684	0.06731
24	2.563	0.39012	39.083	0.02559	15.24696	0.06559
25	2.666	0.37512	41.646	0.02401	15.62208	0.06401
26	2.772	0.36069	44.312	0.02257	15.98277	0.06257
27	2.883	0.34682	47.084	0.02124	16.32959	0.06124
28	2.999	0.33348	49.968	0.02001	16.66306	0.06001
29	3.119	0.32065	52.966	0.01888	16.98372	0.05888
30	3.243	0.30832	56.085	0.01783	17.29203	0.05783
35	3.946	0.25342	73.652	0.01358	18.66461	0.05358
40	4.801	0.20829	95.026	0.01052	19.79277	0.05052
45	5.841	0.17120	121.029	0.00826	20.72004	0.04826
50	7.107	0.14071	152.667	0.00655	21.48218	0.04655
55	8.646	0.11566	191.159	0.00523	22.10861	0.04523
60	10.520	0.09506	237.991	0.00420	22.62349	0.04420
70	15.572	0.06422	364.291	0.00275	23.39452	0.04275
80	23.050	0.04338	551.245	0.00181	23.91539	0.04181
90	34.119	0.02931	827.984	0.00121	24.26728	0.04121
100	50.505	0.01980	1237.624	0.00081	24.50500	0.04081

Table C.4. 5% INTEREST FACTORS FOR ANNUAL COMPOUNDING

	Single Payment		Equal-Payment Series			
n	*Compound-amount factor*	*Present-worth factor*	*Compound-amount factor*	*Sinking-fund factor*	*Present-worth factor*	*Capital-recovery factor*
	SP *i-n* ( )	PS *i-n* ( )	SR *i-n* ( )	RS *i-n* ( )	PR *i-n* ( )	RP *i-n* ( )
1	1.050	0.95238	1.000	1.00000	0.95238	1.05000
2	1.103	0.90703	2.050	0.48780	1.85941	0.53780
3	1.158	0.86384	3.153	0.31721	2.72325	0.36721
4	1.216	0.82270	4.310	0.23201	3.54595	0.28201
5	1.276	0.78353	5.526	0.18097	4.32948	0.23097
6	1.340	0.74622	6.802	0.14702	5.07569	0.19702
7	1.407	0.71068	8.142	0.12282	5.78637	0.17282
8	1.477	0.67684	9.549	0.10742	6.46321	0.15472
9	1.551	0.64461	11.027	0.09069	7.10782	0.14069
10	1.629	0.61391	12.578	0.07950	7.72174	0.12950
11	1.710	0.58468	14.207	0.07039	8.30641	0.12039
12	1.796	0.55684	15.917	0.06283	8.86325	0.11283
13	1.886	0.53032	17.713	0.05646	9.39357	0.10646
14	1.980	0.50507	19.599	0.05102	9.89864	0.10102
15	2.079	0.48102	21.579	0.04634	10.37966	0.09634
16	2.183	0.45811	23.657	0.04227	10.83777	0.09227
17	2.292	0.43630	25.840	0.03870	11.27407	0.08870
18	2.407	0.41552	28.132	0.03555	11.68959	0.08555
19	2.527	0.39573	30.539	0.03275	12.08532	0.08275
20	2.653	0.37689	33.066	0.03024	12.46221	0.08024
21	2.786	0.35894	35.719	0.02800	12.82115	0.07800
22	2.925	0.34185	38.505	0.02597	13.16300	0.07597
23	3.072	0.32557	41.430	0.02414	13.48857	0.07414
24	3.225	0.31007	44.502	0.02247	13.70864	0.07247
25	3.386	0.29530	47.727	0.02095	14.09394	0.07095
26	3.556	0.28124	51.113	0.01956	14.37519	0.06956
27	3.733	0.26785	54.669	0.01829	14.64303	0.06829
28	3.920	0.25509	58.403	0.01712	14.89813	0.06712
29	4.116	0.24295	62.323	0.01605	15.14107	0.06605
30	4.322	0.23138	66.439	0.01505	15.37245	0.06505
35	5.516	0.18129	90.320	0.01107	16.37419	0.06107
40	7.040	0.14205	120.800	0.00828	17.15909	0.05828
45	8.985	0.11130	159.700	0.00626	17.77407	0.05626
50	11.467	0.08720	209.348	0.00478	18.25593	0.05478
55	14.636	0.06833	272.713	0.00367	18.63347	0.05367
60	18.679	0.05354	353.584	0.00283	18.92929	0.05283
70	30.426	0.03287	588.529	0.00170	19.34268	0.05170
80	49.561	0.02018	971.229	0.00103	19.59646	0.05103
90	80.730	0.01239	1594.608	0.00063	19.75226	0.05063
100	131.501	0.00760	2610.026	0.00038	19.84791	0.05038

Table C.5. 6% INTEREST FACTORS FOR ANNUAL COMPOUNDING

	Single Payment		Equal-Payment Series			
n	Compound-amount factor	Present-worth factor	Compound-amount factor	Sinking-fund factor	Present-worth factor	Capital-recovery factor
	SP *i-n* ( )	PS *i-n* ( )	SR *i-n* ( )	RS *i-n* ( )	PR *i-n* ( )	RP *i-n* ( )
1	1.060	0.94340	1.000	1.00000	0.94340	1.06000
2	1.124	0.89000	2.060	0.48544	1.83339	0.54544
3	1.191	0.83962	3.184	0.31411	2.67301	0.37411
4	1.262	0.79209	4.375	0.22859	3.46510	0.28859
5	1.338	0.74726	5.637	0.17740	4.21236	0.23740
6	1.419	0.70496	6.975	0.14336	4.91732	0.20336
7	1.504	0.66506	8.394	0.11914	5.58238	0.17914
8	1.594	0.62741	9.897	0.10104	6.20979	0.16104
9	1.689	0.59190	11.491	0.08702	6.80169	0.14702
10	1.791	0.55839	13.181	0.07587	7.36009	0.13587
11	1.898	0.52679	14.972	0.06679	7.88687	0.12679
12	2.012	0.49697	16.870	0.05928	8.38384	0.11928
13	2.133	0.46884	18.882	0.05296	8.85268	0.11296
14	2.261	0.44230	21.015	0.04758	9.29498	0.10758
15	2.397	0.41727	23.276	0.04296	9.71225	0.10296
16	2.540	0.39365	25.673	0.03895	10.10590	0.09895
17	2.693	0.37136	28.213	0.03544	10.47726	0.09544
18	2.854	0.35034	30.906	0.03236	10.82760	0.09236
19	3.026	0.33051	33.760	0.02962	11.15812	0.08962
20	3.207	0.31180	36.786	0.02718	11.46992	0.08718
21	3.400	0.29416	39.993	0.02500	11.76408	0.08500
22	3.604	0.27751	43.392	0.02305	12.04158	0.08305
23	3.820	0.26180	46.996	0.02128	12.30338	0.08128
24	4.049	0.24698	50.816	0.01968	12.55036	0.07968
25	4.292	0.23300	54.865	0.01823	12.78336	0.07823
26	4.549	0.21981	59.156	0.01690	13.00317	0.07690
27	4.822	0.20737	63.706	0.01570	13.21053	0.07570
28	5.112	0.19563	68.528	0.01459	13.40616	0.07459
29	5.418	0.18456	73.640	0.01358	13.59072	0.07358
30	5.743	0.17411	79.058	0.01265	13.76483	0.07265
35	7.686	0.13011	111.435	0.00897	14.49825	0.06897
40	10.286	0.09722	154.762	0.00646	15.04630	0.06646
45	13.765	0.07265	212.744	0.00470	15.45583	0.06470
50	18.420	0.05429	290.336	0.00344	15.76186	0.06344
55	24.650	0.04057	394.172	0.00254	15.99054	0.06254
60	32.988	0.03031	533.128	0.00188	16.16143	0.06188
70	59.076	0.01693	967.932	0.00103	16.38454	0.06103
80	105.796	0.00945	1746.600	0.00057	16.50913	0.06057
90	189.465	0.00528	3141.075	0.00032	16.57870	0.06032
100	339.302	0.00295	5638.369	0.00018	16.61755	0.06018

Table C.6. 7% INTEREST FACTORS FOR ANNUAL COMPOUNDING

	Single Payment		Equal-Payment Series			
	Compound-amount factor	Present-worth factor	Compound-amount factor	Sinking-fund factor	Present-worth factor	Capital-recovery factor
n	SP i-n ( )	PS i-n ( )	SR i-n ( )	RS i-n ( )	PR i-n ( )	RP i-n ( )
1	1.070	0.93458	1.000	1.00000	0.93458	1.07000
2	1.145	0.87344	2.070	0.48309	1.80802	0.55309
3	1.225	0.81630	3.215	0.31105	2.62432	0.38105
4	1.311	0.76290	4.440	0.22523	3.38721	0.29523
5	1.403	0.71299	5.751	0.17389	4.10020	0.24389
6	1.501	0.66634	7.153	0.13980	4.76654	0.20980
7	1.606	0.62275	8.654	0.11555	5.38929	0.18555
8	1.718	0.58201	10.260	0.09747	5.97130	0.16747
9	1.838	0.54393	11.978	0.08349	6.51523	0.15349
10	1.967	0.50835	13.816	0.07238	7.02358	0.14238
11	2.105	0.47509	15.784	0.06336	7.49867	0.13336
12	2.252	0.44401	17.888	0.05590	7.94269	0.12590
13	2.410	0.41496	20.141	0.04965	8.35765	0.11965
14	2.579	0.38782	22.550	0.04434	8.74547	0.11434
15	2.759	0.36245	25.129	0.03979	9.10791	0.10979
16	2.952	0.33873	27.888	0.03586	9.44665	0.10586
17	3.159	0.31657	30.840	0.03243	9.76322	0.10243
18	3.380	0.29586	33.999	0.02941	10.05909	0.09941
19	3.617	0.27651	37.379	0.02675	10.33559	0.09675
20	3.870	0.25842	40.995	0.02439	10.59401	0.09439
21	4.141	0.24151	44.865	0.02229	10.83553	0.09229
22	4.430	0.22571	49.006	0.02041	11.06124	0.09041
23	4.741	0.21095	53.436	0.01871	11.27219	0.08871
24	5.072	0.19715	58.177	0.01719	11.46933	0.08719
25	5.427	0.18425	63.249	0.01581	11.65358	0.08581
26	5.807	0.17220	68.676	0.01456	11.82578	0.08456
27	6.214	0.16093	74.484	0.01343	11.98671	0.08343
28	6.649	0.15040	80.698	0.01239	12.13711	0.08239
29	7.114	0.14056	87.347	0.01145	12.27767	0.08145
30	7.612	0.13137	94.461	0.01059	12.40904	0.08059
35	10.677	0.09366	138.237	0.00723	12.94767	0.07723
40	14.974	0.06678	199.635	0.00501	13.33171	0.07501
45	21.002	0.04761	285.749	0.00350	13.60552	0.07350
50	29.457	0.03395	406.529	0.00246	13.80075	0.07246
55	41.315	0.02420	575.929	0.00174	13.93994	0.07174
60	57.946	0.01726	813.520	0.00123	14.03918	0.07123
70	113.989	0.00877	1614.134	0.00062	14.16039	0.07062
80	224.234	0.00446	3189.062	0.00031	14.22201	0.07031
90	441.103	0.00227	6287.185	0.00016	14.25333	0.07016
100	867.716	0.00115	12381.661	0.00008	14.26925	0.07008

Table C.7. 8% INTEREST FACTORS FOR ANNUAL COMPOUNDING

n	Single Payment		Equal-Payment Series			
	Compound-amount factor	Present-worth factor	Compound-amount factor	Sinking-fund factor	Present-worth factor	Capital-recovery factor
	SP *i-n* ( )	PS *i-n* ( )	SR *i-n* ( )	RS *i-n* ( )	PR *i-n* ( )	RP *i-n* ( )
1	1.080	0.92593	1.000	1.00000	0.92593	1.08000
2	1.166	0.85734	2.080	0.48077	1.78326	0.56077
3	1.260	0.79383	3.246	0.30803	2.57710	0.38803
4	1.360	0.73503	4.506	0.22192	3.31213	0.30192
5	1.469	0.68058	5.867	0.17046	3.99271	0.25046
6	1.587	0.63017	7.336	0.13632	4.62288	0.21632
7	1.714	0.58349	8.923	0.11207	5.20637	0.19207
8	1.851	0.54027	10.637	0.09401	5.74664	0.17401
9	1.999	0.50025	12.488	0.08008	6.24689	0.16008
10	2.159	0.46319	14.487	0.06903	6.71008	0.14903
11	2.332	0.42888	16.645	0.06008	7.13896	0.14008
12	2.518	0.39711	18.977	0.05270	7.53608	0.13270
13	2.720	0.36770	21.495	0.04652	7.90378	0.12652
14	2.937	0.34046	24.215	0.04130	8.24424	0.12130
15	3.172	0.31524	27.152	0.03683	8.55948	0.11683
16	3.426	0.29189	30.324	0.03298	8.85137	0.11298
17	3.700	0.27027	33.750	0.02963	9.12164	0.10963
18	3.996	0.25025	37.450	0.02670	9.37189	0.10670
19	4.316	0.23171	41.446	0.02413	9.60360	0.10413
20	4.661	0.21455	45.762	0.02185	9.81815	0.10185
21	5.034	0.19866	50.423	0.01983	10.01680	0.09983
22	5.437	0.18394	55.457	0.01803	10.20074	0.09803
23	5.871	0.17032	60.893	0.01642	10.37106	0.09642
24	6.341	0.15770	66.765	0.01498	10.52876	0.09498
25	6.848	0.14602	73.106	0.01368	10.67478	0.09368
26	7.396	0.13520	79.954	0.01251	10.80998	0.09251
27	7.988	0.12519	87.351	0.01145	10.93516	0.09145
28	8.627	0.11591	95.339	0.01049	11.05108	0.09049
29	9.317	0.10733	103.966	0.00962	11.15841	0.08962
30	10.063	0.09938	113.283	0.00883	11.25778	0.08883
35	14.785	0.06763	172.317	0.00580	11.65457	0.08580
40	21.725	0.04603	259.057	0.00386	11.92461	0.08386
45	31.920	0.03133	386.506	0.00259	12.10840	0.08259
50	46.902	0.02132	573.770	0.00174	12.23348	0.08174
55	68.914	0.01451	848.923	0.00118	12.31861	0.08118
60	101.257	0.00988	1253.213	0.00080	12.37655	0.08080
70	218.606	0.00457	2720.080	0.00037	12.44282	0.08037
80	471.955	0.00212	5886.935	0.00017	12.47351	0.08017
90	1018.915	0.00098	12723.937	0.00008	12.48773	0.08008
100	2199.761	0.00045	27484.515	0.00004	12.49432	0.08004

Table C.8. 9% INTEREST FACTORS FOR ANNUAL COMPOUNDING

n	Single Payment		Equal-Payment Series			
	Compound-amount factor	Present-worth factor	Compound-amount factor	Sinking-fund factor	Present-worth factor	Capital-recovery factor
	SP *i-n*	PS *i-n*	SR *i-n*	RS *i-n*	PR *i-n*	RP *i-n*
	( )	( )	( )	( )	( )	( )
1	1.090	0.91743	1.000	1.00000	0.91743	1.09000
2	1.188	0.84168	2.090	0.47847	1.75911	0.56847
3	1.295	0.77218	3.278	0.30505	2.53129	0.39505
4	1.412	0.70843	4.573	0.21867	3.23972	0.30867
5	1.539	0.64993	5.985	0.16709	3.88965	0.25709
6	1.677	0.59627	7.523	0.13292	4.48592	0.22292
7	1.828	0.54703	9.200	0.10869	5.03295	0.19869
8	1.993	0.50187	11.028	0.09067	5.53482	0.18067
9	2.172	0.46043	13.021	0.07680	5.99525	0.16680
10	2.367	0.42241	15.193	0.06582	6.41766	0.15582
11	2.580	0.38753	17.560	0.05695	6.80519	0.14695
12	2.813	0.35553	20.141	0.04965	7.16072	0.13965
13	3.066	0.32618	22.953	0.04357	7.48690	0.13357
14	3.342	0.29925	26.019	0.03843	7.78615	0.12843
15	3.642	0.27454	29.361	0.03406	8.06069	0.12406
16	3.970	0.25187	33.003	0.03030	8.31256	0.12030
17	4.328	0.23107	36.974	0.02705	8.54363	0.11705
18	4.717	0.21199	41.301	0.02421	8.75562	0.11421
19	5.142	0.19449	46.018	0.02173	8.95011	0.11173
20	5.604	0.17843	51.160	0.01955	9.12855	0.10955
21	6.109	0.16370	56.765	0.01762	9.29224	0.10762
22	6.659	0.15018	62.873	0.01590	9.44243	0.10590
23	7.258	0.13778	69.532	0.01438	9.58021	0.10438
24	7.911	0.12640	76.790	0.01302	9.70661	0.10302
25	8.623	0.11597	84.701	0.01181	9.82258	0.10181
26	9.399	0.10639	93.324	0.01072	9.92897	0.10072
27	10.245	0.09761	102.723	0.00973	10.02658	0.09973
28	11.167	0.08955	112.968	0.00885	10.11613	0.09885
29	12.172	0.08215	124.135	0.00806	10.19828	0.09806
30	13.268	0.07537	136.308	0.00734	10.27365	0.09734
35	20.414	0.04899	215.711	0.00404	10.56682	0.09464
40	31.409	0.03184	337.882	0.00296	10.75736	0.09296
45	48.327	0.02069	525.859	0.00190	10.88120	0.09190
50	74.358	0.01345	815.084	0.00123	10.96168	0.09123
55	114.408	0.00874	1260.092	0.00079	11.01399	0.09079
60	176.031	0.00568	1944.792	0.00051	11.04799	0.09051
70	416.730	0.00240	4619.223	0.00022	11.08445	0.09022
80	986.552	0.00101	10950.573	0.00009	11.09985	0.09009
90	2335.526	0.00043	25939.182	0.00004	11.10635	0.09004
100	5529.041	0.00018	61422.674	0.00002	11.10910	0.09002

Table C.9. 10% INTEREST FACTORS FOR ANNUAL COMPOUNDING

	Single Payment		Equal-Payment Series			
n	Compound-amount factor	Present-worth factor	Compound-amount factor	Sinking-fund factor	Present-worth factor	Capital-recovery factor
	SP i-n ( )	PS i-n ( )	SR i-n ( )	RS i-n ( )	PR i-n ( )	RP i-n ( )
1	1.100	0.90909	1.000	1.00000	0.90909	1.10000
2	1.210	0.82645	2.100	0.47619	1.73554	0.57619
3	1.331	0.75131	3.310	0.30211	2.48685	0.40211
4	1.464	0.68301	4.641	0.21547	3.16987	0.31547
5	1.611	0.62092	6.105	0.16380	3.79079	0.26380
6	1.772	0.56447	7.716	0.12961	4.35526	0.22961
7	1.949	0.51316	9.487	0.10541	4.86842	0.20541
8	2.144	0.46651	11.436	0.08744	5.33493	0.18744
9	2.358	0.42410	13.579	0.07364	5.75902	0.17364
10	2.594	0.38554	15.937	0.06275	6.14457	0.16275
11	2.853	0.35049	18.531	0.05396	6.49506	0.15396
12	3.138	0.31863	21.384	0.04676	6.81369	0.14676
13	3.452	0.28966	24.523	0.04078	7.10336	0.14078
14	3.797	0.26333	27.975	0.03575	7.36669	0.13575
15	4.177	0.23939	31.772	0.03147	7.60608	0.13147
16	4.595	0.21763	35.950	0.02782	7.82371	0.12782
17	5.054	0.19784	40.545	0.02466	8.02155	0.12466
18	5.560	0.17986	45.599	0.02193	8.20141	0.12193
19	6.116	0.16351	51.159	0.01955	8.36492	0.11955
20	6.727	0.14864	57.275	0.01746	8.51356	0.11746
21	7.400	0.13513	64.002	0.01562	8.64869	0.11562
22	8.140	0.12285	71.403	0.01401	8.77154	0.11401
23	8.954	0.11168	79.543	0.01257	8.88322	0.11257
24	9.850	0.10153	88.497	0.01130	8.98474	0.11130
25	10.835	0.09230	98.347	0.01017	9.07704	0.11017
26	11.918	0.08391	109.182	0.00916	9.16095	0.10916
27	13.110	0.07628	121.100	0.00826	9.23722	0.10826
28	14.421	0.06934	134.210	0.00745	9.30657	0.10745
29	15.863	0.06304	148.631	0.00673	9.36961	0.10673
30	17.449	0.05731	164.494	0.00608	9.42691	0.10608
35	28.102	0.03558	271.024	0.00369	9.64416	0.10369
40	45.259	0.02209	442.593	0.00226	9.77905	0.10226
45	72.890	0.01372	718.905	0.00139	9.86281	0.10139
50	117.391	0.00852	1163.908	0.00086	9.91481	0.10086
55	189.059	0.00529	1880.591	0.00053	9.94711	0.10053
60	304.482	0.00328	3034.816	0.00033	9.96716	0.10033
70	789.747	0.00127	7887.469	0.00013	9.98734	0.10013
80	2048.400	0.00049	20474.000	0.00005	9.99512	0.10005
90	5313.022	0.00019	53120.222	0.00002	9.99812	0.10002
100	13780.611	0.00007	137796.110	0.00001	9.99927	0.10001

APPENDIX D

FINITE QUEUING TABLES

Table D.1–D.3. Finite Queuing Factors

The probability of a delay, D, and the efficiency factor, F, are given for populations of 10, 20, and 30 units. Each set of values is keyed to the service factor, X, and the number of channels, M. (*These tabular values adapted with permission from L. G. Peck and R. N. Hazelwood, Finite Queuing Tables. New York: John Wiley & Sons, Inc., 1958.*)

Table D.1. FINITE QUEUING FACTORS—POPULATION 10

X	M	D	F	X	M	D	F	X	M	D	F
0.008	1	0.072	0.999		2	0.177	0.990		3	0.182	0.986
0.013	1	0.117	0.998		1	0.660	0.899		2	0.528	0.921
0.016	1	0.144	0.997	0.085	3	0.037	0.999		1	0.954	0.610
0.019	1	0.170	0.996		2	0.196	0.988	0.165	4	0.049	0.997
0.021	1	0.188	0.995		1	0.692	0.883		3	0.195	0.984
0.023	1	0.206	0.994	0.090	3	0.043	0.998		2	0.550	0.914
0.025	1	0.224	0.993		2	0.216	0.986		1	0.961	0.594
0.026	1	0.232	0.992		1	0.722	0.867	0.170	4	0.054	0.997
0.028	1	0.250	0.991	0.095	3	0.049	0.998		3	0.209	0.982
0.030	1	0.268	0.990		2	0.237	0.984		2	0.571	0.906
0.032	2	0.033	0.999		1	0.750	0.850		1	0.966	0.579
	1	0.285	0.988	0.100	3	0.056	0.998	0.180	5	0.013	0.999
0.034	2	0.037	0.999		2	0.258	0.981		4	0.066	0.996
	1	0.302	0.986		1	0.776	0.832		3	0.238	0.978
0.036	2	0.041	0.999	0.105	3	0.064	0.997		2	0.614	0.890
	1	0.320	0.984		2	0.279	0.978		1	0.975	0.549
0.038	2	0.046	0.999		1	0.800	0.814	0.190	5	0.016	0.999
	1	0.337	0.982	0.110	3	0.072	0.997		4	0.078	0.995
0.040	2	0.050	0.999		2	0.301	0.974		3	0.269	0.973
	1	0.354	0.980		1	0.822	0.795		2	0.654	0.873
0.042	2	0.055	0.999	0.115	3	0.081	0.996		1	0.982	0.522
	1	0.371	0.978		2	0.324	0.971	0.200	5	0.020	0.999
0.044	2	0.060	0.998		1	0.843	0.776		4	0.092	0.994
	1	0.388	0.975	0.120	4	0.016	0.999		3	0.300	0.968
0.046	2	0.065	0.998		3	0.090	0.995		2	0.692	0.854
	1	0.404	0.973		2	0.346	0.967		1	0.987	0.497
0.048	2	0.071	0.998		1	0.861	0.756	0.210	5	0.025	0.999
	1	0.421	0.970	0.125	4	0.019	0.999		4	0.108	0.992
0.050	2	0.076	0.998		3	0.100	0.994		3	0.333	0.961
	1	0.437	0.967		2	0.369	0.962		2	0.728	0.835
0.052	2	0.082	0.997		1	0.878	0.737		1	0.990	0.474
	1	0.454	0.963	0.130	4	0.022	0.999	0.220	5	0.030	0.998
0.054	2	0.088	0.997		3	0.110	0.994		4	0.124	0.990
	1	0.470	0.960		2	0.392	0.958		3	0.366	0.954
0.056	2	0.094	0.997		1	0.893	0.718		2	0.761	0.815
	1	0.486	0.956	0.135	4	0.025	0.999		1	0.993	0.453
0.058	2	0.100	0.996		3	0.121	0.993	0.230	5	0.037	0.998
	1	0.501	0.953		2	0.415	0.952		4	0.142	0.988
0.060	2	0.106	0.996		1	0.907	0.699		3	0.400	0.947
	1	0.517	0.949	0.140	4	0.028	0.999		2	0.791	0.794
0.062	2	0.113	0.996		3	0.132	0.991		1	0.995	0.434
	1	0.532	0.945		2	0.437	0.947	0.240	5	0.044	0.997
0.064	2	0.119	0.995		1	0.919	0.680		4	0.162	0.986
	1	0.547	0.940	0.145	4	0.032	0.999		3	0.434	0.938
0.066	2	0.126	0.995		3	0.144	0.990		2	0.819	0.774
	1	0.562	0.936		2	0.460	0.941		1	0.996	0.416
0.068	3	0.020	0.999		1	0.929	0.662	0.250	6	0.010	0.999
	2	0.133	0.994	0.150	4	0.036	0.998		5	0.052	0.997
	1	0.577	0.931		3	0.156	0.989		4	0.183	0.983
0.070	3	0.022	0.999		2	0.483	0.935		3	0.469	0.929
	2	0.140	0.994		1	0.939	0.644		2	0.844	0.753
	1	0.591	0.926	0.155	4	0.040	0.998		1	0.997	0.400
0.075	3	0.026	0.999		3	0.169	0.987	0.260	6	0.013	0.999
	2	0.158	0.992		2	0.505	0.928		5	0.060	0.996
	1	0.627	0.913		1	0.947	0.627		4	0.205	0.980
0.080	3	0.031	0.999	0.160	4	0.044	0.998		3	0.503	0.919

X	M	D	F	X	M	D	F	X	M	D	F
	2	0.866	0.732		4	0.533	0.906		7	0.171	0.982
	1	0.998	0.384		3	0.840	0.758		6	0.413	0.939
0.270	6	0.015	0.999		2	0.986	0.525		5	0.707	0.848
	5	0.070	0.995	0.400	7	0.026	0.998		4	0.917	0.706
	4	0.228	0.976		6	0.105	0.991		3	0.991	0.535
	3	0.537	0.908		5	0.292	0.963	0.580	8	0.057	0.995
	2	0.886	0.712		4	0.591	0.887		7	0.204	0.977
	1	0.999	0.370		3	0.875	0.728		6	0.465	0.927
0.280	6	0.018	0.999		2	0.991	0.499		5	0.753	0.829
	5	0.081	0.994	0.420	7	0.034	0.998		4	0.937	0.684
	4	0.252	0.972		6	0.130	0.987		3	0.994	0.517
	3	0.571	0.896		5	0.341	0.954	0.600	9	0.010	0.999
	2	0.903	0.692		4	0.646	0.866		8	0.072	0.994
	1	0.999	0.357		3	0.905	0.700		7	0.242	0.972
0.290	6	0.022	0.999		2	0.994	0.476		6	0.518	0.915
	5	0.093	0.993	0.440	7	0.045	0.997		5	0.795	0.809
	4	0.278	0.968		6	0.160	0.984		4	0.953	0.663
	3	0.603	0.884		5	0.392	0.943		3	0.996	0.500
	2	0.918	0.672		4	0.698	0.845	0.650	9	0.021	0.999
	1	0.999	0.345		3	0.928	0.672		8	0.123	0.988
0.300	6	0.026	0.998		2	0.996	0.454		7	0.353	0.954
	5	0.106	0.991	0.460	8	0.011	0.999		6	0.651	0.878
	4	0.304	0.963		7	0.058	0.995		5	0.882	0.759
	3	0.635	0.872		6	0.193	0.979		4	0.980	0.614
	2	0.932	0.653		5	0.445	0.930		3	0.999	0.461
	1	0.999	0.333		4	0.747	0.822	0.700	9	0.040	0.997
0.310	6	0.031	0.998		3	0.947	0.646		8	0.200	0.979
	5	0.120	0.990		2	0.998	0.435		7	0.484	0.929
	4	0.331	0.957	0.480	8	0.015	0.999		6	0.772	0.836
	3	0.666	0.858		7	0.074	0.994		5	0.940	0.711
	2	0.943	0.635		6	0.230	0.973		4	0.992	0.571
0.320	6	0.036	0.998		5	0.499	0.916	0.750	9	0.075	0.994
	5	0.135	0.988		4	0.791	0.799		8	0.307	0.965
	4	0.359	0.952		3	0.961	0.621		7	0.626	0.897
	3	0.695	0.845		2	0.998	0.417		6	0.870	0.792
	2	0.952	0.617	0.500	8	0.020	0.999		5	0.975	0.666
0.330	6	0.042	0.997		7	0.093	0.992		4	0.998	0.533
	5	0.151	0.986		6	0.271	0.966	0.800	9	0.134	0.988
	4	0.387	0.945		5	0.553	0.901		8	0.446	0.944
	3	0.723	0.831		4	0.830	0.775		7	0.763	0.859
	2	0.961	0.600		3	0.972	0.598		6	0.939	0.747
0.340	7	0.010	0.999		2	0.999	0.400		5	0.991	0.625
	6	0.049	0.997	0.520	8	0.026	0.998		4	0.999	0.500
	5	0.168	0.983		7	0.115	0.989	0.850	9	0.232	0.979
	4	0.416	0.938		6	0.316	0.958		8	0.611	0.916
	3	0.750	0.816		5	0.606	0.884		7	0.879	0.818
	2	0.968	0.584		4	0.864	0.752		6	0.978	0.705
0.360	7	0.014	0.999		3	0.980	0.575		5	0.998	0.588
	6	0.064	0.995		2	0.999	0.385	0.900	9	0.387	0.963
	5	0.205	0.978	0.540	8	0.034	0.997		8	0.785	0.881
	4	0.474	0.923		7	0.141	0.986		7	0.957	0.777
	3	0.798	0.787		6	0.363	0.949		6	0.995	0.667
	2	0.978	0.553		5	0.658	0.867	0.950	9	0.630	0.938
0.380	7	0.019	0.999		4	0.893	0.729		8	0.934	0.841
	6	0.083	0.993		3	0.986	0.555		7	0.994	0.737
	5	0.247	0.971	0.560	8	0.044	0.996				

Table D.2. FINITE QUEUING FACTORS—POPULATION 20

X	M	D	F	X	M	D	F	X	M	D	F
0.005	1	0.095	0.999		1	0.837	0.866		3	0.326	0.980
0.009	1	0.171	0.998	0.052	3	0.080	0.998		2	0.733	0.896
0.011	1	0.208	0.997		2	0.312	0.986		1	0.998	0.526
0.013	1	0.246	0.996		1	0.858	0.851	0.100	5	0.038	0.999
0.014	1	0.265	0.995	0.054	3	0.088	0.998		4	0.131	0.995
0.015	1	0.283	0.994		2	0.332	0.984		3	0.363	0.975
0.016	1	0.302	0.993		1	0.876	0.835		2	0.773	0.878
0.017	1	0.321	0.992	0.056	3	0.097	0.997		1	0.999	0.500
0.018	2	0.048	0.999		2	0.352	0.982	0.110	5	0.055	0.998
	1	0.339	0.991		1	0.893	0.819		4	0.172	0.992
0.019	2	0.053	0.999	0.058	3	0.105	0.997		3	0.438	0.964
	1	0.358	0.990		2	0.372	0.980		2	0.842	0.837
0.020	2	0.058	0.999		1	0.908	0.802	0.120	6	0.022	0.999
	1	0.376	0.989	0.060	4	0.026	0.999		5	0.076	0.997
0.021	2	0.064	0.999		3	0.115	0.997		4	0.219	0.988
	1	0.394	0.987		2	0.392	0.978		3	0.514	0.950
0.022	2	0.070	0.999		1	0.922	0.785		2	0.895	0.793
	1	0.412	0.986	0.062	4	0.029	0.999	0.130	6	0.031	0.999
0.023	2	0.075	0.999		3	0.124	0.996		5	0.101	0.996
	1	0.431	0.984		2	0.413	0.975		4	0.271	0.983
0.024	2	0.082	0.999		1	0.934	0.768		3	0.589	0.933
	1	0.449	0.982	0.064	4	0.032	0.999		2	0.934	0.748
0.025	2	0.088	0.999		3	0.134	0.996	0.140	6	0.043	0.998
	1	0.466	0.980		2	0.433	0.972		5	0.131	0.994
0.026	2	0.094	0.998		1	0.944	0.751		4	0.328	0.976
	1	0.484	0.978	0.066	4	0.036	0.999		3	0.661	0.912
0.028	2	0.108	0.998		3	0.144	0.995		2	0.960	0.703
	1	0.519	0.973		2	0.454	0.969	0.150	7	0.017	0.999
0.030	2	0.122	0.998		1	0.953	0.733		6	0.059	0.998
	1	0.553	0.968	0.068	4	0.039	0.999		5	0.166	0.991
0.032	2	0.137	0.997		3	0.155	0.995		4	0.388	0.968
	1	0.587	0.962		2	0.474	0.966		3	0.728	0.887
0.034	2	0.152	0.996		1	0.961	0.716		2	0.976	0.661
	1	0.620	0.955	0.070	4	0.043	0.999	0.160	7	0.024	0.999
0.036	2	0.168	0.996		3	0.165	0.994		6	0.077	0.997
	1	0.651	0.947		2	0.495	0.962		5	0.205	0.988
0.038	3	0.036	0.999		1	0.967	0.699		4	0.450	0.957
	2	0.185	0.995	0.075	4	0.054	0.999		3	0.787	0.860
	1	0.682	0.938		3	0.194	0.992		2	0.987	0.622
0.040	3	0.041	0.999		2	0.545	0.953	0.180	7	0.044	0.998
	2	0.202	0.994		1	0.980	0.659		6	0.125	0.994
	1	0.712	0.929	0.080	4	0.066	0.998		5	0.295	0.978
0.042	3	0.047	0.999		3	0.225	0.990		4	0.575	0.930
	2	0.219	0.993		2	0.595	0.941		3	0.879	0.799
	1	0.740	0.918		1	0.988	0.621		2	0.996	0.555
0.044	3	0.053	0.999	0.085	4	0.080	0.997	0.200	8	0.025	0.999
	2	0.237	0.992		3	0.257	0.987		7	0.074	0.997
	1	0.767	0.906		2	0.643	0.928		6	0.187	0.988
0.046	3	0.059	0.999		1	0.993	0.586		5	0.397	0.963
	2	0.255	0.991	0.090	5	0.025	0.999		4	0.693	0.895
	1	0.792	0.894		4	0.095	0.997		3	0.938	0.736
0.048	3	0.066	0.999		3	0.291	0.984		2	0.999	0.500
	2	0.274	0.989		2	0.689	0.913	0.220	8	0.043	0.998
	1	0.815	0.881		1	0.996	0.554		7	0.115	0.994
0.050	3	0.073	0.998	0.095	5	0.031	0.999		6	0.263	0.980
	2	0.293	0.988		4	0.112	0.996		5	0.505	0.943

472

Table D.2. FINITE QUEUING FACTORS—POPULATION 20 (*Continued*)

X	M	D	F	X	M	D	F	X	M	D	F
	4	0.793	0.852		4	0.998	0.555	0.500	14	0.033	0.998
	3	0.971	0.677	0.380	12	0.024	0.999		13	0.088	0.995
0.240	9	0.024	0.999		11	0.067	0.996		12	0.194	0.985
	8	0.068	0.997		10	0.154	0.989		11	0.358	0.965
	7	0.168	0.989		9	0.305	0.973		10	0.563	0.929
	6	0.351	0.969		8	0.513	0.938		9	0.764	0.870
	5	0.613	0.917		7	0.739	0.874		8	0.908	0.791
	4	0.870	0.804		6	0.909	0.777		7	0.977	0.698
	3	0.988	0.623		5	0.984	0.656		6	0.997	0.600
0.260	9	0.039	0.998		4	0.999	0.526	0.540	15	0.023	0.999
	8	0.104	0.994	0.400	13	0.012	0.999		14	0.069	0.996
	7	0.233	0.983		12	0.037	0.998		13	0.161	0.988
	6	0.446	0.953		11	0.095	0.994		12	0.311	0.972
	5	0.712	0.884		10	0.205	0.984		11	0.509	0.941
	4	0.924	0.755		9	0.379	0.962		10	0.713	0.891
	3	0.995	0.576		8	0.598	0.918		9	0.873	0.821
0.280	10	0.021	0.999		7	0.807	0.845		8	0.961	0.738
	9	0.061	0.997		6	0.942	0.744		7	0.993	0.648
	8	0.149	0.990		5	0.992	0.624		6	0.999	0.556
	7	0.309	0.973	0.420	13	0.019	0.999	0.600	16	0.023	0.999
	6	0.544	0.932		12	0.055	0.997		15	0.072	0.996
	5	0.797	0.848		11	0.131	0.991		14	0.171	0.988
	4	0.958	0.708		10	0.265	0.977		13	0.331	0.970
	3	0.998	0.536		9	0.458	0.949		12	0.532	0.938
0.300	10	0.034	0.998		8	0.678	0.896		11	0.732	0.889
	9	0.091	0.995		7	0.863	0.815		10	0.882	0.824
	8	0.205	0.985		6	0.965	0.711		9	0.962	0.748
	7	0.394	0.961		5	0.996	0.595		8	0.992	0.666
	6	0.639	0.907	0.440	13	0.029	0.999		7	0.999	0.583
	5	0.865	0.808		12	0.078	0.995	0.700	17	0.047	0.998
	4	0.978	0.664		11	0.175	0.987		16	0.137	0.991
	3	0.999	0.500		10	0.333	0.969		15	0.295	0.976
0.320	11	0.018	0.999		9	0.540	0.933		14	0.503	0.948
	10	0.053	0.997		8	0.751	0.872		13	0.710	0.905
	9	0.130	0.992		7	0.907	0.785		12	0.866	0.849
	8	0.272	0.977		6	0.980	0.680		11	0.953	0.783
	7	0.483	0.944		5	0.998	0.568		10	0.988	0.714
	6	0.727	0.878	0.460	14	0.014	0.999		9	0.998	0.643
	5	0.915	0.768		13	0.043	0.998	0.800	19	0.014	0.999
	4	0.989	0.624		12	0.109	0.993		18	0.084	0.996
0.340	11	0.029	0.999		11	0.228	0.982		17	0.242	0.984
	10	0.079	0.996		10	0.407	0.958		16	0.470	0.959
	9	0.179	0.987		9	0.620	0.914		15	0.700	0.920
	8	0.347	0.967		8	0.815	0.846		14	0.867	0.869
	7	0.573	0.924		7	0.939	0.755		13	0.955	0.811
	6	0.802	0.846		6	0.989	0.651		12	0.989	0.750
	5	0.949	0.729		5	0.999	0.543		11	0.998	0.687
	4	0.995	0.588	0.480	14	0.022	0.999	0.900	19	0.135	0.994
0.360	12	0.015	0.999		13	0.063	0.996		18	0.425	0.972
	11	0.045	0.998		12	0.147	0.990		17	0.717	0.935
	10	0.112	0.993		11	0.289	0.974		16	0.898	0.886
	9	0.237	0.981		10	0.484	0.944		15	0.973	0.833
	8	0.429	0.954		9	0.695	0.893		14	0.995	0.778
	7	0.660	0.901		8	0.867	0.819		13	0.999	0.722
	6	0.863	0.812		7	0.962	0.726	0.950	19	0.377	0.981
	5	0.971	0.691		6	0.994	0.625		18	0.760	0.943

Table D.3. FINITE QUEUING FACTORS—POPULATION 30

X	M	D	F	X	M	D	F	X	M	D	F
0.004	1	0.116	0.999		1	0.963	0.772		3	0.426	0.976
0.007	1	0.203	0.998	0.044	4	0.040	0.999		2	0.847	0.873
0.009	1	0.260	0.997		3	0.154	0.996	0.075	5	0.069	0.998
0.010	1	0.289	0.996		2	0.474	0.977		4	0.201	0.993
0.011	1	0.317	0.995		1	0.974	0.744		3	0.486	0.969
0.012	1	0.346	0.994	0.046	4	0.046	0.999		2	0.893	0.840
0.013	1	0.374	0.993		3	0.171	0.996	0.080	6	0.027	0.999
0.014	2	0.067	0.999		2	0.506	0.972		5	0.088	0.998
	1	0.403	0.991		1	0.982	0.716		4	0.240	0.990
0.015	2	0.076	0.999	0.048	4	0.053	0.999		3	0.547	0.959
	1	0.431	0.989		3	0.189	0.995		2	0.929	0.805
0.016	2	0.085	0.999		2	0.539	0.968	0.085	6	0.036	0.999
	1	0.458	0.987		1	0.988	0.689		5	0.108	0.997
0.017	2	0.095	0.999	0.050	4	0.060	0.999		4	0.282	0.987
	1	0.486	0.985		3	0.208	0.994		3	0.607	0.948
0.018	2	0.105	0.999		2	0.571	0.963		2	0.955	0.768
	1	0.513	0.983		1	0.992	0.663	0.090	6	0.046	0.999
0.019	2	0.116	0.999	0.052	4	0.068	0.999		5	0.132	0.996
	1	0.541	0.980		3	0.227	0.993		4	0.326	0.984
0.020	2	0.127	0.998		2	0.603	0.957		3	0.665	0.934
	1	0.567	0.976		1	0.995	0.639		2	0.972	0.732
0.021	2	0.139	0.998	0.054	4	0.077	0.998	0.095	6	0.057	0.999
	1	0.594	0.973		3	0.247	0.992		5	0.158	0.994
0.022	2	0.151	0.998		2	0.634	0.951		4	0.372	0.979
	1	0.620	0.969		1	0.997	0.616		3	0.720	0.918
0.023	2	0.163	0.997	0.056	4	0.086	0.998		2	0.984	0.697
	1	0.645	0.965		3	0.267	0.991	0.100	6	0.071	0.998
0.024	2	0.175	0.997		2	0.665	0.944		5	0.187	0.993
	1	0.670	0.960		1	0.998	0.595		4	0.421	0.973
0.025	2	0.188	0.996	0.058	4	0.096	0.998		3	0.771	0.899
	1	0.694	0.954		3	0.288	0.989		2	0.991	0.664
0.026	2	0.201	0.996		2	0.695	0.936	0.110	7	0.038	0.999
	1	0.718	0.948		1	0.999	0.574		6	0.105	0.997
0.028	3	0.051	0.999	0.060	5	0.030	0.999		5	0.253	0.988
	2	0.229	0.995		4	0.106	0.997		4	0.520	0.959
	1	0.763	0.935		3	0.310	0.987		3	0.856	0.857
0.030	3	0.060	0.999		2	0.723	0.927		2	0.997	0.605
	2	0.257	0.994		1	0.999	0.555	0.120	7	0.057	0.998
	1	0.805	0.918	0.062	5	0.034	0.999		6	0.147	0.994
0.032	3	0.071	0.999		4	0.117	0.997		5	0.327	0.981
	2	0.286	0.992		3	0.332	0.986		4	0.619	0.939
	1	0.843	0.899		2	0.751	0.918		3	0.918	0.808
0.034	3	0.083	0.999	0.064	5	0.038	0.999		2	0.999	0.555
	2	0.316	0.990		4	0.128	0.997	0.130	8	0.030	0.999
	1	0.876	0.877		3	0.355	0.984		7	0.083	0.997
0.036	3	0.095	0.998		2	0.777	0.908		6	0.197	0.991
	2	0.347	0.988	0.066	5	0.043	0.999		5	0.409	0.972
	1	0.905	0.853		4	0.140	0.996		4	0.712	0.914
0.038	3	0.109	0.998		3	0.378	0.982		3	0.957	0.758
	2	0.378	0.986		2	0.802	0.897	0.140	8	0.045	0.999
0.040	1	0.929	0.827	0.068	5	0.048	0.999		7	0.115	0.996
	3	0.123	0.997		4	0.153	0.995		6	0.256	0.987
	2	0.410	0.983		3	0.402	0.979		5	0.494	0.960
0.042	1	0.948	0.800		2	0.825	0.885		4	0.793	0.884
	3	0.138	0.997	0.070	5	0.054	0.999		3	0.979	0.710
	2	0.442	0.980		4	0.166	0.995	0.150	9	0.024	0.999

Table D.3. FINITE QUEUING FACTORS—POPULATION 30 (*Continued*)

X	M	D	F	X	M	D	F	X	M	D	F
	8	0.065	0.998		7	0.585	0.938		7	0.901	0.818
	7	0.155	0.993		6	0.816	0.868		6	0.981	0.712
	6	0.322	0.980		5	0.961	0.751		5	0.999	0.595
	5	0.580	0.944		4	0.998	0.606	0.290	14	0.023	0.999
	4	0.860	0.849	0.230	12	0.023	0.999		13	0.055	0.998
	3	0.991	0.665		11	0.056	0.998		12	0.117	0.994
0.160	9	0.036	0.999		10	0.123	0.994		11	0.223	0.986
	8	0.090	0.997		9	0.242	0.985		10	0.382	0.969
	7	0.201	0.990		8	0.423	0.965		9	0.582	0.937
	6	0.394	0.972		7	0.652	0.923		8	0.785	0.880
	5	0.663	0.924		6	0.864	0.842		7	0.929	0.795
	4	0.910	0.811		5	0.976	0.721		6	0.988	0.688
	3	0.996	0.624		4	0.999	0.580		5	0.999	0.575
0.170	10	0.019	0.999	0.240	12	0.031	0.999	0.300	14	0.031	0.999
	9	0.051	0.998		11	0.074	0.997		13	0.071	0.997
	8	0.121	0.995		10	0.155	0.992		12	0.145	0.992
	7	0.254	0.986		9	0.291	0.981		11	0.266	0.982
	6	0.469	0.961		8	0.487	0.955		10	0.437	0.962
	5	0.739	0.901		7	0.715	0.905		9	0.641	0.924
	4	0.946	0.773		6	0.902	0.816		8	0.830	0.861
	3	0.998	0.588		5	0.986	0.693		7	0.950	0.771
0.180	10	0.028	0.999		4	0.999	0.556		6	0.993	0.666
	9	0.070	0.997	0.250	13	0.017	0.999	0.320	15	0.023	0.999
	8	0.158	0.993		12	0.042	0.998		14	0.054	0.998
	7	0.313	0.980		11	0.095	0.996		13	0.113	0.994
	6	0.546	0.948		10	0.192	0.989		12	0.213	0.987
	5	0.806	0.874		9	0.345	0.975		11	0.362	0.971
	4	0.969	0.735		8	0.552	0.944		10	0.552	0.943
	3	0.999	0.555		7	0.773	0.885		9	0.748	0.893
0.190	10	0.039	0.999		6	0.932	0.789		8	0.901	0.820
	9	0.094	0.996		5	0.992	0.666		7	0.977	0.727
	8	0.200	0.990	0.260	13	0.023	0.999		6	0.997	0.625
	7	0.378	0.973		12	0.056	0.998	0.340	16	0.016	0.999
	6	0.621	0.932		11	0.121	0.994		15	0.040	0.998
	5	0.862	0.845		10	0.233	0.986		14	0.086	0.996
	4	0.983	0.699		9	0.402	0.967		13	0.169	0.990
0.200	11	0.021	0.999		8	0.616	0.930		12	0.296	0.979
	10	0.054	0.998		7	0.823	0.864		11	0.468	0.957
	9	0.123	0.995		6	0.954	0.763		10	0.663	0.918
	8	0.249	0.985		5	0.995	0.641		9	0.836	0.858
	7	0.446	0.963	0.270	13	0.032	0.999		8	0.947	0.778
	6	0.693	0.913		12	0.073	0.997		7	0.990	0.685
	5	0.905	0.814		11	0.151	0.992		6	0.999	0.588
	4	0.991	0.665		10	0.279	0.981	0.360	16	0.029	0.999
0.210	11	0.030	0.999		9	0.462	0.959		15	0.065	0.997
	10	0.073	0.997		8	0.676	0.915		14	0.132	0.993
	9	0.157	0.992		7	0.866	0.841		13	0.240	0.984
	8	0.303	0.980		6	0.970	0.737		12	0.392	0.967
	7	0.515	0.952		5	0.997	0.617		11	0.578	0.937
	6	0.758	0.892	0.280	14	0.017	0.999		10	0.762	0.889
	5	0.938	0.782		13	0.042	0.998		9	0.902	0.821
	4	0.995	0.634		12	0.093	0.996		8	0.974	0.738
0.220	11	0.041	0.999		11	0.185	0.989		7	0.996	0.648
	10	0.095	0.996		10	0.329	0.976	0.380	17	0.020	0.999
	9	0.197	0.989		9	0.522	0.949		16	0.048	0.998
	8	0.361	0.974		8	0.733	0.898		15	0.101	0.995

Table D.3. FINITE QUEUING FACTORS—POPULATION 30 (*Continued*)

X	M	D	F	X	M	D	F	X	M	D	F
	14	0.191	0.988		16	0.310	0.977		22	0.038	0.998
	13	0.324	0.975		15	0.470	0.957		21	0.085	0.996
	12	0.496	0.952		14	0.643	0.926		20	0.167	0.990
	11	0.682	0.914		13	0.799	0.881		19	0.288	0.980
	10	0.843	0.857		12	0.910	0.826		18	0.443	0.963
	9	0.945	0.784		11	0.970	0.762		17	0.612	0.936
	8	0.988	0.701		10	0.993	0.694		16	0.766	0.899
	7	0.999	0.614		9	0.999	0.625		15	0.883	0.854
0.400	17	0.035	0.999	0.500	20	0.032	0.999		14	0.953	0.802
	16	0.076	0.996		19	0.072	0.997		13	0.985	0.746
	15	0.150	0.992		18	0.143	0.992		12	0.997	0.690
	14	0.264	0.982		17	0.252	0.983		11	0.999	0.632
	13	0.420	0.964		16	0.398	0.967	0.600	23	0.024	0.999
	12	0.601	0.933		15	0.568	0.941		22	0.059	0.997
	11	0.775	0.886		14	0.733	0.904		21	0.125	0.993
	10	0.903	0.823		13	0.865	0.854		20	0.230	0.986
	9	0.972	0.748		12	0.947	0.796		19	0.372	0.972
	8	0.995	0.666		11	0.985	0.732		18	0.538	0.949
0.420	18	0.024	0.999		10	0.997	0.667		17	0.702	0.918
	17	0.056	0.997	0.520	21	0.021	0.999		16	0.837	0.877
	16	0.116	0.994		20	0.051	0.998		15	0.927	0.829
	15	0.212	0.986		19	0.108	0.994		14	0.974	0.776
	14	0.350	0.972		18	0.200	0.988		13	0.993	0.722
	13	0.521	0.948		17	0.331	0.975		12	0.999	0.667
	12	0.700	0.910		16	0.493	0.954	0.700	25	0.039	0.998
	11	0.850	0.856		15	0.663	0.923		24	0.096	0.995
	10	0.945	0.789		14	0.811	0.880		23	0.196	0.989
	9	0.986	0.713		13	0.915	0.827		22	0.339	0.977
	8	0.998	0.635		12	0.971	0.767		21	0.511	0.958
0.440	19	0.017	0.999		11	0.993	0.705		20	0.681	0.930
	18	0.041	0.998		10	0.999	0.641		19	0.821	0.894
	17	0.087	0.996	0.540	21	0.035	0.999		18	0.916	0.853
	16	0.167	0.990		20	0.079	0.996		17	0.967	0.808
	15	0.288	0.979		19	0.155	0.991		16	0.990	0.762
	14	0.446	0.960		18	0.270	0.981		15	0.997	0.714
	13	0.623	0.929		17	0.421	0.965	0.800	27	0.053	0.998
	12	0.787	0.883		16	0.590	0.938		26	0.143	0.993
	11	0.906	0.824		15	0.750	0.901		25	0.292	0.984
	10	0.970	0.755		14	0.874	0.854		24	0.481	0.966
	9	0.994	0.681		13	0.949	0.799		23	0.670	0.941
	8	0.999	0.606		12	0.985	0.740		22	0.822	0.909
0.460	19	0.028	0.999		11	0.997	0.679		21	0.919	0.872
	18	0.064	0.997		10	0.999	0.617		20	0.970	0.832
	17	0.129	0.993	0.560	22	0.023	0.999		19	0.991	0.791
	16	0.232	0.985		21	0.056	0.997		18	0.998	0.750
	15	0.375	0.970		20	0.117	0.994	0.900	29	0.047	0.999
	14	0.545	0.944		19	0.215	0.986		28	0.200	0.992
	13	0.717	0.906		18	0.352	0.973		27	0.441	0.977
	12	0.857	0.855		17	0.516	0.952		26	0.683	0.953
	11	0.945	0.793		16	0.683	0.920		25	0.856	0.923
	10	0.985	0.724		15	0.824	0.878		24	0.947	0.888
	9	0.997	0.652		14	0.920	0.828		23	0.985	0.852
0.480	20	0.019	0.999		13	0.972	0.772		22	0.996	0.815
	19	0.046	0.998		12	0.993	0.714		21	0.999	0.778
	18	0.098	0.995		11	0.999	0.655	0.950	29	0.226	0.993
	17	0.184	0.989	0.580	23	0.014	0.999		28	0.574	0.973

SELECTED REFERENCES

Ackoff, R. L., *Scientific Method: Optimizing Applied Research Decisions.* New York: John Wiley & Sons, Inc., 1962.

Allen, R. G. D., *Mathematical Economics.* London: The Macmillan Co., Ltd., 1956.

Barish, N. N., *Economic Analysis.* New York: McGraw-Hill Book Company, Inc., 1962.

Barnard, C. I., *The Functions of the Executive.* Cambridge, Mass.: Harvard University Press, 1938.

Baumol, W. J., *Economic Theory and Operations Analysis.* Englewood Cliffs, N.J.: Prentice-Hall, Inc., 1961.

Bellman, R. E., *Dynamic Programming.* Princeton, N.J.: Princeton University Press, 1957.

———, and S. E. Dreyfus, *Applied Dynamic Programming.* Princeton, N.J.: Princeton University Press, 1962.

Bowker, A. H., and G. J. Lieberman, *Engineering Statistics.* Englewood Cliffs, N.J.: Prentice-Hall, Inc., 1959.

Bowman, E. H., and R. B. Fetter, *Analysis for Production Management.* Homewood, Ill.: Richard D. Irwin, Inc., 1961.

———— and ————, *Analysis of Industrial Operations.* Homewood, Ill.: Richard D. Irwin, Inc., 1959.

Buffa, E. S., *Models for Production and Operations Management.* New York: John Wiley & Sons, Inc., 1963.

Churchman, C. W., R. L. Ackoff, and E. L. Arnoff, *Introduction to Operations Research.* New York: John Wiley & Sons, Inc., 1957.

Clough, D. J., *Concepts in Management Science.* Englewood Cliffs, N.J.: Prentice-Hall, Inc., 1963.

Dean, J., *Managerial Economics.* Englewood Cliffs, N.J.: Prentice-Hall, Inc., 1951.

Dorfman, R., P. A. Samuelson, and R. M. Solow, *Linear Programming and Economic Analysis.* New York: McGraw-Hill Book Company, Inc., 1958.

Duncan, A. S., *Quality Control and Industrial Statistics.* Homewood, Ill.: Richard D. Irwin, Inc., 1965.

Ehrenfeld, S., and S. B. Littauer, *Introduction to Statistical Method.* New York: McGraw-Hill Book Company, Inc., 1964.

Feller, W., *An Introduction to Probability Theory and its Applications*, Vol. I. New York: John Wiley & Sons, Inc., 1957.

Grant, E. L., *Statistical Quality Control.* New York: McGraw-Hill Book Company, Inc., 1964.

————, and W. G. Ireson, *Principles of Engineering Economy.* New York: The Ronald Press Company, 1960.

Ireson, W. G., and E. L. Grant, *Handbook of Industrial Engineering and Management.* Englewood Cliffs, N.J.: Prentice-Hall, Inc., 1966.

Llewellyn, R. W., *Linear Programming.* New York: Holt, Rinehart, and Winston, 1964.

Manne, A. S., *Economic Analysis for Business Decisions.* New York: McGraw-Hill Book Company, Inc., 1961.

Maynard, H. B., *Industrial Engineering Handbook.* New York: McGraw-Hill Book Company, Inc., 1956.

McGarrah, R. E., *Production and Logistics Management.* New York: John Wiley & Sons, Inc., 1963.

Miller, D. W., and M. K. Starr, *Executive Decisions and Operations Research* Englewood Cliffs, N.J.: Prentice-Hall, Inc., 1960.

Peck, L. G., and R. N. Hazelwood, *Finite Queuing Tables*. New York: John Wiley & Sons, Inc., 1958.

Putnam, A. O., E. R. Barlow, and G. N. Stilian, *Unified Operations Management*. New York: McGraw-Hill Book Company, Inc., 1963.

Sasieni, M., A. Yaspan, and L. Friedman, *Operations Research: Methods and Problems*. New York: John Wiley & Sons, Inc., 1959.

Schweyer, H. E., *Analytic Models for Managerial and Engineering Economics*. New York: Reinhold Publishing Corporation, 1964.

Starr, M. K., *Production Management: Systems and Synthesis*. Englewood Cliffs, N.J.: Prentice-Hall, Inc., 1964.

Taylor, G. A., *Managerial and Engineering Economy*. Princeton, N.J.: D. Van Nostrand Company, Inc., 1964.

Thuesen, H. G., and W. J. Fabrycky, *Engineering Economy*. Englewood Cliffs, N.J.: Prentice-Hall, Inc., 1964.

Teichroew, D., *An Introduction to Management Science: Deterministic Models*. New York: John Wiley & Sons, Inc., 1964.

Villers, R., *Dynamic Management in Industry*. Englewood Cliffs, N.J.: Prentice-Hall, Inc., 1960.

INDEX